H. v. Helmholtz

Hermann von Helmholtz

by Leo Koenigsberger

Translated by Frances A. Welby

With a Preface by Lord Kelvin

Dover Publications, Inc., New York

Published in Canada by General Publishing Company, Ltd., 30 Lesmill Road, Don Mills, Toronto, Ontario.

Published in the United Kingdom by Constable and Company, 10 Orange Street, London W. C. 2.

This Dover edition, first published in 1965, is an unabridged and unaltered republication of the work originally published by the Clarendon Press, Oxford, in 1906. This edition is published by special arrangement with Oxford University Press, Inc.

The publisher wishes to express his gratitude to the Directors of the Oberlin College Library for supplying a copy of this book for reproduction purposes.

Library of Congress Catalog Card Number 65-27993

Manufactured in the United States of America

Dover Publications, Inc.
180 Varick Street
New York, N. Y. 10014

PREFACE TO THE ENGLISH EDITION

In the historical record of science the name of Helm-holtz stands unique in grandeur, as a master and leader in mathematics, and in biology, and in physics. His admirable theory of vortex rings is one of the most beautiful of all the beautiful pieces of mathematical work hitherto done in the dynamics of incompressible fluids. In 1843, when he was only twenty-two years old, and barely emerged from his undergraduate course as a medical student, he showed, in his first published scientific paper, a clear appreciation of the necessity of distinguishing vital from non-vital phenomena: and he gave experimental evidence tending to prove that putrefaction and fermentation are essentially vital actions: and thus led the way to Pasteur's splendid and beneficent discoveries. His *Erhaltung der Kraft*, published in 1847, was a guide to his own countrymen, and to the rest of the world, in the *doctrine of energy* through the whole range of dynamic action in dead and living matter, then despised and rejected by nearly all the high priests of science; now cherished *by all* as a most fruitful result of modern research. His *Tonempfindungen*, and his *Physiological Optics*, are not mere textbooks: they are ever memorable Principia of the perception of sound, and of light, by living creatures.

The professional career of Helmholtz was unparalleled in the history of professions. He was Military Surgeon in the Prussian army five years; Teacher of Anatomy in the Academy of Arts in Berlin one year; Professor of Pathology and Physiology in Königsberg six years; Professor of Anatomy in Bonn three years; Professor of Physiology in Heidelberg thirteen years; Professor of Physics in the University of Berlin about twenty years, till he became Director of the new 'Physikalisch-Technische Reichsanstalt'. He occupied this post during the last years of his life, still continuing to give lectures as Professor of Physics.

Beginning with the generous aid and co-operation of Werner von Siemens, and ultimately supported by the financial resources of their country, Helmholtz created the Reichsanstalt, which has already conferred inestimable benefits, not only on Germany, but on the whole world. It is an example, tardily and imperfectly followed by Great Britain and other countries only now beginning to learn that scientific research yields results which are valuable, not merely for the discovery of truths appreciated only by scientific workers, but for contributing in many ways to the welfare of the whole people.

The Faraday Lecture, delivered by Helmholtz before the Fellows of the Chemical Society in the theatre of the Royal Institution on Tuesday, April 5, 1881, was an epoch-making monument of the progress of Natural Philosophy in the nineteenth century, in virtue of the declaration, then first made, that electricity consists of atoms. Before that time atomic theories of electricity had been noticed and rejected by Faraday and Maxwell, and probably by many other philosophers and workers; but certainly accepted by none. Now in the beginning of the twentieth century we all believe that electricity consists of atoms. How far-reaching is this theory, and how much science is enriched by it, is splendidly illustrated by Becquerel's discovery of radio-activity, and the magnificent harvests of new and astonishing truth which have been gathered by the numerous and brilliant workers in the field of investigation thus opened to the world.

I cannot conclude this short preface without referring to the great debt which the world owes to Helmholtz, in having given to Hertz the inspiration to find experimental proof of Maxwell's electric waves; and giving him, in the Physical Institute of the University of Berlin, the apparatus and appliances by means of which he carried out the investigation. To this we owe the first practical demonstration of progressive electric waves, and of stationary waves, in air, and therefore inferentially in ether undisturbed by ponderable matter. Thus in Helmholtz we find a prime factor in the grand series of theoretical and experimental researches through which wireless telegraphy has been achieved.

The Oxford University Press has earned the gratitude of all English-speaking scientific workers in giving to them this English version of the very valuable and interesting Life of Helmholtz, by Dr. Königsberger.

KELVIN.

AUTHOR'S PREFACE

I DECIDED at the end of last year, in consequence of my long personal and scientific connexion with Hermann von Helmholtz, and at the repeated wish of his widow, the late Frau Anna von Helmholtz, to compile a Biography of the great investigator.

Thanks to the letters and other communications received from his family and from a vast number of distinguished scholars and friends, to the permission accorded by the Prussian Government to avail myself of the Official Papers relating to the career of Helmholtz, and above all to the active co-operation of his daughter, Frau Ellen von Siemens, I have been enabled to give a connected account of his life; for this help I beg to express my cordial thanks.

It is for the indulgent reader to decide whether it lies within the power of a mathematician to present the epoch-making contributions of von Helmholtz to the most various departments of human knowledge in a form that shall be universally intelligible.

LEO KOENIGSBERGER.

HEIDELBERG,
October, 1902.

In the English edition the Life has been slightly abridged, with the permission of the author and German publishers.

CONTENTS

AND

CHRONOLOGICAL INDEX TO THE SCIENTIFIC CAREER OF HERMANN VON HELMHOLTZ

viii CONTENTS

ILLUSTRATIONS

CHAPTER I

THE PARENTAGE OF HERMANN VON HELMHOLTZ

HERMANN VON HELMHOLTZ was the son of August Ferdinand Julius Helmholtz, who was born on December 21, 1792, in Berlin, and was educated at the Friedrichs-Gymnasium; he matriculated on October 15, 1811, in the Theological Faculty of the University. Notwithstanding a feeble constitution, he took part in the campaign of 1813–1814, was sworn in as a volunteer at Breslau immediately after the Royal Proclamation on March 30, 1813, and was promoted to be second lieutenant on September 8, after the battle of Dresden.

After the Peace of Paris, 1814, he obtained his discharge, and returned to Berlin, but felt himself obliged to give up his theological studies from conscientious motives, since he was unable to reconcile himself to the hyper-orthodox views that prevailed at the time. He therefore chose the study of the classical languages as his profession, although his inclinations would have led him to prefer philosophy.

A protracted nervous fever obliged him to relinquish the campaign of 1815, when he accepted a temporary engagement as private tutor to a couple of talented and industrious lads with whom he was happy and contented; and he only parted from them reluctantly in order to provide for his future, and secure himself a permanent position.

After passing a qualifying examination in Berlin he was appointed form-master at the Potsdam Gymnasium in 1820, and became Professor by Royal Patent in 1828.

Directly after his appointment to the Gymnasium he married Fräulein Caroline Penne, the daughter of a Hanoverian artillery officer, who was born on May 22, 1797. She was descended in the male line from the famous American colonist William Penn, the founder of Pennsylvania, and on her mother's side from a family of French refugees named Sauvage. This happy union lasted till 1854, Frau Helmholtz doing much by her faithful fulfilment of her domestic duties to lighten the heavy calling of her husband, who was weighed down by his sense of duty and scrupulous conscientiousness.

Caroline Helmholtz is described as being excessively simple in appearance, and was profoundly emotional and of quick intellect. Everything she said was incisive, and her homely judgements were clear and luminous. She seemed to penetrate obscure points by intuition, 'without any deep reflection,' expressing her conclusions in simple language. 'A refined officer's daughter,' says her younger son, Otto, 'she was compelled by the straitened circumstances which were all my father could provide for her, to consecrate her whole life to the maintenance of the household, and the education of her children, particularly of the two daughters, since my father was physically much enfeebled by the effects of his campaigns.' His profession, moreover, was onerous, for the strictest discipline prevailed at that time among Prussian officials, greatly to the advantage of the country, and to the ultimate weal of the whole of Germany.

Thus when the young teacher expressed his desire to be associated with the general insurance fund for widows of officials, the Consistory made the following characteristic reply, which is illustrative of the rigid discipline then maintained in Prussian offices, and of the temper in which the rising generation were brought up :—

'Your memorial is incomplete in its contents and most reprehensible in its form. It was your duty definitely to explain that you could, and to engage that you would, provide a pension of at least 100 *thaler* at the General Institute for the Relief of Widows on behalf of your future wife, so that the declaration that you had decided to provide for your wife is obviously not sufficiently definite. We shall expect to receive the amended statement within eight days. . . . With regard to the form, you ought to know, or your sense of propriety should have informed you, that an official statement or memorial to the Board should not be drawn up upon a single page, but should occupy an entire sheet. The leaf you have handed in testifies to the greatest inattention and neglect of the respect due to the Board, and to its President, by whom the communication of the 3rd inst. was issued. We are compelled to call your attention to this carelessness on account of its consequences, and to recommend you to observe the claims of propriety and duty.'

Such reprimands, however, were quietly accepted by the young Prussian official, in whom respect for authority was in-born. He devoted himself whole-heartedly to his profession, giving instruction in German and philosophy, translating and interpreting Plato, *The Odyssey*, Ovid and Virgil with his pupils, while for four years he was further responsible for the teaching of mathematics and physics in the higher forms. Notwithstand-ing this press of work he found time for painting (in which he was self-taught), for philosophical study, and for the publica-tion in the annual School Report of essays, such as 'The Early Development of the Hellenes', 'Historical Problems of the Coming Century', and 'The Arabs, as described in the Hamasêh', the merits of which were recognized at a later time by eminent authorities. Thanks to his wide literary studies, he had acquired a considerable knowledge of aesthetics; his scientific interests were comprehensive; and he was a stimulating and capable teacher, with a pronounced individuality—as shown by the official report of the Head-master, which emphasizes his admirable influence upon the character and achievements of his pupils no less strongly than it is attested by such of the latter as still survive.

In the words spoken fifty years later at the Commemoration Festival of the University of Berlin, by one who has earned undying fame, 'the older among us can remember the men of that period, who had been the foremost volunteers in our army, who were always ready to plunge into a metaphysical discussion, who were well read in the works of Germany's great poets, who burned with wrath at the name of the First Napoleon, and glowed with pride and inspiration in relating the deeds of the war of liberation.'

In respect of Latin, his profession seems to have been merely the 'bread-study' that he was wont to call it, but he was an enthusiastic Hellenist, and had a great influence over his pupils, endeavouring to give them a feeling for poetic beauty, instead of merely providing them with grammatical instruction. As a schoolboy he was unable to acquire the

Ciceronian style, and at a later time was wont to explain his predilection for the Greek language by saying with his greater son, that 'linguistic talent is not one thing, but like all other intellectual functions the sum of different factors'.

He was one of the most distinguished teachers of the Gymnasium, and, with the mathematician Meyer, received frequent ovations from his pupils. A prominent member of the Prussian Civil Service writes: 'We reckoned it one of our happiest hours when we could persuade him to read us poems, dramas, ballads, and the like. Once, for instance, I remember his giving us the first monologue in *Faust*, and another time Bürger's "Lied vom braven Mann" with so much force and feeling that we sat silent and deeply moved ; in later life, and even to the present day, his voice and his expressive countenance have often come back to me.'

Despite the conscientiousness of the pedagogue, however, he was consumed with the enthusiasm and fire of the patriot. Once at the request of his pupils he devoted the three hours of German instruction which he gave the second class as form-master to an account of the feeling that inspired the Prussian people prior to 1813, and they applauded him enthusiastically. But the Headmaster got wind of it, and the favourite teacher received an intimation that any repetition of the indiscretion would be punished by dismissal. This was in the middle of the forties, when the pressure of reaction in Church and State bore heavily upon Prussia, and resulted in the so-called *Treubund* (league of faith) to which the Headmaster and others of the teaching staff belonged.

Hence the discipline of silence was imposed upon Helmholtz for the sake of his family, though his discontent with the political condition of Germany occasionally broke out in private. His eldest son, Hermann, was born in 1821, the daughters Marie and Julie soon after, and twelve years later the second son, Otto. Later again there were two others, Ferdinand and Heinrich, who died in infancy in the years 1836 and 1839. His income was inadequate, his salary only being raised to £160 at the close of his teaching career, and as a good husband and prudent father there was nothing for him to do but to keep his political ideas to himself, and avoid political conversation even in his own house. Henceforward he took his solitary walks to the mill of Sans Souci, and buried himself in philosophical reflections.

But if Ferdinand Helmholtz thus avoided any open expression of political opinion, his philosophical views would not permit him to keep silence in questions of ecclesiastical orthodoxy. An array of sketches and notes for speeches still bears witness to his profound philosophical ideas and noble religious convictions. His relations to his wife and his plans for the education of his children were based on genuine religious and ethical feelings. But he abhorred all ecclesiastical bigotry, and subscribed unhesitatingly to a declaration published on August 15, 1845, by such men as Alschefski, Bellermann, Bonnel, Jonas, Lisco, Meinecke, &c., which began with the words, 'A party has organized itself within the Protestant Church which clings tenaciously to the conception of Christianity inherited from the earliest traditions of the Reformation. This formula is its Pope. Faithful are such as submit themselves to it unconditionally, unfaithful and politically suspect all who have not joined it'; adding, 'We declare that we believe a healthy issue of this contest to be possible only if the right of free development is maintained intact on all sides.'

We are thus able to form some picture of Ferdinand Helmholtz, and to understand the almost exaggerated appreciation of the friend with whom he maintained a life-long correspondence, and made many a journey. This was Imanuel Hermann Fichte, son of Gottlieb Fichte, and Professor of Philosophy in Tübingen from 1842, who writes of 'unalterable, and ever increasing affection—a reciprocal attachment that was of the weightiest consequence in both our lives'.

Helmholtz pursued his vocation as teacher faithfully till 1857, with the utmost devotion to his duties. He followed the later career of his children with affection and interest, but was always, in virtue of his serious philosophical temperament, a somewhat exacting critic. Finally, when his energies began to fail, he applied for a pension, which was granted with a gratifying recognition of his long and faithful service.

CHAPTER II

BOYHOOD: 1821-1838

HERMANN LUDWIG FERDINAND HELMHOLTZ was born on August 31, 1821, at Potsdam, in the house known as No. 8 Hoditzstrasse, and was baptized on October 7 in the Lutheran Church of the Holy Spirit.

For the first seven years of his life he was an ailing child, confined to his room for long periods, and often to his bed, but he was energetic in work and play: his time was occupied with picture-books and games, more especially with wooden blocks, and his mental powers were carefully fostered by his parents. Each infantile disorder from which he suffered renewed the anxiety of his tenderly attached family. ' I heard,' writes Frau von Bernuth, his father's cousin (and the daughter of Surgeon-General Mursinna of Berlin), 'that your son had scarlet fever; and feared the worst as he is so delicate. Thank God that he has recovered! You must not be distressed because he has learned little so far. I am sure it will be for his good not to begin before his eighth year. Alexander von Humboldt learned nothing before he was eight, and now the King has made him President of the Academy of Sciences, with the title of Excellency, and a big yearly stipend—and this is what I predict for your son.'

When he was seven years old, Hermann, though still in delicate health, was sent to the Normal School of Potsdam, and even there astonished his masters in the Geometry Class, because (thanks to his toy blocks) he knew all the facts which they expected him to learn. His health improved by degrees with gymnastics and daily bathing, and his great love of Nature was developed at the same time by frequent walks with his father in the beautiful environs of his native town. In the spring of 1832, he was admitted to the lowest form of the Gymnasium, where he followed the teaching easily enough, and gave satisfaction to his masters. His handwriting indeed was criticized, and his mathematical home-tasks were inadequately performed: but his power of working by himself, and the attention, zeal, and thought which he bestowed upon his studies, were highly commended. At the outset, in the lower classes, he was hampered by the want of a good memory for disconnected facts: 'this showed itself,' he says fifty years later, 'in the difficulty which I still distinctly remember of distinguishing between right and left; later on, when I got to languages in my school-work, it was harder for me to learn the vocabularies, grammatical irregularities, and idiomatical expressions, than for the others. History, in particular, as it was taught in those days, was quite beyond me. It was a real torture to learn prose extracts by heart. This defect has of course increased, and is a nuisance in my old age. I found no difficulty in learning the poems of the great masters, but the more laboured verses of second-rate poets were far less easy.'

The father's influence was the most important factor in the boy's intellectual development. At home he occupied himself in arousing his children (with whom he was always on cordial, if not affectionate, terms) to a sense of the ideal in poetry, art, and music, while at the same time he strove to make them good patriots. As a keen teacher of Greek, he read Homer with his pupils, and as their instructor in German he gave them great facility of expression by means of prose essays and metrical exercises.

The first three years of school-life were thus devoted mainly to grammatical studies, and to the aesthetic side of young Helmholtz's education, but with his entry into the second class the curriculum was widened to include mathematics and physics. The teaching of Prof. C. Meyer, Helmholtz's first mathematical tutor, is still praised by his surviving students. His treatise on 'The Caustic Curves produced by the Reflection of Light from Curves of the Second Order', which was published in the School Report for 1838, proves that Meyer combined scientific with pedagogic interests, and it may have been thanks to him that young Helmholtz, while his class were reading Cicero or Virgil, which did not interest him, would often be engaged beneath the table in working out the passage of rays of light through the telescope, or in learning some of the optical theorems that served him in good stead later on in the construction of the ophthalmoscope.

He was more fascinated by the elements of physics as taught in the Gymnasium, than by his purely geometrical and algebraic studies. And when he began to follow the physical and chemical experiments which Professor Meyer demonstrated in the laboratory to his students, and listened to the scientific discussions between his father and his mathematical colleague (in which, among other matters, the question of a *perpetuum mobile*, and the futile attempts to realize it, was continually cropping up), the boy's desire to immerse himself in these problems waxed stronger and stronger, and he burned to enlarge his mental horizon by independent and original experiments. It was at this time indeed (as Helmholtz often attested in later days) that he conceived the idea which increasingly dominated him, that the knowledge of natural laws should give us not only a spiritual mastery over Nature, but an actual material control of her processes. The vigorous young scholar was consciously outgrowing the narrow circle of his home and school relations.

With no other appliances than some spectacle glasses and a little botanical lens belonging to his father, young Helmholtz and a friend contrived to make up optical instruments, modifying the construction again and again until he hit off some practicable arrangement. The necessary knowledge had to be acquired from a few antiquated textbooks on physics and chemistry possessed by his father, 'to which the discoveries of Lavoisier and Humphry Davy had not yet penetrated, while phlogiston still played its part and galvanism ended with the voltaic pile.'

At fifteen, Helmholtz was described by his fellow-students as reserved and self-contained, showing invariable kindness to those weaker than himself. As regards his studies, he was by no means devoted exclusively to the exact sciences, for his first school-report in the first class testifies to a fairly level interest in all branches of his studies, his progress in Latin, Greek, Hebrew, religious instruction, mathematics, and physics being characterized as good, and history and geography as excellent: while the same appears from the decision of the masters' meeting in August, 1837, that at the Michaelmas speeches Helmholtz should reply with a Latin ode to the farewell oration delivered in German by one of the *Abiturienten*.

While still in the second class Helmholtz announced to his father that he wished to devote himself to science, but when the worthy man, who had the education of four children on his hands, explained that he could not afford to provide him with instruction in physics unless he took up the study of medicine as well, he accepted the situation cheerfully.

As early as 1835 his father applied for his admission to the Royal Friedrich-Wilhelm Institute of Medicine and Surgery in Berlin, which gave considerable assistance to medical students, inasmuch as it guaranteed them a complete course of study and means of livelihood, in return for a certain number of years' service as army surgeons.

The competition for entry to this Institute was, however, too keen for it to be promised to Helmholtz's father two years in advance, and the application had to be renewed when Hermann had reached the first class. It was then successful, and he was summoned to an examination in Berlin during the Easter vacation of 1837.

'Dear Father,' writes the lad of sixteen, on March 30, from Berlin, 'I arrived the day before yesterday in a raging snowstorm. Tell mother, however, that I hardly felt the cold, except in my hands, which were quite numb. Yesterday morning I went to the Pépinière at 9.30, and was called up at 10.30. Surgeon-General Schulz was very kind. He inquired after you, tested my eyes to see if I were short-sighted, and asked three of the staff-doctors to guess my height. They decided that I was about four inches high (*sic*). He questioned me about my health, admonished me to emulate my *quasi*-ancestor Mursinna, and prove myself worthy of him, and not be afraid of the examination : even if I could not answer all the questions exhaustively it would not matter, as this was only to be a general test of my acquirements.

'He then gave me a note for Dr. Figulus, who was to examine me. The doctor was not at home then, or an hour later, and I only found him after dinner. He gave me an appointment for this morning. Yesterday afternoon I went about in the

town, and got pretty tired. This morning at eight I commenced
my doctor's examination. I had to do my *curriculum vitae*
in German and Latin. There was not time to make a fair
copy of the Latin. The examination is all in writing. I don't
know how long it will last.'

Helmholtz returned with the news of his success to his
delighted parents at Potsdam, and then gave himself up once
more to severe and regular study of the most heterogeneous
subjects, devoting himself to each in turn with the same interest
and enthusiasm, though he could not forbear to say in his
curriculum vitae a year later: ' quorum (veterum scriptorum)
cognitio quantum valeat ad conformandum animum, nemo est,
qui ignoret; deinde maxima atque plurima debeo Schmidtio
professori, quum aliis in disciplinis, tum in historiis, quibus
nihil est praestantius ad cognoscendam naturam hominum et
populorum. Pater meus artis poeticae et oratoriae praecepta
mihi dedit, quarum illa et iucundissima est et utilissima ad
elocutionem elegantem et copiosam. Omnium disciplinarum
autem maxime iam a pueritia me delectavit physice et mathe-
matice, quibus eruditus sum a Meierio, viro harum rerum
peritissimo.'

After a full year's work, in which he not only prepared
for the *Abiturienten* examination, but also, in view of his
medical career, embarked on the scientific studies that had
hitherto been outside his curriculum—such as botany and
zoology, with the elements of anatomy from Oken's *Natur-
geschichte für alle Stände*, and physiology from Magendie's
Textbook—his father sent him off with some other boys of
his class to the Harz Mountains. They took long walks,
to the great benefit of his none too robust constitution, absorbing the influences of Nature and Art at the various places
where they halted.

Refreshed in mind and body by this expedition, Helmholtz
and one fellow-student embarked upon the written part of the
Abiturienten examination, which lasted from August 20-25.
His translation of sixty lines of the *Hecuba* of Euripides was
marked 'very satisfactory'; his French version of a piece of
two columns called *Die Katakomben* was ' excellent'; while the
Hebrew professor gave him the highest praise for his Latin
commentary on Deut. ix. 1-3, which was not a compulsory

item for the medical student. As might have been expected, his father's judgement of his German essay on 'The Ideas and Art in Lessing's *Nathan der Weise*' was a little severe, although he could not refrain from praising its simple and expressive diction.

Helmholtz solved his four mathematical tests, two being geometrical and two arithmetical, correctly, his treatment of them showing 'great lucidity and grip' of the elements of mathematics. In addition, he presented a fifth and voluntary exercise on 'The Laws of the Free Fall of Bodies'. This essay, as it now lies before us, shows unusual precision of thought and expression, and it is obvious that the author had pondered deeply and often over physical problems.

The *viva voce* examination took place on September 12, 1838, and young Helmholtz left the Gymnasium with brilliant testimonials.

In later years the staff of the Potsdam Gymnasium might well be proud of the education for which the young man was in part at least indebted to it. ' Our teachers encouraged us to read a great deal, and we were eventually able to peruse the authors to whom they introduced us with comparative ease, and did so at home after school hours, in addition to the study of foreign languages. I took up English and Italian privately at school, as well as Hebrew, and got a very good mark in Hebrew. I even began Arabic in the first class with a master who knew it, and found plenty of time for all these things.' Later on he read the *Fables* of Lokmân in the original, in his leisure moments.

As soon as he had received the *Abiturienten* certificate, his father wrote on September 16 to Surgeon-General v. Wiebel: ' I recommend this good boy, my dearest treasure, on whose education I have expended my best energies, to the fatherly care of one who is so valued for his goodness.' The father had to guarantee a monthly allowance of 18s. during his son's term of study, to be paid quarterly, in advance, to the account of the Institute, while the student was bound after his five years' education at the King's expense to serve as surgeon to a company or squadron for eight consecutive years.

And so Hermann Helmholtz, permeated with a thirst for knowledge, and inspired with a deep love for natural science, to which his future was to be consecrated, was launched into a new life. Happily for himself, and to the great advantage of the world of science, his education had not been one-sided. By reason of his natural endowment, and thanks to the ceaseless efforts of his parents, whose intellectual standard was ever set to high ideals, he was filled with passionate enthusiasm for music and poetry, as well as for art and science.

CHAPTER III

STUDENT AT THE ROYAL FRIEDRICH-WILHELM INSTITUTE FOR MEDICINE AND SURGERY IN BERLIN: 1838-1842

On his arrival at the Royal Friedrich-Wilhelm Institute (October, 1838), Helmholtz gave his parents a brief description of the strictly regulated conditions of his new life:—

'I got here safely on Friday. My things arrived shortly after. The servant and the porter made difficulties at first on account of the piano, as there was no place for it in my quarters. The room next this is intended for two, and has ample space. Accordingly I deposited it there, and said that Surgeon-Major Grimm had given me leave to bring it. The place is fairly roomy for the two of us; it is up two flights of stairs at the end of the building opposite the entrance, so that I have to go half the length of the Hoditzstrasse to reach the street. The room has one inconvenience—the three students who live in the next rooms invariably pass through it, although this is forbidden, and they ought to go across the yard; but it can't be helped. It would be hard for them if they wanted to call the servant to have to go down two long flights of stairs, and then all the way up again. In order to make this plainer I will draw you a little plan. . . . My room-fellow is the son of a Silesian engineer; he has already been one half-year at the Academy, that is to say, has attended classes and lectures, but did not lodge or take food there. He has extraordinary execution on the piano, but only cares for florid pieces and for modern Italian music. A few other fellows have also been coming to our room, as they had sent away their hired instruments during the vacation, but we hope this will stop now. Frau v. Bernuth has so far fed me sumptuously, so much so indeed that often I can hardly get up the two flights of stairs to my room. Each time I leave the table she tells me everything I have done amiss, and flatters herself I have improved a little already. There are a few new pictures at the Exhibition, but they are not worth much, the only one I care for being a Jephtha.... We have not yet got our plan of studies. As soon as I know a little more of the real life here I will write to you again. I am so far unpleasantly conscious of separation from you, as everything has to be paid for, and the senior students who come in pretty frequently to inspect the freshmen (*Füchse*) rob us of nearly all our leisure moments. . . .'

On November 2 he received a letter from his father, full of good advice, and anxiety for the hope and joy of the family :—

'Dear Son! We were very glad to learn from your letters that you have arrived safely, and have received your things; your mother could hardly wait until a letter came from you; she was positively ill from her anxiety for news. Your room is not far from that in which I passed my own years at the University; my windows looked on to the Friedrichstrasse, and were above the gateway nearest to you. May you be as happy in your abode, and enjoy as many happy moments of a higher life there, as fell to my lot! Your first disagreeable reception as a "fox" was only to be expected—no one is let off—but you may comfort yourself with the reflection that it is the last time you will have to go through it, and if you take it wisely, and hold your own, it will soon be over. I only hope your comrade is a stout-hearted, industrious lad; if he is, it will be great luck for you. His playing the piano so well is your best chance of improving yourself, and do not be so accommodating as to leave all the playing to him because he does it better than you, for it was under similar circumstances that I forgot all I ever learned: and, above all, don't let your taste for the solid inspiration of German and classical music be vitiated by the sparkle and dash of the new Italian extravagances—these are only a distraction, the other is an education. Be thankful for Cousin Bernuth's lessons, even if they are given somewhat crudely; behind these conventional social forms there lies in reality a deeper meaning, which is forgotten though it is still there, so that the forms help people to get on in society; to give them life so that they cease to be empty form and convention is the task of the individual. . . . We are all well, and all love you dearly, and hope you will still, as ever, be our delight and pride. Be good, and devote yourself seriously and whole-heartedly to your profession, to science, and to virtue. Write as soon as possible to describe your studies and your every-day life. We shall be delighted to see you, provided your work allows it. If your companion is a good fellow, and you think it would improve your relations with him, you can bring him with you later on.'

The young student soon accommodated himself to his new surroundings, and affectionately reassures his parents, who were anxious about his food and lodging on account of his weak health :—

'I am well. The classes have commenced to-day, and regular work, which we hope will bring more quiet to our room. So far these visitors have been rather unwelcome, especially when I was practising, as they often expected me to play valses, &c., for them. At last I would not do it any more, and got my chum to play, while they sometimes danced till, as Dr. Knapp told me, the company-surgeon below complained of them. I have not sought their company very much, so that K. tells me I am called unsociable. He advises me to be patient, and says he also had to put up with the seniors coming to his room and playing there (which is forbidden in the Institute), though he and his friend did not play with them. My room-mate is good-natured, but not exactly clever, as I see by his note-books, from which I wanted to fill in my own, as I was not able to take notes myself to-day, and also missed the first lecture on Splanchnology. I went with him, as he has already been studying a whole half-year, and he took me to the lecture-room in the University, where Professor Schlemm generally lectures, and where on the time-table at the door we saw " Mondays, 9–10, Prof. Schlemm", and a number of students already waiting. However, as we did not find the others from the Institute, he went round to make inquiries, and I waited for him near the notice-board, but he lost himself in the crowd, and never reappeared. I went back to the lecture-room, where more students had collected meantime, but the Professor did not turn up. At last we went to the anatomical theatre, behind the Garrison Church, and heard that Professor Schlemm was really lecturing there. As the lecture was almost over it was no use going in, so I looked at the subjects which had been brought for dissection, and had been partly cut up. I did not experience any disagreeable sensations.

'We have forty-eight lectures in the week: six on Chemistry in Mitscherlich's house, six on General Anatomy, four on Splanchnology, three on Osteology, three on the Anatomy of the Sense-organs. All these in addition to the Osteology at the anatomical theatre. Then four on Physics by Turte, two on General Medicine with Hecker at the University, two on Logic by Wolf—in the anatomical theatre! three on History by Preuss, two on Latin by Hecker, one on French by Pastor Gosshauer in the Institute. Besides these we have twelve hours of revision classes, but these only begin in a fortnight's time.

'You must not be afraid that I shall give up my music, for the new style my comrade admires so much does not satisfy me, and I am obliged to play myself to hear anything better. Besides which, other people's expression and execution seldom satisfy me; I always care much more for music when I am playing it myself. The food in the Institute is not so bad as most people make out, though less good than in a private home. We can have two helpings of soup and vegetables, but only one of meat. Or instead of vegetables we may have sauce over the meat, with potatoes. Dr. Grimm has been in to see if everything was right; he came to me, and asked about the classes, what I thought of the food, and so on.'

In spite of these good accounts the anxious mother sent her husband off to Berlin to make sure of their son's welfare, and only after that does she write cheerily to her boy that 'all beginnings are hard', and crack jokes with him in her usual merry fashion. 'Wilhelm Wilkens,' she says, 'was here the other day, to ask what father found when he went to see you. He hurried along to school with him without speaking; but father understood, and gave him all the news of you. Oh you dumb, self-contained, reserved creatures! Unless you alter, people will have nothing to say to you. ... Write to me of your classes, your chilblains, your tempers, your discontent, and the good things that happen to you. God grant you may do the right, and leave the wrong undone.'

Young Helmholtz devoted himself impartially to the study

of physics, chemistry, and anatomy, and worked hard to acquire the necessary knowledge of these subjects from books and lectures, but in leisure moments his thoughts always turned to his home, and notwithstanding his occasional Sunday visits to Potsdam, he was wont in any passing fit of depression to disburden himself of his thoughts and feelings by writing to his anxious parents:—

'Since I was with you work has begun in earnest. The revision classes, including two in osteology, have all started, and we often have to sit through the evening learning one muscle after another till our heads split. It is easier to me than to the others, but even I have had an attack of chagrin against God and the world, such as every one here is subject to occasionally. But it generally goes off in a few hours, and our youthful ardour reasserts itself. Any spare time I have during the day is devoted to music, and so far, even on the worst days, I have put in about an hour, and more on Friday, Saturday, and Sunday. By myself I play sonatas of Mozart and Beethoven, and often with my chum the new things he gets hold of, which we run through at sight. In the evenings I have been reading Goethe and Byron, which K. borrowed for me, and sometimes for a change the integral calculus.

'The day after I went to Potsdam I received an invitation from Geheimrath Langner, to whom Mrs. Wilkens gave me an introduction. I met several young people there, mostly law students, but they made us play whist! Happily one of the players in my rubber knew as little as I, and the others hardly more. It was a fine game, and a fine mistake too, to set us down to whist. It lost me the chance of making friends with the young people, among whom was a sailor, just back from North America. Aunt Bernuth was much amused at it; she has presented me with a pair of gloves, which come in very handy this weather. Every morning we have an anatomical revision class in an unwarmed room, and going across to the dissecting-room is a treat without one's cloak! Our rooms have been rather better during the last few days, as we have twice had a fire; before that it was so cold that one could not write at all, and could hardly play.'

After spending Christmas at home, and working industriously through the second half of the first term, Helmholtz returned to his parents and brothers and sisters for a longer holiday at the close of the session.

'We are through with all our lectures now except Mitscherlich's, as he only breaks up next Saturday. So I must stay here all this week, and see how I can pass the time; till now I have employed it in reading Homer, Byron and Biot, and Kant; I am a little out of touch with all these studies, especially the last, and need to apply myself to them again. That once done, they fascinate me only the more. In particular I could hardly tear myself away from Homer, and devoured two or three books one after the other in an evening. I shall be with you next Saturday or Sunday.'

In the second term Helmholtz began to feel more at home in his quarters; his studies assumed a serious aspect, and he became especially engrossed in Johannes Müller's lectures on physiology. In his leisure moments he studied Kant, and the Second Part of *Faust*, and having been appointed assistant-librarian of the Institute, found opportunities of enlarging his knowledge by means of the more recondite works contained in the library. In April, 1839, he writes to his parents:—

'Two important changes have been made in our section: my comrade has moved into the next division above, where some one has left, and another, who is bored with the Institute, has asked for and obtained his discharge; so that there were two vacancies for University students. Meantime I have become acquainted with several good fellows, and did not intend to trust to luck a second time in the choice of a companion, so I proposed to the worthy Königsberger, who has improved very much during the term, that we should join forces. We could either have occupied my room or his. In order to escape the passing through, and to have more space, I went to him, his room being really intended for three men. So now I am living in the third room of the wing in which I formerly inhabited the first, and can use the right of way. My present chum is a lanky fellow, unskilful and untidy in all mundane things, but good-natured, conscientious, and talented. He has a vast memory, e. g. last term he amused himself by learning the *Hecuba* of Euripides by heart in odd quarters of an hour at anatomy; he makes metrical translations from the English, and from Euripides his favourite tragic author, and paints moonlight landscapes with body-colour; in fact he is altogether rather sentimental, especially when he is reading aloud and playing the flute, in which, however, he does not excel, since he has no idea of time. He is the one in the division who has his work most at heart, and gets into discussions, although he is tolerably orthodox—and he has some curious notions about art. Another advantage is that my room is no longer crowded with the people who were attracted by the playing of my former comrade.

' I am one of the assistant-librarians for this term. It loses me some two hours weekly, but is the only way to find out what there is of any value in the library, among the endless heaps of antiquated literature.

'We are expected to go to forty-two lectures a week in the summer term. According to the time-table (which, however, only accounts for thirty-nine, as they left out History) we have only one lecture from four to five, or five to six, on the three first afternoons of the week; the three last are free. But most mornings we go straight on from six till one. Mitscherlich's Zöo-chemistry is a new lecture. We have six hours Botany and six of Natural History with Link, six of Physiology with Müller, six of Chemistry, six of Zöo-chemistry with Mitscherlich. The house lectures are three on History with Preuss, two Latin with Hecker, one French with Gosshauer. Revisions—four in Chemistry, three Physiology (with Herr v. Besser, who sits opposite Klotz at Müller's lectures), two Osteology, one Botany. No Logic or Psychology, nor does Link ever lecture on Mineralogy, although we have to take all these subjects in the first examination.'

In spite of the many lectures and necessary study which these involved, Helmholtz found time to enjoy a splendid performance of *Euryanthe*, and to admire Seydemann's Mephistopheles, and Clara Stich as Gretchen in a representation such as he had never before seen of *Faust*. His time became more and more filled up, for all the free afternoons were struck out on account of the many lectures. Müller's physiology pleased him immensely, and Mitscherlich's zöo-chemistry also interested him, the experimental chemistry being, as he says, ' chock-full, but the least bit tedious.' Link, however, seemed to him to suffer ' from a superabundance of intellect; after two months' lectures on Natural History he is still at the philosophical introduction (good heavens!)'. And along with all this, Helmholtz was taking fencing and swimming lessons, so as to come up to the standard required from a student, hoping thereby to be rid of his savings, 'since otherwise the confounded spring will strew them to the winds.'

In December Helmholtz passed his *tentamen philosophicum.* He writes :—

'I got through the examination for the *philosophicum* all right yesterday, and received a good certificate. The report in chemistry was excellent, in physics, psychology, zoology, and botany very good, in mineralogy pretty good. This last is the best Weiss gives as a rule ; at least I have been told that he said no more for examinees who knew a great deal of mineralogy. Of us four I had the best certificate, and Kunth congratulated me on it as he handed it to me. Even if the examination requires not so much special knowledge as a bird's-eye view of the whole, it has its uses as an incentive for going deeper into the sciences, and becoming interested in them.'

Directly after this, on December 12, he demonstrated one of his own anatomical preparations of the peritoneum at a students' meeting. It was neatly done, and explained in a capital lecture, which was highly commended by Dr. Frost, a London botanist who happened to be present.

The end of the year brought anxiety for the health of his dearly-loved mother, but she was able to join in the family festivities at Christmas, and he utilized the rest of the winter term and the Easter holidays in preparation for the clinical lectures given during the summer.

The hospital work again tried his health severely, and on August 25, 1840, he received ten weeks' leave for a journey to Silesia, Prague, and Dresden.

At the beginning of the winter term of 1840 Helmholtz took his anatomical examination, the prospect of which was alarming, though he was well prepared for it. On October 30, however, he announces the successful issue of the two days' examination to his anxious parents, with the news that both his tests had been got through without comment from the professors :—

'I still have to make an anatomical preparation, but this can only mean a higher or lower mark. W. and F., who were a term ahead of me, have also been in now; and had the same good fortune. Although none of us ever went up to an examination with better consciences than to this anatomy, we were all on thorns over the demonstrations, especially in the first public one, where we each had to give a full description of the tissues in one of the body-cavities, selected by lot, before a crowd of other students, who all arrived on the scene owing to some alteration of arrangements in the examination. The examiners, Müller and Gurlt, sat there—they yawned and looked horribly bored. The second demonstration, on a preparation of bone, and one of intestine preserved in spirit, came off before the examiners alone, when they were even more bored, and only too pleased if the candidate in his haste omitted something. At the end we only regretted that we had spent so much labour over our anatomy, and tried to reassure the crowd who are still trembling at the idea of it.'

As soon as the second part of the examination was over, Helmholtz was free to plunge into the independent scientific work he thirsted for. His visits to Potsdam became less frequent, the letters to his parents fewer, and he was already considering the subject of his doctor's thesis. The winter session of 1840–1, and the summer of 1841, were devoted to the extension of his knowledge on all sides, more particularly in mathematics and recondite branches of mechanics. Still he always found time and opportunity to take part in amateur theatricals with his friends, and he followed the growth of national feeling and consequent political developments with keen interest. The witty lampoons and satires with which the Berliners revenged themselves for their deluded hopes, after the accession of Frederick William IV, were a perpetual source of amusement to him.

Hardly, however, had he embarked on the anatomical and physiological researches that were to serve for his doctor's thesis, when he was prostrated for several months by a severe attack of typhoid fever. He was able to return to Berlin in the winter of 1841, and once more took up the question suggested to him (that is, in a general sense) by his master Johannes Müller. From this time he lived entirely in the circle of Müller's pupils, since he had already formed a friendship with the physiologists

Brücke and du Bois-Reymond, who were two years senior to himself, and like him devotedly attached to their teacher. Friendly intercourse with each other, and daily exchange of ideas with the great investigator, who showed them 'the working of the mind of an independent thinker', ennobled their lives and efforts. 'Whoever,' said Helmholtz half a century later, 'comes into contact with men of the first rank has an altered scale of values in life. Such intellectual contact is the most interesting event that life can offer.'

Müller's pupils were united in a common attempt to connect physiology with physics, and to place its conclusions upon a more exact basis, but, as they often confessed at a later period, Helmholtz had a decided advantage over the rest, since in mathematics he gained a tremendous power in the clear formulating of problems and the precise determination of appropriate methods of solution. Yet his wealth of mathematical knowledge had been won by private study of the works of the great mathematicians; for among all the different lectures he attended there was strangely enough not one on this subject, while he said so little about his mathematical learning that even his close friends Brücke and du Bois-Reymond were unaware of it. The time had not yet come when he was to dominate the problems of physiology and physics as one of the greatest of mathematicians.

Müller had indeed emancipated himself from the earlier and essentially metaphysical views of the nature of life, and demanded an empirical foundation for all scientific concepts, but, as his pupils recognized, he had been unable to free himself entirely from the traditions of nature-philosophy and from metaphysical conceptions. Under his influence Helmholtz endeavoured to lay the foundations of a strict physical science by ascertaining the facts in certain definite problems, thereby co-operating with the ceaseless efforts of his master.

And with how modest an equipment Helmholtz set about his colossal investigations! During his illness in the Charité Hospital, where he was nursed free of charge as a student, he saved enough of his little monthly allowance to procure a small and very ordinary microscope, and it was with this instrument, supplemented by a few antiquated textbooks of physics and chemistry, that he attacked his task.

He passed his oral examination at the end of June, but his hopes of receiving the doctor's degree in the summer term were disappointed.

On August 1, 1842, he writes to his father: 'I went to-day to Professor Müller with my thesis. He received me very kindly, and after inquiring what my conclusions were, and on what evidence they were based, declared the subject to be of the greatest possible interest, since it proves the origin for nerve-fibres that was conjectured in the higher animals, but had never been determined. But he advised me to work it out upon a more complete series of animals than I have at present, so as to get more cogent proof than is possible from the examination of three or four only. He mentioned several animals as being the most likely to yield good results, and invited me to use his instruments at the Anatomical Museum if my own were inadequate. If I were not obliged to hurry in taking my degree, he advised me to employ the vacation for further work, so as to produce a fully-developed thesis that need fear no future attack. As I had nothing reasonable to urge to the contrary, and had said most of the same things to myself already, you will have to give up your twenty-year-old doctor, and content yourself with having him at twenty-one. If this distresses you too much, send me a line, and I will translate the discourse I delivered here at Easter, at the Institute, and shall be doctor next week. The Potsdam worthies will presumably conclude that I have failed in my examination, and those in Berlin that I wanted to get off the doctor's banquet, but they shall all be satisfied sooner or later. I was rather surprised myself, and did not like the delay, but, as I said, I can find no good reason against it.'

After a four weeks' tour in the Harz Mountains he returned to Berlin on September 30, and was appointed house-surgeon at the Charité.

It was an arduous post, unsatisfactory 'on account of the tedious and for the most part incurable diseases', and occupied him from 7 a.m. to 8 p.m., with only short breaks of an hour, or even a half-hour; but the work was congenial and instructive, and Helmholtz found time to follow the advice of his teacher, verifying and extending his previous researches with the aid of the instruments provided at the Anatomical Museum.

'I am working hard at my thesis. Once I thought I had arrived at a conclusion of the utmost importance; on closer observation the day before yesterday I found the contrary, and then on looking into it again more carefully yesterday discovered that the first idea was right with certain limitations. To-day I am going for the point more carefully.' His only recreation from this labour was the Art Exhibition, and he greatly admired Lessing's *Huss*, 'a picture that is perhaps worth more than all the earlier exhibitions put together; at any rate here in Berlin we have no picture so profound, so inspired, and so characteristic. Every one is charmed with it, except the Berlin professors.'

Müller ultimately declared the thesis to be satisfactory, and Helmholtz took his doctor's degree on November 2, 1842; his Inaugural Dissertation, *De Fabrica Systematis Nervosi Evertebratorum*, or 'The Structure of the Nervous System in Invertebrates', being dedicated to Johannes Müller. His microscopical discovery, that the nerve-fibres originate in the ganglion cells discovered by Von Ehrenberg in 1833, has been recognized by all physiologists as the histological basis of nervous physiology and pathology: the connexion till then sought in vain between nerve-fibres and nerve-cells, and therewith the proof of the central character of these cells, was established by him for invertebrates in this first-rate contribution to minute anatomy.

As soon as Helmholtz had overcome the initial difficulties of his post, he devoted himself gladly to his calling, but managed to find time to pursue the many-sided studies of the previous year, and develop them profitably. He became so absorbed in his work that he could not tear himself away, and for the first time failed to convey his birthday congratulations in person to his father. In writing, he refers the older man (who cared little for practical realities) to the ideals of a brighter future, but his own scientific thoughts were turning more and more away from the metaphysical, idealistic views by which science was then held in bondage. He directed his hopes entirely to the real world, the world of fact, thus laying the foundation of the mighty structure which was to be erected in the second half of the nineteenth century.

The theoretical methods which obtained in that period of

the development of medicine were fast approaching their end. The methods were rejected, and the facts as well, and it was seen that medical science, like all the other sciences, had to be reconstructed. After physics and chemistry first shaped themselves on scientific lines in France in consequence of the epoch-making labours of Coulomb and Lavoisier, Mitscherlich and Liebig established chemistry as a science in Germany, while Ohm, Franz Neumann, Gauss, and Wilhelm Weber built up methods of experimental and mathematical physics upon a solid foundation. Yet it required a titanic labour to transfer these principles of methodic investigation from inorganic to organic Nature.

After Ernst Heinrich Weber had demanded that vital phenomena should be explained in terms of physical processes, Johannes Müller endeavoured in all his physiological work to clear the way for inductive methods of investigation, and to push deductive reasoning and metaphysical conceptions more and more into the background. But he could not emancipate himself from the notion of a separate, individual, vital force, distinct from the chemical and physical forces working within the organism, and capable of binding and loosing the action of the same. This is only abolished by death; the forces which it restrained are then set free, and produce corruption and putrefaction; the vital force has vanished, and is not replaced, nor converted into any other perceptible form of energy. Müller did not attempt to disguise the inconsistency of his position, and as a result the four gifted young investigators, Brücke, du Bois-Reymond, Helmholtz, and Virchow, were all striving to develop a logical and unified physiology according to the principles of exact investigation. Each sought to abolish the notion of vital force from the department of physiology which he regarded as his own, and to cultivate physiology as a branch of physics and chemistry.

But, in the mind of Helmholtz, the conflict between realistic and metaphysical principles had become a resolute fight against the dominating ideas in a wider field than physiology: a vanishing vital force for which nothing was substituted appeared to him a physical paradox—a disappearance of energy and matter was unthinkable. He had never heard a mathematical lecture, but the Pépinière possessed the works of Euler, Daniel Bernouilli, d'Alembert, and Lagrange, mathematicians of the previous century, and arming himself with a small textbook of higher analysis he had plunged even as a student, during the time of his assistant-librarianship at the Institute, into the fundamental investigations of these great mathematicians—penetrating into the significance of the principles of mechanics, as laid down by these immortal thinkers, with which such metaphysical views were incompatible.

The time was not yet ripe for bringing forward these universal and comprehensive ideas ; Helmholtz had learned from the stern methods of Johannes Müller that only definite and methodical experiment could make the general principles of science intelligible, and set them on a sure foundation. As soon as his doctor's examination was over, he applied himself in Müller's laboratory to a problem which, on account of Liebig's work, was then in the forefront of interest. Helmholtz attacked it on far wider grounds, with the intention of bringing the so-called ' vital forces ' within the scope of scientific study.

Liebig was engaged in a fierce campaign against the organized nature of yeast, as discovered by Schwann and Cagniard-Latour, and its *rôle* in alcoholic fermentation, and upheld the essentially chemical theory of fermentation and putrefaction, based on Gay-Lussac's experiments. Helmholtz immediately recognized the crucial importance of this question, and its close connexion with the possibility of perpetual motion, and set himself to decide the point. The economies of his winter's illness had provided him not only with a microscope for the morphological investigations described in his thesis, but also with the recently published *Organic Chemistry* of Mitscherlich ; and in the early months of the year 1843, when he was not much hampered by his duties in the children's ward, he plunged into extended physico-chemical investigations which henceforward absorbed him.

In this arduous and exhausting work he had to trust entirely to himself, as he knew little of even the most important publications on the subject. On July 25 he applies to his father to procure him the necessary literature : ' Could you be so good as to borrow of Professor Meyer, or through his intermediation, by next Sunday afternoon, that treatise of Mitscherlich on Fermentation which you mentioned the other day, or to ask him where I could meet him to hear the results of these experiments, if he is unable to lend it?' and in spite of the heavy work of the summer months on the out-patient post at the Charité, he adds, 'I am now so far advanced with my experiments that I am ready to begin writing, and it is essential to acquaint myself with the work of Mitscherlich.'

The main object of this paper, published in *Müller's Archiv* in 1843, with the title 'On the Nature of Fermentation and Putrefaction', was to support Liebig in his attack on vitalism by proving that there can be no such thing as spontaneous generation. Helmholtz found, however, that the transformations known as fermentation and putrefaction are not the result of chemical action, as supposed by Liebig, and therefore due to the action of oxygen, or the introduction of residual disintegration products of the putrefying substances. He showed (and the clear and precise wording of his results is of especial interest in view of the great discoveries of Pasteur at a later time) that putrefaction can occur independently of life, but that it offers a fertile soil for the development and nutrition of living germs, and is modified in its aspects by them. Fermentation is one such putrefactive process modified by organisms, and correlated with them ; it strikingly resembles the vital process in the similarity of the substances it attacks, in its rate of growth, and the similarity of the conditions determining its continuance or check.

These observations, which Helmholtz was unable to pursue from the inadequacy of the means at his command, seemed actually to give fresh support to vitalism, and his experiments were accordingly regarded with suspicion, above all by the physicists. Magnus, indeed, whose generous liberality knew no scientific jealousy, invited him to make use of his private laboratory, and to take advantage of 'methods of investigation that would throw more light on the subject than such as a young army surgeon living on his pay could provide for himself'; but it was not until two years later that Helmholtz was able to convince him by a series of new experiments of the accuracy of his previous work. Nor did he publish anything further on the subject, which had occupied him almost daily for three months. He was already engaged on other and far profounder problems, the solution of which was to condemn

that aspect of physiology against which he and Liebig had
been contending, and to found an entirely new era in science.

In the meantime Helmholtz, after receiving a prize in May
for his excellent hospital work, was on duty in the eye wards
during August; after which, on the recommendation of his
superiors (who had long since recognized his merits), he was
appointed assistant-surgeon to the Royal Hussars at Potsdam,
under the regimental doctor Branco. His Government Examination was not due for two years, so that he could reckon
on a protracted period of leisure, not unduly interrupted by
official duties, for the development of all the weighty thoughts
that had pressed on him since the beginning of his student
life, of which the investigations already accomplished were
merely the preliminary verification.

CHAPTER IV

ARMY SURGEON AT POTSDAM : 1843-1848

As Hussar-Surgeon, Helmholtz was now obliged to forgo the scientific atmosphere in which he had lived, under the inspiration of Johannes Müller, in constant intercourse with such congenial intellects as his chosen friends du Bois-Reymond and Brücke. His peace-loving, retiring nature was harassed at first by the rude five o'clock awakening, when the bugler blew the reveille at his door to rouse the barracks, and interrupted his slumbers, but he soon grew accustomed to this, and attended with alacrity to his official duties. He arranged a small laboratory for physics and physiology in the barracks, where he was frequently visited by du Bois-Reymond and Brücke, who came out from Berlin to discuss their plans for the future reconstitution of physiology. Though restricted to the most elementary instruments (he constructed an electrical machine for himself, which he presented later on to his brother), Helmholtz was always backed up by advice and help from du Bois-Reymond, who, he writes, 'tended me like a mother, to enable me to attain a scientific position.' He plunged at once into his projected investigations on the metabolism in muscular activity, and embarked on a series of laborious experiments on the conduction of heat in muscle, and the rate of transmission of the nervous impulse.

All was well with his parents ; he himself lived a quiet and retired life, wholly immersed in his work. His brother's friends have not yet forgotten the impression made upon them by the young man of twenty-three, who, with a contour of head and a manner inherited from his mother, was distinguished by an expression of absolute calm and intellectuality. All that he said gave an impression of truth and vigour. His extraordinary gift of observation excited the admiration of his friends; on every walk he discovered new things they had not seen. When watching the play and splashing jets of a fountain at Sans Souci he heard melodies and chords in the murmur which they were unable to perceive, even when he drew attention to them. His duties with the squadron left him much spare time, but he devoted every moment to science; his brother tells us that he made use of the midday recreation to study the *Fundamenta Nova Functionum Ellipticarum* of Jacobi, and his much-read copy still shows traces of industrious work, and endeavour to render these difficult matters (with which even the mathematicians were unfamiliar at that time) clear to himself and applicable to physiology.

But the family life in Potsdam reacted unfavourably, though not for long, upon the relation between father and son. The more the young man's thoughts, the direction of his labours, and his whole scientific attitude (which was so soon to be adopted by the entire world of science) took him away from metaphysical speculation, the stronger and for some time the more irreconcilable became the contrast with the wholly speculative philosophy of his father. While Ferdinand Helmholtz admitted only the deductive method in science, and held inductive reasoning to be inimical to it, Hermann on the contrary bore the latter upon his shield, proclaiming it to the end of his life the salvation of science in general and not merely of the physical sciences. The father (secure in the consciousness that he must be the better able as a philosopher to appreciate the relation in which man stands to experience, and with the best intentions in the world of directing his son, his 'dearest treasure', into the right paths of scientific discovery) missed no opportunity in their daily intercourse of bringing his general philosophical convictions and metaphysical conceptions to bear upon the young man, doing all he could to shake him in his methods of thought and experiment.

Helmholtz, who was already concentrating himself upon the experimental evidence that was to establish his world-famed Law of the Conservation of Energy, saw that no agreement in scientific investigation and method was possible upon such divergent grounds, and that it was wiser not to discuss his work with his father. The old man naturally felt this keenly, but at least it kept their domestic relations in good train, and the future soon gave him cause to rejoice over the famous son, by whom the family name was to become known throughout the world.

Since Helmholtz was entirely thrown upon his own re- sources during these years in Potsdam, the need of scientific intercourse often drew him to Berlin to forgather with his great teacher Johannes Müller, and his devoted friends du Bois-Reymond, Brücke, and Ludwig (who was his senior by five years). The young men were all striking out new paths in their chosen sciences, but they willingly and ungrudgingly gave the palm to Helmholtz, as du Bois-Reymond and Brücke loved to relate in after years.

Nor was it long before Helmholtz made his mark in a wider circle. Müller's distinguished pupils at Berlin had become acquainted with other students in physics and chemistry, at the informal classes of their master, Gustav Magnus, and in 1845 the Physical Society had been founded by du Bois-Rey- mond, Brücke, Karsten, Beetz, Heintz, and Knoblauch. Du Bois introduced young Helmholtz to the Society, where he was warmly welcomed as its greatest ornament, and for over ten years contributed reports to the *Fortschritte der Physik* on certain departments of physics and physiology.

The riddle of the existence and nature of vital force—the question whether the life of organisms was the effect of one special, self-engendered, definitely directed force, or merely the sum of the forces that are effective in inorganic nature also, modified only by the manner of their concurrence—such were the questions raised again and again by Müller, and trans- formed by Liebig into the far more concrete problem of whether the mechanical energy and the heat produced in an organism could result entirely from its own metabolism, or not. Helmholtz soon perceived that all these questions were inti- mately connected with the validity of that law of the Conserva- tion of Energy which had for years seemed incontestable to him; but it was necessary to prove the accuracy of his mathematico-physical propositions by a vast number of experi- ments in different regions of physiology and physics, before he could hope to see the principle admitted by science. He began, therefore, in 1845, by testing the accuracy of his physical conceptions upon a highly complex physiological

problem, in a paper published in *Müller's Archiv* with the
title, ' Metabolism during Muscular Activity.'

Lavoisier had already shown that a man who is doing work
requires more oxygen than a man at rest, but while it was
admitted that certain ponderable or imponderable substances
were consumed in the production of mechanical effects, and
were perpetually renewed by the vegetative vital processes,
and also that the amount of certain excreted nitrogenous
matters was increased by muscular activity, all data in regard
to the initial and intermediate steps of the process and the
seat of its occurrence were wanting. Helmholtz accordingly
set himself to investigate the modifications produced in
the chemical constitution of muscle by its own activity.
Resorting to the frog, 'that ancient martyr to science,' he
succeeded by means of the little electrical machine constructed
by himself, and of a Leyden jar, in showing that the components within a muscle undergo chemical transformation during
its activity in virtue of the chemical processes described in his
account of fermentation and putrefaction ; and these conclusions led him after protracted experiment to a series of
important results, which were for a long time the only exact
data in connexion with this subject. Yet, as he was perpetually studying the inter-connexion of all these problems,
and their relation with the great law that governed his imagination, Helmholtz soon perceived that before he could obtain
exact data as to metabolism, it would be necessary to ascertain
the relations between muscular action and the heat therein
developed. This, however, entailed a fresh series of experiments, which had to be left over for a later period.

At Michaelmas he was to go up for the Government Examination at Berlin, and only had time before it to write an article
for the *Encyclopaedia of Medical Science* (issued by some
members of the Medical Faculty of Berlin), entitled ' Heat,
physiological,' which comprised the most recent observations
on animal heat. In this he strove to bring order into the
distorted conceptions then prevailing as to the nature of heat,
and the essay is distinguished by that grasp of the historical
development of the most heterogeneous branches of natural
science, for which Helmholtz was afterwards so generally
admired.

After giving an historical and critical review of the facts that relate to the regulated high temperature of the more perfectly organized animals, which persists throughout life, and only disappears with its extinction, and a table of the differences of temperature in different kinds of animals, he investigates the origin of animal heat. In a very interesting discussion of the different views that have been held as to its nature, Helmholtz states the most important results of the prevailing theories in the form of the law that is fundamental to organic heat, viz. that the total heat liberated by the union of two or more elements to form the same compound must be the same, whatever the intermediate processes through which the system may have passed. But since quantity of substance can neither be increased nor diminished in nature, it follows from the accepted theories of heat that its quantity in nature must be an absolute constant, whence he concludes that the actual temperature of an organism can only be due to a supply of heat from without, either free or latent, and, inasmuch as sources of free heat exist only in exceptional cases, organic heat must necessarily be derived from the latent heat of the food. The work that had been done on production and loss of heat, and on animal metabolism, justified the conclusion that the materials supplied to the body in respiration and digestion provide the entire sum of vital warmth during the successive stages of their combination within the body. According to Helmholtz the only alternative is to admit that organisms are the seat of a special force (the so-called vital energy), by which the forces of nature can be engendered *ad infinitum*—a hypothesis that contradicts all known laws of mechanical science, but cannot theoretically be objected to, if physiologists choose to assume that such an incomprehensible phenomenon is the distinguishing characteristic of the life-process.

In October, 1845, Helmholtz received six months' leave, in order to pass the State Examination in medicine and surgery, during which time he was attached as surgeon to the Friedrich-Wilhelm Institute. By the terms of his engagement, he was subsequently bound to serve twice this period as surgeon to the King's army. On February 7, 1846, he returned to his official duties with full credentials.

The five months of his stay in Berlin were spent in hard work, and in close scientific intercourse with his friends du Bois-Reymond and Brücke, who, when separated later on, communicated all their scientific projects, and the results of their work, to each other in writing. This was the first Christmas that Helmholtz had not spent with his parents. He was doing his clinical tests at the Infirmary, and at the same time working steadily in the laboratory of Magnus at his researches on fermentation and putrefaction, while he regularly attended the meetings of the Physical Society.

In January, 1846, he announces in a letter to his parents that he had done well in the examination as physician and surgeon, but did not pass as an 'operator'.

Immediately after his return to his military duties at Potsdam we find him busy again with his experiments on the heat evolved in muscular activity, and from this time he exchanged ideas regularly with du Bois-Reymond, partly in letters written about once a fortnight, partly at meetings between the two friends in Berlin or Potsdam. Up to July 1, he was on duty in the field hospital, after which he was 'happy again with leisure to experiment'. After satisfying himself 'with great difficulty as to the constancy of the frog-current between copper electrodes in a solution of copper sulphate', he proceeded to investigate the nature of the chemical processes which he had discovered in muscle.

At the beginning of October, 1846, Helmholtz sent a 'Report on Work done on the Theory of Animal Heat for 1845', at du Bois' request, to the *Fortschritte der Physik*, issued by the Physical Society. This was merely an abstract from the article in the Encyclopaedic Dictionary above mentioned, but it anticipates more definitely the conclusions of his great work. He states without hesitation that the material theory of heat is no longer tenable, and that a kinetic theory must be substituted for it, since heat originates in mechanical forces, either directly by friction, or indirectly from an electrical current produced by the motion of magnets. This conception of heat as motion involves the conclusion that mechanical, electrical, and chemical forces must always be the definite equivalent of one and the same energy, whatever the mode by which one force is transformed into another. The empirical confirmation of this law must be the imperative duty of physicists and physiologists.

The last months of 1846 were wholly taken up with experiments on the heat evolved during muscular action. After much discussion with du Bois-Reymond by word of mouth and letter as to the conversion of a thermo-multiplier of extreme sensitivity, by empirical graduation, into a thermometer for thousandths of a degree, Helmholtz begs the loan of the portable balance made for du Bois by Halske, 'in order to experiment on the ash of muscle and the composition of nerve with regard to their possible alteration by muscular contraction.' But though du Bois himself brought the balance to Potsdam, Helmholtz was compelled by stress of official duties to break off his experiments for a long time at the end of 1846. The New Year diverted his scientific enterprises into another and wider field, and was also destined to be the most important of his life in aspects other than scientific.

After the death of Surgeon-Major von Velten, his widow had moved from Riesenburg to Potsdam with her two daughters, in order to profit by the advantages of the intellectual society to which she was there introduced by her brother (a surgeon-major in the Hussars), and to obtain a good education for her children. Her husband was the son of that Cornet Velten of the Ziethen Hussars, who during the retreat at the battle of Kunersdorf came upon the King, standing alone on an eminence in the field, with his sword driven into the ground in front of him, facing death or captivity. Velten cut his way through, along with Captain von Prittwitz, and helped the King to escape on his own horse, for which he was ennobled, and received the order *pour le mérite*. Frau von Velten was the daughter of the late Hofrath Puhlmann, Court Painter and Director of the Picture-Gallery founded by Frederick the Great. Helmholtz soon obtained an introduction to this distinguished family, though 'at first he was somewhat of a foreign element'.

His sister-in-law relates that he was 'grave and reserved, a little awkward and shy among other more lively and sociable young men. Some one made the characteristic remark, when Helmholtz was introduced to us, that he was a very clever man if only you could dig him out,—and that proved treasure-trove indeed'. Before long he was accepted as one of the household, which, he declared, seemed to him less a part of ordinary life than of some beautiful romance; while his judgement in all matters was soon accepted as conclusive. He played the piano a great deal with the younger sister, Olga, who sang exceedingly well, displayed his talent for reading aloud, made pretty verses for the young ladies, and acted comedy almost like a professional, taking the humorous parts for choice, especially those with a touch of the grotesque. A still existing play-bill tells us that he took the chief *rôle* of Herr Petermann in a piece called *Lodgings to Let*, performed on December 27, 1846, at the house of Rigler, the Director of the Gymnasium. It is on record that Helmholtz gave up his time most amiably, and worked hard at the performance, although it was obvious from his acting that his mind was occupied with other and higher thoughts; in fact, he was just then writing the Introduction to his memoir on the 'Conservation of Energy'. 'He was becoming,' writes his sister-in-law, 'an inseparable part of our existence, and there was a ripening sense between him and my sister that their lives were bound up together. Olga was not beautiful, but she was refined and agreeable; she never put herself forward, but listened with attention and keen observation. Her mind was alert, amusing, witty, almost sarcastic; but there was about her a breath of femininity and simple purity that was irresistible.'

The betrothal took place on March 11, 1847, and Helmholtz writes a characteristic letter to his bride-elect on a day when he had vainly expected her at a symphony-concert at the *Sing-Akademie* in Berlin. 'You did not come, and so my ear went wrong also. I fancied it must always have been your soul, with your deep musical perceptions, that had governed the harmonies in my brain. My ear heard only musical figures, and my soul heard naught. Needless to say this was in the Mozart Symphony, one of his finest, with which every one else was delighted. But forlorn as I was, bereft of the better half of my soul, I might as well have been listening to scales upon the piano. I only recovered myself in the *Coriolanus* Overture. That is a jewel—so short, so convincing, so decided, and proud amid a host of restless and entangled *motifs*, while it dies off

so sadly in melancholy strains . . . an unsurpassable master-
piece.'

The wedding could not take place until Helmholtz received
some permanent appointment, so the young man embarked
courageously upon his great scientific enterprise.   By the
middle of February, 1847, he had sent du Bois-Reymond the
sketch of his Introduction to the 'Conservation of Energy'. 'Not
because I think it is ready, for even in reading it over I see
that most likely none of it can stand, but because I do not
yet see how many times I shall have to rewrite it before it is
done, and I want to know if you think the style in which it
is written one that will go down with the physicists.   I pulled
myself together at the last reading, and threw everything over-
board that savoured of philosophy, wherever it was not absolutely essential, so this may have made some gaps in my logic.
Still you will be able to see the nature of the argument from
it.   Don't put yourself out to read it; do it at your leisure, and
then write to me: where you find obscurities or lacunae in the
details note them on the margin.   I may come to Berlin myself
after a while to talk to you about it.'

Du Bois received the Introduction with enthusiasm, and
declared that it must remain as it was, '*an historical document
of great scientific import for all time.*'

It was during the first quarter of 1847, while he was on
field-hospital duty, that the young investigator found opportunity to formulate the ideas which he had cherished since
the beginning of his studies, and had tested by experiments
in the most disparate branches of physiology and physics with
a view to publishing the results.   Neither he nor his friends
had any notion that other workers were engaged on the same
problems.   When free of the hospital post, Helmholtz at once
resumed his experimental work, and reconstructed the apparatus
for his thermal experiments on muscle, giving much good
advice from his own experiences to du Bois about his experiments, while he 'waited impatiently for the spring and the frogs'.
But once more he had to interrupt his experiments, since Halske
kept him waiting too long over the construction of a Neef's
interruptor for his electrical apparatus, till finally the moment
for producing the 'Conservation of Energy' before the world
arrived.

On July 21 he announced to du Bois-Reymond that he would
bring forward his 'Conservation of Energy' on the 23rd at the
Physical Society.   The meeting was one of the most memorable
in the annals of the Society; as du Bois tells us, Helmholtz
revealed himself at one bound, to the surprise of all his friends,
as a master of mathematical physics.   The members of the
Physical Society were acquainted with the Law of the Conservation of Energy when it was still unknown to all the rest
of the world.

As soon as the meeting was over Helmholtz sent the manuscript to Magnus, with whom he was on very friendly terms,
begging him to arrange for its publication in *Poggendorff's
Annalen*.   But Magnus, though he willingly and cordially
recognized the merits of Helmholtz's essay, took exception to
the character of his work.   He regarded experimental and
mathematical physics as separate departments, and warned him
repeatedly against undue partiality for mathematics, and the
attempt to bring remote provinces of physics together by
its means.   Accordingly he only sent the memoir with
a few words of general recommendation to Poggendorff, and
this apparently not till he was constrained to it by du Bois-
Reymond, who, with Brücke, had all the younger physicists
and physiologists of the Physical Society upon his side.
Poggendorff replied that the subject-matter was not in his
opinion sufficiently experimental to justify him in publishing it
in the *Annalen*, though he acknowledged its importance as
a theoretical treatise.   Both he and Magnus therefore advised
the author to bring it out as an independent publication.   Du
Bois forwarded these letters to Helmholtz with forcible expressions of his annoyance with Poggendorff and Magnus,
urging him if possible to get the essay published by Reimer
in Berlin as a pamphlet, and recommending him to restore
the Philosophical Introduction.   Helmholtz did not allow
his satisfaction in the work to be destroyed by the reservations of the older physicists, but he altered certain
parts of the Introduction in order still further to emphasize
his position in regard to the prevailing scientific conceptions.   This Introduction was the foreword of modern
science in the second half of the nineteenth century, while
its fine and simple style already proclaim its author a

master of language : hence it may be fitly cited in this connexion :—

'The principal contents of the present memoir show it to be addressed to physicists chiefly, and I have therefore thought it judicious to lay down its fundamental principles purely in the form of a physical premise, and, independent of metaphysical considerations, to develop the consequences of these principles, and to submit them to a comparison with what experience has established in the various branches of physics. The deduction of the propositions contained in the memoir may be based on either of two maxims ; either on the maxim that it is not possible by any combination whatever of natural bodies to derive an unlimited amount of mechanical force, or on the assumption that all actions in nature can be ultimately referred to attractive or repulsive forces, the intensity of which depends solely on the distances between the points at which the forces are exerted. That both these propositions are identical is shown at the commencement of the memoir itself. Meanwhile the important bearing which they have upon the final aim of the physical sciences may with propriety be made the subject of a special introduction.

'The problem of the sciences just alluded to is, in the first place, to seek the laws by which the particular processes of nature may be referred to, and deduced from, general rules. These rules—for example, the law of the reflection and re-fraction of light, the law of Mariotte and Gay-Lussac regarding the volumes of gases—are evidently nothing more than general ideas by which the various phenomena which belong to them are connected together. The finding out of these is the office of the experimental portion of our science. The theoretic portion seeks, on the contrary, to evolve the unknown causes of the processes from the visible actions which they present ; it seeks to comprehend these processes according to the laws of causality. We are justified, and indeed impelled in this proceeding, by the conviction that every change in nature *must* have a sufficient cause. The proximate causes to which we refer phenomena may, in themselves, be either variable or invariable ; in the former case the above conviction impels us to seek for causes to account for the change, and thus we proceed until we at length arrive at final causes which are unchangeable, and which therefore must, in all cases where the exterior conditions are the same, produce the same invariable effects. The final aim of the theoretic natural sciences is therefore to discover the ultimate and unchangeable causes of natural phenomena. Whether all the processes of nature be actually referable to such, or whether nature is capable of being completely comprehended, or whether changes occur which are not subject to the laws of necessary causation, but spring from spontaneity or freedom, this is not the place to decide; it is at all events clear that the science whose object it is to comprehend nature must proceed from the assumption that it is comprehensible, and in accordance with this assumption investigate and conclude until, perhaps, she is at length admonished by irrefragable facts that there are limits beyond which she cannot proceed.

'Science regards the phenomena of the exterior world according to two processes of abstraction; in the first place it looks upon them as simple existences, without regard to their action upon our organs of sense or upon each other; in this aspect they are termed *matter*. The existence of matter in itself is to us something tranquil and devoid of action: in it we distinguish merely the relations of space and of quantity (mass), which is assumed to be eternally unchangeable. To matter, thus regarded, we must not ascribe qualitative differences, for when we speak of different kinds of matter we refer to differences of action, that is, to differences in the forces of matter. Matter in itself can therefore partake of one change only, a change which has reference to space, that is, motion. Natural objects are not, however, thus passive; in fact we come to a knowledge of their existence solely from their actions upon our organs of sense, and infer from these actions a something which acts. When, therefore, we wish to make actual application of our idea of matter, we can only do it by means of a second abstraction, and ascribe to it properties which in the first case were excluded from our idea, namely, the capability of producing effects, or, in other words, of exerting *force*. It is evident that in the application of the ideas of matter and force to nature the two former should never be separated: a mass of pure matter would as far as we and nature are concerned be a nullity, inasmuch as no action could be wrought by it either upon our organs of sense or upon the remaining portion of nature. A pure force would be something which must have a basis, and yet which has no basis, for the basis we name matter. It would be just as erroneous to define matter as something which has an actual existence, and force as an idea which has no corresponding reality. Both, on the contrary, are abstractions from the actual, formed in precisely similar ways. Matter is only discernible by its forces, and not by itself.

'We have seen above that the problem before us is not to refer back the phenomena of nature to unchangeable final causes. This requirement may now be expressed by saying that for final causes unchangeable forces must be found. Bodies with unchangeable forces have been named in science (chemistry) elements. Let us suppose the universe decomposed into elements possessing unchangeable qualities, the only alteration possible to such a system is an alteration of position, that is, motion; hence the forces can only be moving forces dependent in their action upon conditions of space.

'To speak more particularly: the phenomena of nature are to be referred back to motions of material particles possessing unchangeable moving forces, which are dependent upon conditions of space alone. Motion is the alteration of the conditions of space. Motion, as a matter of experience, can only appear as a change in the relative position of at least two material bodies. Force, which originates motion, can only be conceived of as referring to the relation of at least two material bodies towards each other; it is therefore to be defined as the endeavour of two masses to alter their relative position. But the force which two masses exert upon each other must be resolved into those exerted by all their particles upon each other; hence in mechanics we go back to forces exerted by material points. The relation of one point to another, as regards space, has reference solely to their distance apart: a moving force, therefore, exerted by each upon the other, can only act so as to cause an alteration of their distance, that is, it must be either attractive or repulsive.

'Finally, therefore, we discover the problem of physical natural science to be, to refer natural phenomena back to unchangeable attractive and repulsive forces, whose intensity

depends solely upon distance. The solvability of this problem
is the condition of the complete comprehensibility of nature.
In mechanical calculations this limitation of the idea of moving
force has not yet been assumed: a great number, however, of
general principles referring to the motion of compound systems
of bodies are only valid for the case that these bodies operate
upon each other by unchangeable attractive or repulsive forces;
for example, the principle of virtual velocities; the conservation
of the motion of the centre of gravity; the conservation of the
principal plane of rotation; of the moment of rotation of free
systems; and the conservation of *vis viva*. In terrestrial matters
application is made chiefly of the first and last of these principles, inasmuch as the others refer to systems which are supposed
to be completely free; we shall, however, show that the first
is only a special case of the last, which therefore must be
regarded as the most general and important consequence a
the deduction which we have made.

'Theoretical natural science therefore, if she does not rest
contented with half-views of things, must bring her notions
into harmony with the expressed requirements as to the
nature of simple forces, and with the consequences which
flow from them. Her vocation will be ended as soon as
the reduction of natural phenomena to simple forces is complete, and the proof given that this is the only reduction of
which the phenomena are capable.'[1]

Helmholtz accepted du Bois-Reymond's advice and wrote to
G. A. Reimer, who replied that he was only too glad, since
du Bois answered for the value of the treatise, to undertake
its publication. He brought it out in 1847, and presented
Helmholtz, to his great surprise, with an honorarium.

The Law of the Conservation of Energy as put forth by
Helmholtz suffered the vicissitudes incident to the birth of
all great thoughts. However much a generalization may be
foreshadowed by experiment in different directions, and suggested and discussed by speculative thinkers, yet when it
finally appears in concrete form it is sure to encounter doubts
as to its accuracy, or, if the magnitude and worth of the discovery are recognized, suspicions of its originality, and

[1] J. Tyndall, 'The Conservation of Force,' *Scientific Memoirs* [Natural
Philosophy], I, pp. 114 seqq.

disputes as to priority. While the memoir was enthusiastically welcomed by the younger physicists and physiologists of Berlin, who were led by du Bois-Reymond, and Helmholtz to his high delight was praised by the military authorities 'for the splendid practical turn that he had given to his studies', the older scientists with hardly an exception rejected the ideas which the work expressed, fearing, strangely enough, that such speculations would revive the phantasm of Hegel's 'nature-philosophy', against which they had fought so long, and in the end so successfully. There was but one, after Johannes Müller the most gifted scientific thinker of the day, the mathematician Joh. Jac. Jacobi, who from his profound studies of the principles of mechanics clearly recognized the close connexion between the work of Helmholtz and that of the great French mathematicians of the preceding century. Notwithstanding the doubts of his distinguished colleagues Lejeune-Dirichlet and Eisenstein, he unhesitatingly proclaimed the significance of Helmholtz's work, and by this gave confidence and self-assurance to its author. In the original treatise Helmholtz had only attempted to give a critical survey and arrangement of the facts in the interests of physiology, expecting the physicists at most to reproach him for having, as a young doctor, brought forward as new what was well known to them, but he now realized from the general opposition that he had been the first to set forth a universal law of experimental science, and to purify and free it from vague philosophical and speculative reflections.

The elementary scientific discussions about perpetual motion in his parents' house had never proved its impossibility conclusively for Helmholtz, and while still a student at the Friedrich-Wilhelm Institute he resorted to the works of Daniel Bernouilli, d'Alembert, and other mathematicians of the eighteenth century which he found in its library. From these he obtained the strictest and most convincing proof that a *perpetuum mobile* cannot be produced by purely mechanical forces. Just as the works of a clock have no energy of their own, and can only distribute evenly, over a considerable period, what is supplied to them from without, so, as these great thinkers showed by rigid mathematical proof for all pure motive forces, our machines and apparatus have no intrinsic energy, but merely give out in other forms what is communicated to them from the store of energy in the universe.

Yet it still remained an open question whether perpetual motion might not be possible in the great field of the other natural forces, which cannot be reckoned as purely motive—heat, electricity, magnetism, light, chemical affinity—but are all, nevertheless, in manifold relations with the mechanical processes, since in almost every natural process mechanical effects are produced, and mechanical work is performed.

Helmholtz's medical studies, and his knowledge of the biological side of natural phenomena, led him in the first instance to consider the possibility of perpetual motion in these processes, which he had studied since 1841.

After his physiological observations had led him time after time to the conclusion that there could be no *perpetuum mobile* for the natural forces that here come under consideration, and when he had convinced himself that such a thing was altogether impossible, he inverted the problem hitherto propounded by the scientists, as to how the relations between natural energies could be utilized to construct a *perpetuum mobile*, and asked himself what the relations between the forces of nature must be, if perpetual motion were indeed impossible.

As a matter of fact, this reversal of the problem had been previously made for heat, though in less general terms, and with less conscious intention, by Robert Mayer and Colding, with whose investigations Helmholtz was not acquainted, and by Joule, whose experiments he heard of first when his own work was completed. Helmholtz found that all known relations of forces lead to the conclusion that perpetual motion is impossible : he plotted out a further series as yet unknown, the actual existence of which had to be ascertained, and endeavoured to formulate all the relations between the different processes of nature which could be deduced from his assumption. The result proved that there is no cycle throughout the entire range of natural processes by which mechanical energy can be generated without corresponding expenditure ; the quantity of working force may indeed be lost to the particular machine, but not to the universe as a whole. 'Nature as a whole possesses a store of energy which cannot in any wise be added to or subtracted from: the quantity of energy in inorganic nature is as eternal and unalterable as the quantity of matter,' the constancy of which had been established as a fundamental law of chemistry by Lavoisier half a century before.

Helmholtz termed this universal principle, now known as the Law of the Conservation of Energy, the Law of the Conservation of Force; it asserts that each transformation of energy takes place under exactly measurable quantitative relations, whether the form of energy be the *vis viva* of motion, or electrical and magnetic energy, or heat, whence again the impossibility of perpetual motion follows.

In order to include within the scope of his considerations such natural forces as may be still unknown, he affirms with the care of a great investigator that the validity of the law of the constancy of the sum of *vis viva* and of what he called the 'tensional forces', i.e. of actual and potential energy, is in the highest degree probable, since it contradicts none of the known facts of science, and is on the contrary confirmed by many of these in the most striking manner. He tests the energy-equivalents of heat, of electrical action, of magnetism and electro-magnetism, and after finding the law to be universally valid, turns as physiologist to the natural processes of organic existence, and shows that the problem of the conservation of energy is here a question of whether the oxidation and metabolism of the nutritive substances generate an equivalent quantity of heat to that given off by animals, a problem which had already occupied him for some months in Potsdam.

'I have endeavoured,' he says at the close of this masterly treatise, 'to state in the most complete manner possible the inferences which flow from a combination of the law with other known laws of natural phenomena, and which still await their experimental proof. The object of this investigation was to lay before physicists as fully as possible the theoretic and practical importance of a law whose complete corroboration must be regarded as one of the principal problems of the natural philosophy of the future.'

At the time when Helmholtz began his analytical study of the natural sciences, the law of the persistence of matter (by which the elements may alter in regard to the mode of

their distribution in space, but are unalterable in their properties) was admitted by all physicists to obtain in every
change of organic and inorganic nature. The great principle of the conservation of energy, which Helmholtz placed
beside this law, postulates that all forces are to be measured
in terms of mechanical force, and that all forms of energy are
ultimately kinetic, so that the final aim of natural science
must be to reduce itself to mechanics.

Equipped only with such literary matter as the library of
the Gymnasium could afford him during his residence in
Potsdam, unaware of Robert Mayer's nine-page note 'On
the Forces of Inorganic Nature', published in Wöhler and
Liebig's *Annalen der Chemie* in 1842, after it also had been
rejected by Poggendorff, and of the same author's treatise published in 1845, on 'Organic Motion in relation to Metabolism',
Helmholtz had by 1843-4 completed the essentials of the
work which Kirchhoff estimated twenty years later as the
most important contribution to natural science made in our
era, while Hertz, Helmholtz's great pupil, says of it that
'Physical research had been diverted by the close of the
century into an entirely new channel. Under the over-
mastering influence of Helmholtz's discovery of the conservation of energy, its object was henceforward to refer all
phenomena in last resort to the laws which govern the
transformation of energy'.

But while the great significance of Helmholtz's work was
immediately recognized by the younger generation of scientific
men, the older physicists still held aloof from it, on the ground
that it was a relapse into the 'nature-philosophy' of Hegel.
In other quarters, again, where the importance of the great
law was admitted, the honour of its discovery was withheld
from Helmholtz. It was said that he had borrowed the idea
from Dr. Julius Robert Mayer, a Heilbronn physician, who
had published a thesis on the same subject, and had even
determined the mechanical equivalent of heat. 'This report,'
says du Bois-Reymond, 'has lasted, like the fame of Helmholtz's
treatise, to the present day, and has been greedily accepted
by those who love to trail shadows across the sunlight.'

As regards priority, Helmholtz, after he had become
acquainted with the writings of Robert Mayer, took every

opportunity, in discussing the discovery of the Law of the Conservation of Energy, of insisting that it was Mayer who had first expressed his conviction that the sum of energy in the universe could neither be destroyed nor added to, and who formulated this view in his law of 'the equivalence of heat and work'. The English physicist Joule had also undertaken an extensive series of experiments, independent of Mayer, with the object of determining the equivalence between heat and work empirically, and a lively controversy as to the priority of Mayer's work had therefore already been raised by those 'who attach more weight to the collection of data than to the formulation of general principles'.

Helmholtz himself, both in his original treatise and in discussing the subject afterwards, used to say that the work which he then undertook was one of pure criticism and arrangement, since its principal aim could only be to test the earlier conclusions derived from inductive methods, upon the newly-acquired material. If a law is to hold good throughout the universe for the vast complex of natural processes, it was not in his estimation sufficient merely to state this as Mayer had done; evidence sufficient to enforce conviction of its probability must be produced, so that scientific men may bear it in mind for future confirmation.

'In those days it was far more important than might possibly now be the case, to make clear from beginning to end that the law was a law of facts, abstracted from the facts, and to be confirmed again by facts.'

Helmholtz consistently recognized that when the Law of the Conservation of Energy had made its way later on, and its accuracy was generally accepted, every one would admit that Mayer had in 1842 reached a perception of its meaning and universal significance, just as Faraday must have had a presentiment of the same law long before Joule gave definite scientific expression to it, and filled up the most important gap in the empirical evidence in its favour.

But Mayer had not arrived at this perception by scientific methods. After the data (which were familiar enough to many of his predecessors) had arranged themselves in his consciousness, 'the creative idea presented itself suddenly, not as a demonstrated truth, but as a problem, for the solution of which empirical facts must be investigated.' Unlike Helmholtz, he did not test the accuracy of the law (conceived as it were by inspiration, and by a certain creative activity of his brain), or rather its consequences, upon all the natural processes known at that time: the recognition of the principle in fact involved other, and deeper mathematical, knowledge than any Mayer could command.

Helmholtz by his discovery gave an impulse to the whole later development of mathematical physics, and showed by rigid mathematical proof that whenever natural bodies act upon each other by attractive or repulsive forces, which are independent of time and velocity, the sum of their *vires vivae* and 'tensional forces' must be constant; but if these forces depend upon time and velocity, or act in other directions than the straight lines which unite the two active material points, then (provided the action and reaction are equal) combinations of such bodies will be possible in which energy may be either lost or gained *ad infinitum*. When in this sense the above forces are described as 'conservative', the Law of the Conservation of Energy says no more than that all elementary natural forces are conservative.

The work which the great French mathematicians had done in mechanics was familiar to Helmholtz, and to him it was no new induction, but merely the definite statement and complete generalization of an established conviction, to say that all elementary forces are conservative. In Helmholtz's opinion those great thinkers must have made the same conjecture, but did not state it in terms, since they could not prove it, having 'set themselves the particular task of educating men from the false rationalism of scholasticism to the strict appreciation of experimental data'. Helmholtz termed his theorem the law of the 'Conservation of Energy' (*Erhaltung der Kraft*), to mark that it was an extension of the already known law of the 'Conservation of *Vis Viva*' (*Erhaltung der lebendigen Kraft*), and to make its relation clear with the old question of the possibility of a *perpetuum mobile*.

Mayer, by trying to get rid of the conception of force in mechanics, and defining as *Kraft* (force) what had previously been defined as work, i.e. the product of force into the distance through which it acts, obscured the meaning of the

well-known law of the conservation of *vis viva*, and delayed
the strict mathematical expression of the law which he divined.
Helmholtz, on the other hand (by analogy with the name
'quantity of *vis viva*', which was used by Leibniz to express
the work-equivalent of the velocity of the moving masses),
gave the name 'quantity of tensional force' to this product,
and in thus expressing the work-value of those forces which
are actually engaged in the stress of producing motion, he
established a connexion between actual and potential energy,
the sum of which is constant for all transformations.

This conception of a definite store of energy in the universe
was quite new and due to Helmholtz alone; it was defined
'as a quantity which can no more be destroyed nor added to
than a substance, which acts in space and yet cannot be sub-
divided with space like a material substance, because each
division of space would not involve the portion of "tensional
energy" which exists between the particles of matter on either
side of the dividing surface,'—a conception familiar to modern
science, and founded solely upon the mighty work of Helmholtz and the splendid pioneering achievements of Lord
Kelvin.

Twenty years later Helmholtz again took occasion to ascribe
priority in the conception of the conservation of energy to
Robert Mayer, as against the claims of Joule. In a letter
to Tait on the occasion of a dispute about priority in the
question of absorption and radiation, he puts Kirchhoff forward, since he was the first to formulate the law, and thus
made the great discoveries that are involved in it possible.
Helmholtz maintained that Kirchhoff's work in this field
represented one of the most instructive cases in the history
of science. Many investigators had been on the verge of
the same discoveries, but the development of spectral analysis
as a whole became possible only after Kirchhoff had theoretically determined those general properties of heat which are
its fundamental basis. He clearly enunciates the relation of
Mayer to Joule, and thus indirectly to himself also:—

'Robert Mayer was not in a position to carry out experiments. He was repulsed by the physicists with whom he
was acquainted, and could hardly find acceptance for his
first condensed statement. While no one can deny that Joule

did more than Mayer, and that many particulars are confused in Mayer's first note, we must, I think, regard him as a man who of and for himself conceived the idea which has rendered the great recent advance of natural science possible, nor is his merit in any way lessened by the fact that another man, in another country and different sphere of activity, had simultaneously made the same discovery, and worked it out afterwards with greater completeness.'

Robert Mayer himself was far from claiming priority over Helmholtz in his epoch-making work, and the Naturforscher-Versammlung at Innsbruck in 1868, at which Helmholtz acknowledged Mayer's priority clearly and without ambiguity wherever it was due, left the two distinguished men on the best possible understanding.

With this work on the Conservation of Energy, Helmholtz took first rank not only among physicists, but among physiologists also, who recognized that his law afforded them an invaluable weapon for the attack upon vitalism; and he now went on to verify it for the natural processes of living organisms, by continuing his earlier experiments on the development of heat during muscular activity. His results were given to the Physical Society in November, 1847, and published the next year in *Müller's Archiv*.

This research, which is a model of the application of the most delicate physical methods to physiological problems, was intended to determine whether the rise of temperature in a working muscle takes place in the substance of the muscle itself, in consequence of internal processes brought about during contraction by a disturbance of equilibrium, or whether it is merely the result of increased flow of arterial blood. While the previous thermo-electric determinations of temperature in animals had been made with only a Becquerel couple, Helmholtz employed a triple junction of iron and German-silver which trebled the electromotive force, and found with the finest measurements, and ingenious contrivances for the exclusion of every other increase of temperature, that in excised and isolated thighs of the frog, there was a rise of temperature derived solely from molecular processes, when the muscle was caused to contract by stimulating the spinal cord with a Neef's interruptor modified for the purpose. The heat in contraction was therefore actually produced in the muscle substance, while attempts to demonstrate a rise of temperature in nerve during the transmission of excitation from spinal cord to muscle yielded negative results. These data all made for the verification of Helmholtz's great law, though the investigations could not then be held conclusive.

The close of 1847 was devoted to severely theoretical studies, as appears from the many notes on classical problems in pure mathematics found among Helmholtz's papers, but his medical duties hindered him more than was desirable in the free disposal of his time, until at the beginning of 1848 the current of his life was altered by a fortunate development.

His friend Brücke, who was teacher of anatomy at the Academy of Arts and assistant at the Museum of Anatomy and Zoology, was appointed Professor of Physiology and General Pathology at Königsberg, and the reversion of the posts thus vacated in Berlin devolved on his intimate friend and contemporary du Bois-Reymond, who was two years older than Helmholtz. But since du Bois' private means made it possible for him to devote himself entirely to his investigations in animal electricity, without taking up professional duties, he retired from the competition for the Academy post in favour of his younger friend, arranging with Brücke that Helmholtz should be brought forward.

On the strength of an excellent testimonial received from Johannes Müller, Helmholtz was invited (August 19, 1848) to give a trial lecture before the Senate and Professors of the Academy. This was found among his papers, and has never before been published:—

'I shall endeavour, in the lecture which I have the honour of giving before you, to develop those points which seem to me the most essential in the teaching of anatomy to art-students, and the methods that should be employed. I must from the outset claim the forbearance of this distinguished assembly, since I am well aware what varied capacities and kinds of knowledge should be combined in any one who endeavours to fulfil the duties of this post successfully, and how difficult is the handling of this science, if it is to be raised from the dry and often barren forms of a colossal effort of memory to a living thing that can be applied to Art.

'The end to be aimed at is one so special, so totally different from what is usually expected from a teacher of anatomy, that I venture to say that but few of its postulates can be theoretically laid down beforehand; the majority must follow from practice and experience. The new lecturer must indeed draw up some system of instruction, but little may possibly remain of his scheme by the time it has been carried into execution.

'Anatomy, taught as an exact science to the medical student, has quite other aims, other proportions, and a widely different method. It starts with the necessity of giving the sharpest and most abstract definitions that are possible; for the physician and surgeon cannot limit himself to the appearance of the parts as they are in the sound body. His principal business is to discover sharp and simple characteristics that will not leave him in doubt, even where illness or lesion has so distorted the appearance of the parts, that the untrained eye could no longer find its way among them; and medical anatomy is thus in its essentials a collection of dry concepts, very difficult to realize, of evil repute even for the long-suffering memory of the medical student, and the obvious appearance is hardly ever called in as more than an aid to the memory, while on the other hand it is all-essential to the artist.

'For the doctor, for instance, what is of importance in any particular muscle besides the point of attachment which determines its action, is the situation of the vessels and nerves upon or beneath it, the lie of the fascia that surround it, and control the flow of pus, and so on. What the muscle looks like, whether thin or thick, round or flat; to what extent it consists of flesh, and where its tendons begin; whether it can be seen through the skin—to these and similar questions he is for the most part quite indifferent, while it is just these points that make the muscle interesting to the artist.

'Art anatomy is therefore distinct from medical anatomy not merely in its content (since it embraces a portion of the latter, but has to work it up more specially), but still more essentially in its methods.

'How anatomy should be taught for the artist is best decided by determining wherein and why it can help him. The artists of antiquity were ignorant of the internal aspects of the human body. The ancients had a natural, unconquerable aversion to the dissection of corpses, and were also hampered by their religious convictions, which made all desecration of the dead an unpardonable trespass against the most awful and sacred laws of the gods. Even late into the Middle Ages human bodies were never dissected by physicians—those of apes at most. A medical student may have obtained some essential knowledge from the dismemberment of these man-like animals, but the works of even the most renowned medical authors of antiquity, e.g. Galen, contain anatomical observations which are incorrect for man, and true of apes only. This substitute for human anatomy could have been of no use to artists; they were restricted to careful observation of the surface of the body, and at most could only learn the connexions of the bones, muscles, and tendons from animals, and compare these as well as might be through the skin by eye and touch in man, and endeavour to guess at the form of them.

'And yet despite these limitations, how marvellous a perfection is exhibited by the art of antiquity—not only in the most accurate knowledge of the resting form, with a delicate sense of beauty in all its proportions, but in the finest observation of the play of living muscles. This knowledge of the human form is so perfect in the ancient masters that they were able to dominate their subject with admirable inspiration and freedom, the freedom that modern art strives after, too often vainly, and which is only attained by a few favourites of genius.

'We are tempted to inquire the need of anatomy, when the acme of sculpture was reached in ignorance of it. Why study below the surface, when it is the surface only that art has to render? To this we must reply that even in these works of inimitable talent, exquisite beauty, and laborious industry, there are some not inconsiderable errors which a good anatomist would have been able to avoid, though possessing far less skill than these sculptors. A muscle, e.g., is often visible only as a little swelling, but the slightest increase or displacement of this swelling is sufficient in many cases to produce an anatomical absurdity, into which the most skilful copyist would readily fall if he were ignorant of the meaning of the protrusion, while any one familiar with the lie of the muscles in the figure would avoid it. It would be useless to multiply examples unless we had the statues here to illustrate them; I will only, to make myself intelligible, adduce one instance, taken from a well-known and not ignoble statue of a Greek orator, usually known as the *Germanicus*, which was the work of the younger Cleomenes, in the post-Alexandrian period of Greek Art. The curve of the leg that stands free is so exaggerated, that the extensor muscles of the lower thigh (*m. rectus femoris* and *sartorius*), which lie below it, and are felt in the living subject close beneath the skin, or even protrude a little, are altogether obliterated. In a " Shooting Apollo " in the Berlin Museum the posterior part of the deltoid muscle is constructed as if its insertion lay at right angles to the arch of the shoulder-blade, whereas it is parallel with it.

'You may say that such an error, since it is patent only to the expert's eye (had it been more obvious, the Greek artist would never have perpetrated it), is of no consequence to the general effect of the statue, and that it is splitting hairs to dwell upon it. The creative artist produces the form which he has conceived without troubling about particulars, he is led on only by the sense of ideal beauty which hovers before his brain and eyes; and with the same unconsciousness of details and their causes, the connoisseur revels in the spectacle of living harmony afforded him in the work of the artist. Yet the artist's genius lies in the mysterious power of forming an original conception, and expressing it in a form that deliberate reflection subsequently acknowledges to be true and perfect. And just as it is certain that the spectator will be elevated in proportion with the splendour and fidelity of the artist's conformity to and interpretation of the ideal content of his work, so surely will every failure in this respect detract from the living beauty of the figure, even when the critic is unable to say wherein the fault consists, and what has caused it.

'It cannot be denied that the lack of anatomical knowledge among the ancients is often perceptible as a defect in their productions, however much their marvellous talent for the representation of truth and beauty may have obviated its consequences. Then again it must be remembered that the ancients had far more abundant opportunity of observing the human form than is possible in modern times, and that the curriculum of the art-school has to supplement this want as far as possible. The modern, who can only study the human form in the model-room, or at best in a bathing establishment (where indeed he seldom finds a wholly pleasing subject under the one-sided and distorting conditions of our civilization), is at a great disadvantage as compared with the ancients, and would be on very unequal terms of competition if he were not equipped with accessory instruction. He further has to reckon with the factor that, for the same reason, the public know much less of the human body. Anatomy can no more than any other branch of study be a substitute for genius in the artist, whether in regard to capacity for reproduction or to sense of beauty, but it can set him forward on his way, and sharpen his powers of observation.

'The question of the benefit of anatomy to the artist may therefore be reduced to this: What more can the knowledge of the internal structure of the body give him than he has acquired from the external study of it on the living model? In reply I would submit the following considerations:—

'1. It facilitates appreciation of the different forms of various parts of the body in different postures, since these forms can all be referred to the same underlying anatomical mechanism; it therefore makes the work of the artist easier when he has to do without a model. (Instance the different curves of the upper arm, and the different positions of the hand in turning the fore-arm.)

'2. It teaches the distinction between the essential and non-essential parts of the human form. The prominences and depressions on the surface of the human body are of very different importance according as they correspond with bones, muscles, or folds of skin. Even when the sculptor only wants to reproduce a given model, he may err, as we pointed out, in the reproduction of some swelling which is essential to the anatomical structure. But the sculptor never should imitate slavishly, since his model is always that of a man who has grown up with human imperfections, and falls short of the ideal: he must modify the individual form till he obtains the most perfect expression of its spirituality. Given a muscular man for the model, with the intention of making a figure as strong and tense as possible, a sort of Hercules, he must not thicken the folds of skin and the muscles equally to produce his effect, but, on the contrary, must rather reduce the skin to bring out the muscularity; or conversely, if he is planning a Silenus. It is further to be noted that the emphasizing of the more important anatomical features at the cost of the less essential, adds clearness and simplicity to the figure.

'3. Finally, it is impossible to study the gestures of the moving figure upon models, which must always be supported in order to maintain their posture without effort. This brings us to the important study of the variation in shape of active muscles. The model stands with relaxed muscles, even if he be successfully propped up in the required attitude. The artist must know what muscles swell and protrude in movement, unless his work is to give the effect of standing still, like the model. And even if he makes the model perform the action sometimes, and strives to fix the gestures in his memory, he still cannot entirely forego his knowledge of synthetic muscular action, since a noble, well-formed body moves differently from one that is less well developed. The former at each movement utilizes only so many limbs and muscles, with so much force, as are indispensable to the motion, giving an impression of grace and ease, while the less skilled and weakly individual works harder and uses more muscles simultaneously.

'Still, we must never forget that Anatomy is but an instrument to further the more exact knowledge of the human form, and that, like all other helps to artistic study, it can never replace the immediate perception of the forms themselves, nor the artistic sense of beauty. To the artist it is a means of lightening the mental conquest of the ever-changing complexities of his material object, the human form, sharpening his perception of what is essential, making the whole form transparent to him, and arming him with the instruments of a searching criticism of the work he has accomplished. Art, however, begins where anatomy ends; the spirit of the artist is shown in the wise application of the forms whose connexions and simple outlines have been taught by anatomy, and in the distinguishing characteristics of his figures. Here the artist, as in a Hercules, suggests the muscles lying in hard lumps beneath the skin; there in the female figure they are merely indicated by slight changes in the curvature of the limb; in children again they are entirely concealed by the plump rolls of fat; he alters the normal magnitudes of the parts according to his subject, and determines their position and motion. The display made by the artist who puts too much anatomical science into his figures, as has so often been alleged of Michael Angelo, and with more justice of his less inspired followers, is as unpleasant and false as the neglect of anatomical accuracy which produces lifeless or distorted figures.

'It is important for the student to study forms with very decided development of muscle, but he must not subsequently reproduce them with absolute fidelity on all occasions. It is interesting in this connexion to compare the frequent blunders of modern art with the work of the old masters: e.g. the *Discobolos* of Myron, from the zenith of Greek Art, who is in an attitude of the most violent exertion. He has checked his run to fling the discus, while, with the finest observation of actual movement, the spectator is only shown the great and almost continuous bulging of the limbs, although an impression of great vitality is imparted. Many another would have overladen such a figure, since even in a simple resting form it appears impossible to some to show enough muscles.

'It is essential for the artist, and therefore a principal aim in instruction, that anatomy shall give him as clear and complete a picture as possible. He must not only bear the position, attachment, and function of the different muscles in mind, so that when he thinks of them he can form a correct notion, as is perhaps sufficient for medical studies, but he must be accustomed to see the underlying parts clearly through the intervening veil of skin, and never to picture the arm without realizing the bundles of muscles that lie within it. Nor must he fail in knowledge of the positive anatomical details, since they will serve as a criterion in the searching criticism which he must apply to the figures he has created, in order to facilitate the discovery of errors. The cardinal point in a lecture on anatomical details must therefore be its application to the living and unblemished form. The student must be trained to compare the appearance of a dead subject, that has all its anatomical parts exposed, with living forms, and to recognize anatomical details in life-models and works of art, where they are more or less concealed, in order by such exercises to sharpen his perception of anatomical errors. It follows as a matter of course that anatomy for art-students should only treat of such parts of the body as are of significance for its external form. Instruction in anatomy must therefore embrace:—

'1. Bones and such cartilages as are externally visible, forming the fixed skeleton of the body, which determine the permanent relations of the several elements. This section, with the exception of the cranial bones, must be treated in as much detail as for medical anatomy, since even the smaller prominences on a bone are important as points of insertion for the muscles.

'2. Joints and ligaments, also treated in detail, notably in regard to limitations of movements.

'3. Muscles, briefly as regards the deeper, in detail for the more superficial, with particular reference to their appearance through the skin. Besides the functions of single muscles, systems of composite movements must be included.

'In addition, some instruction in animal anatomy should be given, say on the horse, so far as our teaching apparatus will admit.'

The lecture gave complete satisfaction to the authorities, and on September 30, 1848, Helmholtz was released from the three years' military service for which he was still indentured, and entered on a civil career. The transfer was accomplished with little trouble, at the instance of 'the good genius who then presided over science in Berlin—Alexander von Humboldt'.

The post at the Academy of Arts carried a salary of £60 per annum, and he was further appointed assistant at the Anatomical Museum, with a salary of £30, on the recommendation of Johannes Müller, who testified to his being as skilful in anatomy as he had proved himself in physiological experiment.

Thus, in 1848, Helmholtz left the military service, to which he had belonged since October, 1838, and he also ceased to practise as a doctor from the moment he was emancipated from his official obligations. But he always kept up his connexion with medical science, and frequently asserted later on that to a certain extent he felt more at home in it than in any other department, while he looked back to his education at the Military College with affection, and owed to it, as Ludwig justly remarks, 'the care he invariably bestowed upon his personal appearance, and the general decorum of his attitude.'

CHAPTER V

LECTURER TO THE ACADEMY OF ARTS, AND ASSISTANT IN THE ANATOMICAL MUSEUM IN BERLIN: 1848-1849

ALTHOUGH Helmholtz was now set free from his duties as army surgeon, the preparing of his winter's lectures to the Academy, and still more the task of making preparations in comparative anatomy at the Anatomical Museum during the summer, took up so much time that, save for a short report to the *Fortschritte der Physik* on the theory of physiological heat, he was unable to bring any fresh work to completion.

By the beginning of the winter session, in which, besides his lectures on osteology and myology (given to an audience of five), he had to make preparations of the human subject for the lectures and for the Museum, his work grew a little oppressive, since his brain was teeming with scientific ideas, and urged him on to original research. Accordingly he wrote to his friend Brücke, to ask if he were taking the duties of his new post too seriously. Brücke advised him to abate his pedagogic ardour, and in the following January he writes to his brother Otto, 'Tell the parents that all goes well; I have less to do with my artists now, because I let them draw a good deal from specimens, and can generally leave them after a short lecture.'

Helmholtz was, moreover, eager to justify the expectations of Brücke and his other friends. On March 16, 1849, he read a paper to the Physical Society, entitled 'Principles of Construction of a Tangent Galvanometer', in which he suggested precisely the same construction of galvanometer as was subsequently communicated to the Académie in Paris by Gaugain in 1853. Helmholtz was unable to claim priority for it, since the minutes of the meeting of the Physical Society had been lost. In the next place he sketched out the plan of the epoch-making researches by which he opened fresh paths in the physiology and pathology of nerve and muscle, and created new methods of investigation. But he had scarcely embarked on this work when his life took another and decisive turn, which made it possible for him to follow his great aims undisturbed.

Brücke had been called to the University of Vienna, and the Medical Faculty of Königsberg had nominated du Bois-Reymond, Helmholtz, and Ludwig as candidates for the vacant post (April 1, 1849). Du Bois was not inclined to leave Berlin until he had completed his work on Animal Electricity, and Ludwig, though senior, was passed over on political grounds, so that on May 19, 1849, Helmholtz was by order of the Cabinet appointed Extraordinary Professor of Physiology at Königsberg, with a salary of £120. He was commanded to go at once to Königsberg to commence his lectures on physiology in the summer term, while the Academy of Arts was desired by the Minister to release Helmholtz from his post as teacher of anatomy, in which he was succeeded by du Bois-Reymond.

CHAPTER VI

PROFESSOR OF PHYSIOLOGY AT KÖNIGSBERG:
1849–1855

The fact that Helmholtz should, at such an early age, be appointed Extraordinary Professor and Director of the Physio-logical Institute, with a salary of £120 (which his father had only obtained after years of painstaking activity), completely revolutionized the old man's views as to the value of his son's achievements, and he often remarked that his Hermann had advanced much farther than he, who was only Professor at a Gymnasium. For the last two years the relations between father and son had rarely permitted any exchange of ideas, owing to the wide divergence of their scientific views, but from this time the elder Helmholtz was keenly desirous of becoming acquainted with all his son's work, and, whenever possible, of taking part in it. With Hermann's call to Königsberg, accord-ingly, begins a most interesting correspondence between father and son, which extended over a period of ten years, and affords us many glimpses into the development of the great thinker's projects.

Now that Helmholtz had a settled position he was able to put an end to his long engagement, and bring home his beloved bride. The marriage took place on August 26, 1849, at Dahlem, near Berlin, in the house of the bride's sister. 'The ceremony was performed in the little, old village church, which was filled with a festive procession of friends, parents, and relatives on either side.' The young couple set out for Königsberg directly after the ceremony. Helmholtz's parents were overjoyed, and looked forward hopefully to the future. 'Dear children,' writes the father on September 16, 'I wish I knew what and how to write, to give you as much satisfaction from my letter as yours has given me! Here our quiet life goes on as usual; your present is so beautiful that you can scarcely appreciate the happiness of recollecting what is past. Or should I as a wise parent check your transports by sad legends of the envious gods who leave nothing perfect to us poor mortals?—advise you like Polycrates to sacrifice your dearest jewel, and commend you to bitter renunciation in order that you may remember that you are mortals called to sorrow? Olga, make your Hermann tidy, for that is his weakest point, and when he is a father, he must set his children a better example than I have given him. Now I have quite done; for what to me is so important, that you should be assured of my love, will seem to you in the fullness of your own like a drop in the ocean.'

The new house was soon got ready. 'As soon as we had put our house in order,' Helmholtz writes in the middle of October to du Bois, 'everything was very comfortable, and we were able to enjoy the best part of our life without let or hindrance. I can only recommend you with the best conscience in the world to provide yourself at the first opportunity with just such a dear wife as I have found. Marriage makes one so fully contented with the present, so certain of one's portion, that my working power has substantially increased.' And in fact he employed the vacation in sketching out new enterprises, and continuing his former work, bringing an entirely new method to bear on the experiments already commenced upon the nature of muscular movement during a single twitch. His young wife gave him valuable assistance by observing the divisions of the galvanometer scale, and long series of tables in her handwriting still exist among his papers.

In the first half of the winter session he was almost entirely absorbed in the preparation of his lectures, and could only undertake such minor experiments as were necessary for purposes of demonstration.

'A larger bit of work,' he writes to his father in December, 'from which I was getting a good many results in the October vacation, must now be put off till Christmas. Seven students have entered their names for my lecture, three to five of whom generally appear, according to weather. I am still much handicapped in physiological experiments because the proper equipment of my laboratory is hindered from want of funds. But now I have been allotted £15 for this year, and the same for next, for expenditure on instruments and experiments; so I shall be, and am, better off in this respect than I was in Berlin.'

The father's reply, at once admonitory and soothing, was sent on December 28 as a Christmas and New Year greeting:—

'May 1850 bring you as much of happiness and of God's blessing as 1849. Above all may you both be kept in health: and to you may it bring good results in your scientific labours. I am sorry that you have so small an audience, for nothing inspires a teacher so much as applause, and the response of numbers to what he offers. You have all the more reason to cultivate a fluent style and popular manner, as well as depth and solidity; in this way you will gratify the wishes of the authorities, who have doubtless sent so young a man, with this remarkable salary for an Extraordinary Professor, to Königsberg in order to awaken a keener interest for what is really profound and scientific, as one might say fundamental, in Medicine, and thus initiate further developments of this practical art in Königsberg also. Physiology is so closely related to Philosophy, and has such important general interests, that you will doubtless discover a form of lecture and choice of subject that will attract many from other Faculties, notably from the Philosophical, especially if you make friends with Rosenkranz, whose fame attracts many philosophers to Königsberg. Professor Meyer says that the Königsberg students of his day were distinguished by keen activity and industry, especially in science and mathematics. So we must hope that you will be more successful in this respect next year, for the sake of your own affairs as well, for you will soon find that, even while you are only two, your stipend is small enough in the circle in which you and your wife are moving; and you decline to practise, which is really the most lucrative, though I grant you the most disturbing and fatiguing profession.'

Helmholtz used the Christmas holidays as he had planned, to complete the experiments broken off in October, and was able by January 15, 1850, to send du Bois a short report 'On the Rate of Transmission of Excitation in Nerve', with the request that he would communicate it to the Physical Society, 'to secure priority in their Proceedings.' He sent the notice at the same time to Johannes Müller for the Academy in Berlin, and to Alexander von Humboldt for Paris, contenting himself for the moment with the statement of his discovery, that during the excitation of nerve with the current induced in a coil by the opening of the circuit in another coil, a measurable time (some 0·0014–0·0020 second) elapses, before the stimulus of an instantaneous electrical current applied to the sciatic plexus of large frogs, with nerves 50–60 millimeters in length, is transmitted to the point at which the nerve enters the gastrocnemius muscle. He tells du Bois-Reymond how, 'after a severe struggle, I have converted a bold mathematician, who gets somewhat confused over non-mathematical logic, and is himself lecturer on mechanics, to the doctrine of the conservation of energy, so that it is now official doctrine in this University. Neumann is rather difficult to get at; he is hypochondriacal, shy, but a thinker of the first order.'

Du Bois was again the only man who understood the brief note thus published by Helmholtz merely to establish his priority. 'Your work, I say with pride and grief, is understood and recognized in Berlin by myself alone. You really have, begging your pardon, expressed the subject so obscurely that your report could at best only be an introduction to the rediscovery of the method. The consequence was that Müller failed to rediscover it, and the Academicians decided after he had spoken that you had not eliminated the time lost during the contraction of the muscle. I had to explain it separately to one after the other—to Dove, to Magnus, to Müller himself, who would have nothing to do with it. I brought it forward at the Physical Society, where at any rate we did not have the same difficulty. Humboldt was quite mystified, and refused to send your note to Paris, so I offered to make it plainer. I have done this on my own responsibility; you will observe that I have not altered a single detail, but kept rigidly to what you gave me, while I have developed it inductively. The note on rapidity per second is not mine, but Humboldt's.' In conclusion du Bois-Reymond expresses his wish that Helmholtz would continue these researches: 'The lay of experiment you are on is wonderfully lucky—do oblige me by keeping to it; we could work into each other's hands, and get something out of it.'

It was not surprising that this brief communication from Helmholtz should again arouse questioning and contradiction on the part of the older physiologists and physicists. Johannes Müller had expressly stated six years before that we never should be able to determine the rate of the nervous impulse, since we had no means of experimenting over enormous distances, by which the velocity of light, in this respect analogous with the activity of nerve, had been calculated. He held that the time occupied by the passage of a sensation from periphery to brain and cord, and the efferent reflex that produces a contraction, is too infinitesimal to be measured. And, indeed, so long as the nervous impulse was referred by physiologists to the diffusion of an imponderable agent, or to a psychical principle, it necessarily appeared incredible that the velocity of this current could be measurable within the short compass of the animal body. Du Bois' work had, however, made it more than probable to Helmholtz that the propagation of excitation in nerve is essentially conditioned by altered arrangement of the molecules, whence he conjectured that rate of propagation is a measurable, and even a moderate magnitude, since it is a case of molecular action in ponderable bodies.

These investigations all fell into place in the chain of Helmholtz's thoughts and opinions, which were directed, to the exclusion of any metaphysical speculation, towards the discovery of facts alone. It is interesting to find that while the opponents of 'nature-philosophy' had set themselves against the Law of the Conservation of Energy, because they saw in it merely a philosophical play of ideas with no strong scientific basis, the next, strictly physico-physiological, work of Helmholtz provoked doubt and remonstrance not only from the physiologists, but from the philosophers also, as they were unable to admit a time-interval between the idea and the concomitant physiological action.

In order to explain this antagonism it is only necessary to remember the views that prevailed at that time in regard to the connexion of the sciences, more particularly of physiology and physics. Helmholtz himself tells how a Professor of Physiology, celebrated for his literary activity, and a witty speaker, replied with annoyance when invited by a physicist, during a discussion upon the images in the eye, to accompany him to his home to see the experiment, that 'a physiologist had nothing to do with experiments, though they might be well enough for the physicists': while a Professor of Pharmacology and academic reformer, who tried to persuade Helmholtz to divide his physiology, taking the intellectual part himself, and leaving the lower experimental side to a colleague, gave up all hopes of him when he explained that he regarded experiment as the true basis of science.

When at last Johannes Müller and A. von Humboldt were convinced (before the full publication of the experiments) of the correctness of his work, Helmholtz sent a short account of it on March 29 to his father:—

'I have another six weeks' vacation, and am using this time to prosecute my discoveries in regard to the transmission of nervous activity, extending it to as many cases as possible, and getting it ready for publication. Since my first note to the Academies of Paris and Berlin I have been studying the point in man also, and here too have found it possible to demonstrate that the time required for a message from any part of the body to reach the brain (e. g. $\frac{1}{30}$ second from the great toe) is longer in proportion to the distance it has to travel, while another interval of time is required before the process that excites contraction can be transmitted from the brain through the nerves to a muscle. I expect to finish the experiments, and get them worked up these holidays. My first communication has been published in the *Monatsberichte* of the Academy in Berlin, and the *Comptes Rendus* of the Académie in Paris, and I have had two very appreciative letters about it from J. Müller and A. von Humboldt. I call this work a bit of good luck, for it will not fail to excite attention. That it will be noticed in Paris, though perhaps not with a very good grace, is shown by a scoffing article in the *National*, by the reporter who has already been heckling du Bois-Reymond. Unluckily I have not been able to get hold of the article here. Don't let this distress you: one cannot expect the French to take such things kindly from a German, and I have got all I want for the moment if they are alive to it. Du Bois is in Paris these holidays to give his own things at the Académie, and writes that he will bring mine forward also. He is very clever at that job, and I have no doubt that he will present the German scientists in quite an imposing light to the Frenchmen. Königsberg is a splendid place to work in, because it does not tempt one to do much else, and yet there is plenty of intellectual life about it. The apparatus which I used in my work was made quite well for me here.'

In a few days, however, Helmholtz received a letter of affectionate criticism from his father, intimating that with all deference to his son's authority, he found difficulty in understanding the result of his investigations :—

'As regards your work, the results at first appeared to me surprising, since I regard the idea and its bodily expression not as successive, but as simultaneous, a single living act, that only becomes bodily and mental on reflection : and I could as little reconcile myself to your view, as I could admit that a star that had disappeared in Abraham's time should still be visible.'

Helmholtz was far from wishing that his father should accept his results upon the scientific appreciation of others, contrary to his own convictions, and lost no time in sending him the following lucid explanation of the meaning of his work :—

'I am adding a note intended so far as may be to remove your doubts about the rate of propagation in nerve. You must remember that the interaction of mental and bodily processes is initiated in the brain, and that consciousness, intellectual activity, has nothing to do with the transmission of the message from the skin, from the retina, or from the ear, to the brain. In relation to intelligence this transmission within the body is as external as the propagation of sound from the place at which it takes origin, to the ear. Just as in this case it is the elasticity of the air that conveys the concussion of the resonant body to the nervous apparatus of the ear, so it is here the motions of the minute material particles of the nervous substance which are propagated from the end of the nerve to its origin in the brain, where they are first recognized as a message to consciousness. That the velocity of this trans-

mission in nerve is by no means so enormous as that of light
or electricity may be conjectured from du Bois' discovery that
electricity is developed in nerve during the propagation of a
message or stimulus; whence we must conclude that the
material particles of the nerve are altered in position during
the process.   Transmission is in this case, as a matter of fact,
extremely slow, slower than that of sound.   The reason why
the time occupied by this propagation seems to us so infinitesimal lies in the fact that we are unable to perceive more
quickly than our nervous system can act, and thus the intervals
required for its operations appear to us imperceptibly small.
The inaccuracy of our time-perceptions when based upon a
comparison between our perceptions by two different sense-
organs has recently been demonstrated in the most striking
manner.   Astronomers vary in their estimation of the moment
at which a star crosses the web of their telescopes by more than
a whole second, while the estimates of any individual taken by
himself agree within one-tenth of a second if frequently repeated.   Still more surprising is the difficulty of determining
whether the beats of two gently-ticking watches coincide, or
fall between each other, if held to either ear, while nothing
is easier than the same determination if both are held to the
same ear.   I picture the matter to myself in this way: two
perceptions of different organs can only be estimated as regards
their time-relations, when there is a sufficient interval between
to reflect "now you have perceived one, but not as yet the
other".   Our thought is not so rapid as we usually believe,
as I have proved from my experiment of taking an electric
shock at any point on my skin, and then trying to move my
hand as quickly as might be, measuring the time between
the shock and the first commencement of the movement.   With
great attention, when the will is ready to act the instant it
receives the message, the message is only delayed about one-
tenth of a second in the brain, and is carried on with such
mechanical regularity to the motor nerve as a motor stimulus,
that I think the delay must here be caused only by the necessary mechanical molecular processes.   When, on the contrary,
the attention is fatigued, so that on receiving the message it
becomes necessary to think what is to be done, a much longer
and quite irregular interval is required.

'I have not yet completed my work on the frog, as there are still various experiments to make, diagrams of apparatus to be drawn, &c., but I expect to finish in the Whitsuntide holidays. The experiments on man must be varied and repeated before I can publish them later on.'

While working out his experiments on the frog, Helmholtz was actually taking time-measurements on himself and other men, which seemed to establish the rate of transmission in the motor and sensory nerves of man at fifty to sixty metres per second. At the end of April he announces the completion of the first part of his paper, for *Müller's Archiv*, to du Bois-Reymond, and dispatches it on July 26 along with the news that he is 'father of a well-formed healthy girl'. As regards new discoveries, he announces a theorem on the form of the rise of electrical currents in a coil, which act inductively either upon this or any connected system of other coils—a task which, however, took him nearly a year more before he was able to deduce a conclusion.

In the meanwhile (July 19, 1850) du Bois presented Helmholtz's comprehensive work on 'Measurements of the Time-relations in the Contraction of Animal Muscles, and Rate of Propagation in Nerve,' to the Physical Society. It was at once published in *Müller's Archiv* under du Bois' supervision, Helmholtz consenting, for the benefit of 'those who are only half acquainted with Ohm's Law', to certain alterations advised by du Bois-Reymond. He now realized from the report of the latter, who had returned in a somewhat exasperated mood from Paris, where his lecture on Helmholtz's method of measuring the propagation of the nervous impulse was not very favourably received at the Académie des Sciences, that the novelty of the work demanded a thorough exposition. The article was through the press by December, and in the same month Helmholtz gave a lecture to the Society of Physics and Economics in Königsberg, of which he was this year Director (being elected President two years later), which dealt in a generally comprehensible manner with the subject, and was entitled, 'On Methods of measuring very small Intervals of Time, and their Application to Physiological Purposes.'

In Part I of this great work (Part II only made its appearance two years later), 'which opened a new and unbounded field of investigation to physiologists,' Helmholtz set himself in the first place to study the processes that take place in a simple muscle-twitch, consequent on a stimulus of infinitesimal duration, when the muscle in order to do work must pass from a state of rest to a state of motion, and the quantity of work done depends essentially upon the rapidity of this transition. From these facts he went on to the question of the rate at which excitation is propagated in nerve. From his first experiments at the beginning of 1849 he had concluded, from the curves obtained by plotting the height to which a weight is lifted against time, that the energy of the muscle was not at its maximum immediately after the excitation, but that it rose for some time, and then dropped again. In order to show these facts plainly, and at the same time to determine the time-relations and the stages in which the mechanical activity, the energy of the muscle, rises and falls after an instantaneous excitation, Helmholtz, at the outset of his experiments, contrived a very ingenious piece of apparatus. He attached a metal ring to the muscle, which carried a scale-pan of light weight; the upper part of the ring was supported in such a way by a metal pin, that it could not drop lower when the load was increased. On then closing a current, part of which passed through the muscle, part through a galvanometer, the pin, and the ring, the galvanometer circuit was broken by the contraction of the muscle and consequent lifting of the ring off the pin, and by placing weights in the pan it became possible to compare the elastic force of the muscle in the resting state with that after excitation. In order to follow the very rapid twitch of the muscle in its successive stages, and to investigate the propagation of excitation in the nerve, new methods for the measurement of infinitesimal fractions of time were devised by Helmholtz, who thus provided fresh appliances for the delicate and complicated investigations of physiological processes.

The need of some method by which it should be as possible to measure minute fractions of a second, as it is with a powerful microscope to estimate fractions of length, had long been felt in a variety of astronomical and physical observations. Two such methods, invented mainly for the exigencies of artillery, had already been devised on widely different principles. In the one, perfected by Werner Siemens, the intervals of time are measured in terms of intervals of space; in the other, the mechanical effect produced by a force of known intensity during the interval is measured, and the time of action is subsequently calculated from it. This second method, discovered by Pouillet in 1844, consisted in the measurement of very small intervals of time by the deflection of a galvanometer needle after the passage of a very short electric current, and was elaborated by Helmholtz for physiological purposes. He made the electro-magnetic determinations by means of a mirror attached to the magnet, as introduced by Gauss and Weber, and established the constant factor necessary to convert the differences of oscillation into the corresponding time-differences, by a strictly accurate method.

Starting from the simplest cases, he next attacked the more complicated problem, whether there is any appreciable lost time during the propagation of a message from the remote ends of the sensory cutaneous nerves, or from the nerve-endings in the sense-organs, to the brain, or from the brain to the muscles *via* the motor nerve trunks. He first determined in the frog, by a long series of most delicate experiments, that when the muscle or nerve of an animal is excited by an instantaneous electrical shock, a short time, about one-hundredth of a second, elapses, during which the elastic tension of the muscle is not appreciably altered—the so-called latent period of excitation—after which the muscular tension gradually rises to a maximum, and then as gradually falls again. If, further, two different points of a motor nerve are excited by an instantaneous stimulus, and if the magnitude of the excitation is alike for both, the time-relations of the corresponding contractions will also be the same, but the total effect makes its appearance later when the stimulus is applied to a more distant point of the nerve. The transmission of excitation through nerve to muscle therefore occupies a measurable time, and its speed is actually found to be more than ten times less than the velocity of sound in air. 'Happily,' says Helmholtz, 'the distances our sense-perceptions have to traverse before they reach the brain are short, otherwise our consciousness would always lag far behind the present, and even behind our perceptions of sound.'

Two points in this lecture gave rise to an interesting correspondence with du Bois-Reymond. Helmholtz, using what is now a familiar figure, compared the nerve-fibres with the wires of the electric telegraph, which in an instant transmit intelligence from the outposts to the controlling centre, and then convey its orders back to the outlying parts to be executed there; and at the close of his discourse he illustrated the rapidity of nervous conduction by saying that the whale probably feels a wound near its tail in about one second, and requires another second to send back orders to the tail to defend itself. On March 18, 1851, du Bois sends Helmholtz a lecture which he had given at the Sing-Akademie before the 'familiar audience of non-working classes', and remarks: 'Your surprise on reading this will be little less than my own on reading your lecture. Apparently we have hit on the same thing in two illustrations, and in various other points, even to the expressions we make use of, so that no stranger would absolve me from plagiarism. I feel greatly flattered at this conformity in the motions of our brain molecules. Give my lecture to your good wife to read. The ladies are angry because I made myself comprehensible to them—what do I take them for?—they expected something more scientific from me.' He then describes the difficulty he finds in devising an instrument which shall be set going by a muscle so as to close the circuit during a given fraction of the twitch, and ends with the words: 'Write and tell me what avalanche of ideas this tinkling of a mule-bell rouses in your brain.' After congratulating du Bois in his answer of April 11 on his election to the full membership of the Academy, Helmholtz replies:—

'As regards the coincidence in our lectures I concede you priority in the matter of the electric telegraph, since you long ago suggested the hypothesis that the ganglia represent the intermediate stations of the electric telegraph in the nerve circuit. But in the story of the whale the truth is so romantic that no one will believe it. The moral is that people can easily be mistaken about plagiarism. . . . My wife joins forces with those who say that you have made yourself too intelligible. It is impossible to please every one on these occasions, but one generally gets more thanks for not making one's stuff too plain to the audience, and for leaving the majority a few riddles, which are probably only understood by a handful of one's hearers.'

His father, to whom he had sent his lecture on February 27, was by no means of this opinion, and writes on April 19 to du Bois-Reymond :—

'Dear Doctor, heartiest thanks for the copy of your interesting lecture to the scientific society. I rejoiced in the clearness of your style, which enables even the uninitiated to glance into the secrets of your science, and by its wit and poetic taste redeems it from its usual dryness. It is admirable in you amid your heavy labours thus to find time to refresh yourself with the poets, and to round the realism of your nature-studies with art and poetry. I wish my son had something of your spirit: he is so little able to escape from his scientific rigidity of expression, even in an essay read before a Society in Königsberg, that I am filled with respect for an audience that could understand and thank him for it. I confess that when I read it much remained very obscure to me.'

While Helmholtz was thus engaged in fundamental researches which had the common aim of building up a mechanical conception of the universe (in the best sense), he lighted casually, and as the fruit of his lectures at the end of 1850, upon his discovery of the ophthalmoscope, which 'revealed a new world' to the ophthalmologists, and which, with the doctrine of the Conservation of Energy, did most to establish and extend his reputation. 'The excellent discipline every University teacher is subject to, in being obliged each year to treat the whole of his subject so as to convince and satisfy the best of his students,' resulted on his own avowal in this splendid harvest.

After communicating his invention to the Physical Society in Berlin, on December 6, he wrote on December 17, 1850, to his father:—

'In regard to time-measurements I have at present no new results, but have devoted myself to the construction of fresh apparatus and necessary preliminaries. But I have made a discovery during my lectures on the Physiology of the Sense-organs, which may be of the utmost importance in ophthalmology. It was so obvious, requiring, moreover, no knowledge beyond the optics I learned at the Gymnasium, that it seems almost ludicrous that I and others should have been so slow as not to see it. It is, namely, a combination of glasses, by means of which it is possible to illuminate the dark background of the eye, through the pupil, without employing any dazzling light, and to obtain a view of all the elements of the retina at once, more exactly than one can see the external parts of the eye without magnification, because the transparent media of the eye act like a lens with a magnifying power of twenty. The blood-vessels are displayed in the neatest way, with the branching arteries and veins, the entrance of the optic nerve into the eye, &c. Till now a whole series of most important eye-diseases, known collectively as black cataract, have been *terra incognita*, because the changes in the eye were practically unknown, both during life, and, generally speaking, after death. My discovery makes the minute investigation of the internal structures of the eye a possibility. I have announced this very precious egg of Columbus to the Physical Society at Berlin, as my property, and am now having an improved and more convenient instrument constructed to replace my pasteboard affair. I shall examine as many patients as possible with the chief oculist here, and then publish the matter.'

The ophthalmoscope was, however, some time in making its way, on account of the mathematical and physical knowledge presupposed by the 'Description of an Ophthalmoscope for the Investigation of the Retina in the Living Eye', published in the autumn of 1851, and people were at first very shy of employing it. One distinguished surgical colleague told Helmholtz he should never use the instrument—it would be too dangerous to admit the naked light into a diseased eye; another was of opinion that the mirror might be of service to oculists with defective eyesight—he himself had good eyes and wanted none of it. But by December 16 of the same year Helmholtz was able to write to his father:—

'Eighteen orders for the ophthalmoscope have dropped in, one after the other, so that my mechanician is doing a good trade. The world is getting to hear of it.'

Forty years later he tells the story of its discovery:—

'While preparing my lectures I hit upon the invention of the ophthalmoscope, and then on the method of measuring the velocity of nervous impulses. The ophthalmoscope became the most popular of my scientific achievements, but I have already pointed out to the oculists that good fortune had more to do with it than merit. I had to explain the theory of the emission of reflected light from the eye, as discovered by Brücke, to my students. Brücke himself was but a hair's breadth off the discovery of the ophthalmoscope. He had only neglected to ask himself what optical image was formed by the rays reflected from the luminous eye. For his purpose it was not necessary to put this question. Had it occurred to him, he was just the man to answer it as quickly as I, and to invent the ophthalmoscope. I was turning the problem over and over, and pondering the simplest way of making it clear to my audience, when I came on the further issue.

'The oculist's perplexity in dealing with the condition known at that time as black cataract was familiar to me from my medical studies, and I at once set to work to manufacture the instrument out of spectacle lenses and the cover-glasses used for microscopical objects. At first, however, it was very difficult to use. I might not have persevered save for my conviction that it must succeed; but after about eight days I had the great joy of being the first to see a living human retina exposed before me.'

As a matter of fact the discovery of the ophthalmoscope had not been quite such a simple invention as Helmholtz describes it. The principle underlying the apparatus was difficult to grasp without considerable knowledge of optics, and its introduction was therefore a comparatively slow matter, and was delayed until improved mechanical conditions rendered the handling of it much simpler—although Donders, the celebrated physiologist at Utrecht, held the original form of Helmholtz's instrument to be optically perfect.

The familiar fact that the eyes of certain animals, such as cats and owls, glisten in the dark, had already been correctly interpreted by Johannes Müller to mean that these so-called 'glowing' eyes do not really glow but only reflect light, and that the retina of the eyes that glisten most are provided with a background specially adapted for the reflection of light. Brücke had shown that the eyes of animals seem to glisten most when the beam of a dark-lantern is thrown into the eye that is to be examined, the observer looking past it. All eyes can be made to glisten, both in animals and in man. The first human eye purposely made to shine in the dark was du Bois-Reymond's, illuminated by Brücke. Brücke's subsequent attempts at constructing an instrument for the illumination of the retina failed (according to Graefe) on account of the mode of illumination he adopted.

Helmholtz asked himself in the first place, as he related in the monograph published in Berlin, 1851, why all that we can see of the background of the uninjured eye appears absolutely dark; he ascribed this to the refractive media of the eye, which under normal circumstances prevent us from seeing illuminated points of the retina behind the pupil. The first requisite therefore was to find a source of illumination by which just that portion of the retina that we see through the pupil may be adequately illuminated. By means of a little camera obscura blackened inside he proved by calculation and experiment that for any system of refractive surfaces, the reflected rays, even when they have passed through the re-fracting media and left the eye, must be wholly congruent with the incident rays, and that they all return ultimately to the original point of illumination.

Since the observer's eye cannot be brought into line with the reflected light without intercepting the incident rays, no light can be returned to his pupil from the recesses of the observed eye that has not emanated from his own. Only those points of the retina will accordingly be visible on which the dark image of his own eye is projected. Further, if the observed eye is not a perfect refracting system, part of the light reflected from it will indeed return to the luminous point, but part passes by it, and it becomes possible for an observer, placed as nearly as possible in the line of the incident light, to perceive a little of the light that emerges; and this produces the luminosity of the human eye as discovered by Brücke. In order to obtain an exact image, some method is required which makes it possible to look into the eye not only in the approximate, but in the exact line of the incident light, and Helmholtz found, in trying to make the image as bright as possible, that this can be done by superposing three parallel glass plates, in which the light from a source of illumination placed at one side of the observing eye is reflected. A portion of this light will then enter the subject's eye, and illuminate its fundus; the rays of light reflected from the illuminated background on to the glass plates will now return partially from the surface of these to the source of light, but another part of the reflected rays will pass through the glass plates, and reach the eye of the observer. But the visual field of the latter, limited by the pupil of the observed eye, is so small, on account of the relatively considerable distance of one eye from the other, that it would be impossible to combine the observed details into a whole; it is therefore imperative to bring the two eyes as close to one another as possible. This causes the image as a rule to fall behind the observer, who cannot distinguish it plainly, and since a normal eye can only combine parallel and diverging rays upon its retina, and not those that are convergent, Helmholtz (as the readiest means of making the converging beams diverge) inserted a concave lens between the mirror and the eye of the observer, and by this simple contrivance provided the essentials of his ophthalmoscope. He also suggested a number of other practical methods of constructing the instrument.

'The construction of the ophthalmoscope,' says Helmholtz at a later time, in discussing his medical and physiological work, 'was a turning-point in my position in the eyes of the world. From that moment I found favour with authorities and colleagues, and was left free to follow the promptings of my scientific curiosity. I attribute my subsequent success to the fact that circumstances had fortunately planted me with some knowledge of geometry and training in physics among the doctors, where physiology presented a virgin soil of the utmost fertility, while on the other hand I was led by my acquaintance with the phenomena of life to problems and points of view that are beyond the scope of pure mathematics and physics.'

The invention of the ophthalmoscope, with the mechanical constructions and modifications which it entailed, as well as a series of experiments in physiological optics undertaken with the instrument, took up no more than the early weeks of 1851. Helmholtz discovered among other points that light which impinges directly on the optic nerve does not give rise to any sensation, but that it must fall on a nerve-ending in the retina before it can be perceived. He then returned to the work that had been so happily interrupted, on the stimulation of nerve. In his earlier experiments he had assumed the induction shock by which the nerve was excited to be instantaneous, and he now proceeded, in order to justify this view for the minute time-intervals involved, to answer the question previously raised as to the exact time at which an induction current produces its physiological effect. It was important not to ascribe to some action in the nerve a loss of time which might have occurred in the electrical apparatus. This is especially true of experiments on man, when the currents are of such a strength that serious errors might creep in. In the middle of April he sent du Bois a short note on this physical preliminary to his further work on nerve, for the Academy, together with the longer paper for *Poggendorff's Annalen*. Du Bois-Reymond replies:—

'My brain reels at your appalling industry and encyclopaedic knowledge. How can you get up new lectures and still carry on all this work? All the same I am not quite satisfied with your exposition. I have read your essay and the abstract several times without understanding what you did, or how you did it. At last I discovered the method for myself, and then I saw what you are driving at. Don't be vexed if I say that you must take more pains to get away from your own standpoint, and place yourself on the level of those who do not yet know what it is all about, and what you want to tell them.'

This reproach, however, was unjustified, for in the nature of the case the treatise presupposed that its readers would be trained physicists and mathematicians. Both then and later Helmholtz was in the habit of writing and re-writing many parts of his papers four and even six times, altering the arrangement before he was satisfied, and never holding an investigation to be finished till it presented itself to him in logical completeness, correctly formulated. Accordingly he replies: 'As regards the form of the essay, I took particular pains with it, and finally satisfied myself. But it is true that the more one elaborates a thing the harder it often becomes to understand. It is a very difficult subject to deal with.'

In 'The Duration and Nature of the Electrical Currents induced by Variations of Current' (*Poggendorff's Annalen*) he begins by stating a mathematical law, which he had verified by a long and difficult series of experiments. By means of this law F. Neumann was enabled to solve the problem he had previously laid aside, as to the distribution of current in a copper disk rotating below the two poles of a magnet— carrying out the integrations without neglecting secondary inductive actions, and propounding theorems that could be experimentally tested. If an electric circuit contains voltaic cells and a coil, and if I be the intensity of the battery current, W the resistance of the circuit in absolute units, t the time, and P the self-induction of the coil which depends only upon geometrical relations, then a stationary magnet will be deflected by the inducted current alone through an angle directly proportional to P and I, and inversely proportioned to W; but if the battery current alone acts on the magnet for the very brief time t, a deflection proportional to the products of I and t will result; hence it follows directly that the battery current in the time represented by the quotient of P and W produces the same effect as the whole of the induced current. Dove had already pointed out that the intensity of the counter-current induced on closing the circuit is always less than that of the inducing current, while the weaker current requires more time to produce the same effect than the stronger, whence it follows that the minimum duration of the counter-current at closure is the quotient P/W. Now, since this minimum can be augmented at will, by reducing the resistance W of the circuit, and increasing the self-induction P of the coil by increasing its mass, it is experimentally possible (and this is the cardinal point of the theorem) to make the time required by the current to reach the same value at all parts of the circuit very small by comparison with the above-mentioned interval, and conditions can be brought about under which the rate of transmission of the electric current in the circuit is imperceptibly small as compared with the fractions of time, in which the intensity of the current is not perceptibly altered. This, however, gives the necessary conditions for the application of Ohm's Law, i.e. the equalizing of current-strength throughout the circuit; for the alterations in intensity of induced currents are effected so slowly that the strength of current is equalized in the entire circuit, and the intensity of current in a simple circuit is then determined by Ohm's Law, in the form of an exponential function of time, on the assumption that the induced electromotive force lags by a very small interval behind the variations of the inducing current. After Helmholtz had extended this exponential law mathematically to divided circuits, he tested it experimentally by means of a new type of galvanic contact-key, which made it possible to vary the interval between the opening and closing of any current, as required. Instead of measuring the time directly, he calculated it from the action of the currents upon a magnet, by a modification of Pouillet's method. Thus he proved that, subject to the assumption that the induced electromotive force coincided in time with the inducing variations of current, no inducing action was present $\frac{1}{10000}$ second after breaking the current in a coil. By this means the time-intervals due to the electric current were distinguished with mathematical accuracy from those due to nerve-action, and Helmholtz was free, after this absolute verification of his methods, to devote himself to the complicated experiments on the excitation of nerve that occupied him during the remainder of 1851.

In the autumn holidays of 1851 Helmholtz carried out his project of inspecting some other physiological laboratories. After taking his wife and child to Dahlem, he went in the first place for a few days' rest to his Berlin friends, Professor Heintz and his family, at Halle. Then after a short stay in Kassel he went on to Göttingen. His first visit was to Professor Ritter, one of his former teachers at the Gymnasium of Potsdam, and his father's faithful friend, in whose company he 'saw the little town, rather better built than Halle and Königsberg, with the University as its fulcrum'; after which he called on the professors, though somewhat hampered by the presence of the King. He describes them in a letter to his wife as 'the aristocracy of the town; one can see that they are alive to their own merits, and a little inclined to over-estimate the accomplishments of their circle—not specially in regard to myself, but obviously in referring to any third person'. His lively descriptions show that he much enjoyed this visit to the Göttingen doctors:—

'I have found even more people to visit here than I expected, and Institutes where no money has been grudged on the equipment. The physiologist Wagner, an old man, who is conscious of his own importance, and evidently appreciates the notice taken of him by the King (the title *Hofrath* counts for more here than Professor), is not quite up to the level of the physical knowledge required nowadays, but he feels that, and is careful not to give himself away. The physicist Weber, who, next to Neumann, is certainly the greatest mathematical physicist in Germany, showed me a great deal of very interesting and very perfect physical apparatus, but with less apparent cordiality than his brother in Leipzig. I also met a young anatomist and physiologist Bergmann; an oculist Ruete, who has done important work on the physiology of the eye; an accomplished surgeon Baum, recently imported from Greifswald; a mathematical optician Listing, whom I had not heard of before, but who certainly deserves to be known; and lastly a philosopher Lotze, who has worked a great deal at the principles of pathology and physiology, but is unfortunately too hypochondriacal and self-centred for one to get any exchange of ideas out of him in such a short time. All these people received me with the greatest sympathy and cordiality, and gave me all the time they could spare; it was agreeable to find that they were in touch with my somewhat intricate nerve work, and approved of it, or at least had apparently sufficient confidence in my physical knowledge (for which Weber is responsible) to accept my results. The ophthalmoscope is a splendid toy to travel with; I demonstrated it this morning, and it is making quite a sensation here. This evening several of them are going to take me out walking, if they are not summoned to the King. On the other hand, I was surprised to find that they do not take kindly to du Bois-Reymond's conclusions: they query here and there, and do not see the importance of the work, and I have had to stand up for it. Their objections are based on the opinion of the Weber who is here, and on the Paris Commission, and are also due to imperfect comprehension of the subject. Little inventions like the ophthalmoscope make a better impression. I am demonstrating my frog-curves everywhere.'

From Göttingen, Helmholtz went on by Marburg, where he
called on Knoblauch and the physiologist Nasse, to Giessen,
in the hope of making acquaintance with Liebig, for whom
he had a great admiration.

'Liebig, the king of chemists, as he himself and his scholars
think him, was unfortunately away; he has gone to London
to see the Exhibition, and be *fêted* by the English. I much
wanted to meet him. All I could do was to see his empty
laboratory, to which students flock from the whole of Europe
and America, for practical work, and which was shown me
by his son, a young doctor who studied physiology with du
Bois-Reymond at one time, but will probably go into practice.
I was surprised to find no remarkable appliances; on the contrary everything was covered with dirt; there were very few
people working. It presented an extraordinary contrast to
the laboratories of Heintz and others, which are at least as
convenient, far better equipped, clean, and tidy. But externals
matter little. For in spite of his vanity Liebig is the greatest
of living chemists, and his renown as a teacher has spread
far and wide.'

He next went by Frankfurt, where he revived his old
admiration of Lessing's Huss, the Ezzelino, and two small
landscapes by the same master, to Heidelberg, where he
found Henle, and comments on his laboratory as being excellent for anatomy, but poorly equipped for physiology.
Henle explained that he had only taken on physiology and
general pathology in addition to anatomy, as a temporary
arrangement, in consequence of a disagreement with Tiede-
mann, and hoped he would soon be given a physiological
colleague. 'He suggested to me,' writes Helmholtz to his
wife, 'what may make a great difference to our future: viz.
he and the younger professors of the Medical Faculty are
desirous that I should be offered the Chair at Heidelberg.
We must consider this. Heidelberg would not be a bad
place to work in: the Germans have rather left it, because
there is a dearth of teachers for the moment, but students
are still coming from North America, Brazil, England, France,
Greece, and Russia.'

After staying some hours in Baden-Baden, Helmholtz
went to Kehl, and crossed the bridge over the Rhine into

the French Republic. 'There was plenty to amuse one. *Liberty, Fraternity,* and *Equality* were flaunted everywhere; *Property of the Nation* was posted on all the public buildings, and many private houses displayed other frightfully democratic devices. The country people and the lower classes in the town looked just the same as in Baden, only they seemed to be more stupid, but the better parts of the town appeared thoroughly French.'

After admiring the Cathedral of Freiburg, he visited the 'World's Wonder' at Schaffhausen, and was greatly impressed with it.

'I went down the hill to the bank: it certainly looked rather bigger, more like a waterfall, but still I went to bed somewhat disappointed. Next day, however, I got a different impression of it. One does not appreciate its proportions in the evening, because it is surrounded by rocks 200 to 300 feet in height, so that the 60-foot waterfall looks small beside them, and one cannot see the chief beauty, the wonderful dark-green colour of the water, which makes a magnificent effect as it mixes with the white foam. The effect, however, is overwhelming when one goes to a stage that has been erected at the edge of the Fall, where the appalling mass of water dissolved in foam and mist plunges down close to one. At first the sight is hardly bearable, one loses breath, and feels drawn after it. Afterwards, in spite of the constant shower of spray, I revelled in the spectacle of this force and motion, and could hardly tear myself away. . . . On Friday evening I reached Zürich, and looked up Ludwig, who received me with great cordiality. He has a noble and delightful nature, and is greatly improved since he has got rid of that Bohemian manner. This is apparently thanks to his wife, whom I have only learned to know at present by her quiet, sensible ways. . . . He is a man of the utmost kind-heartedness, and has formed an extravagant opinion of my excellences, related to him partly by du Bois. If you heard all the praises he showered upon me, you would certainly have been satisfied with him. He is extraordinarily industrious, works continuously in the right direction, and is adored by his students, as many of them said and showed me, so that besides all the good work he has done I hope still better from him. But he is somewhat weary and hypochondriacal, perhaps from his arduous work. He was ceaselessly engaged in finding amusement for me, and kept every one else away, so that he might talk to me alone. And talk we did, about every conceivable subject in physiology and physics. . . . In the morning I generally went to the Anatomy Department with Ludwig, and looked at experiments, instruments, and collections; in the afternoon we went out into the country, except on one day when it rained.'

From here Helmholtz set out on his first Swiss journey, and went to all the places he afterwards revisited so many times. In the letters to his wife he gives his impressions with youthful vigour and enthusiasm, along with many a scientific and aesthetic appreciation, such as we find so frequently later in his papers and lectures.

After climbing the Rigi, he wandered on by Fluelen over the Gothard and the Furka Passes to the Rhone Glacier, whose blue ice-slopes made a deep impression on him. 'By glacier you must not picture the snow-covered tops of mountains, but masses of ice that have slidden down into the valleys, to melt there while they are perpetually renewed from above. Picture the Brauhausberg in Potsdam made of ice, and packed into a narrow valley between gigantic peaks of rock, above that another precipice of 1,000 feet, on which the ice-blocks are piled up, and tumble thence to renew the lower masses, while the whole is pierced with innumerable sky-blue rifts, and then you have a picture of the Rhone Glacier.' He rejoiced in the enchanting loveliness of the Rosenlaui Glacier, where the sun streams through the ice into heavenly blue caverns and fissures; climbed the Faulhorn; visited the upper Glacier at Grindelwald; and then stayed a few days in Interlaken, where he resumed the scientific correspondence with his friends du Bois-Reymond, Brücke, and more particularly Ludwig, with whom his stay in Zürich had united him more closely than ever. One of his letters to Ludwig is interesting from its reference to a candidate for the Chair of Physics at Zürich: 'On the contrary I think you might do great things by joining forces with Kirchhoff; he is extraordinarily clear-headed and perspicacious in the most complicated questions; I much wish for your sake and that of physiology that Kirchhoff might go to Zürich.'

After crossing the Gemmi he went to Leukerbad, thence partly on foot, partly on horseback, to Lago Maggiore, and on by Como to Milan, 'a great and splendid town with all the brilliancy of Italian life. In beauty of form the Cathedral, Milan's pride, is far behind the Gothic cathedrals of Germany. Its Gothic forms are mere arbitrary decoration; but they are tastefully applied, and the innumerable pillars and arches, and well-carved statues, all standing out in white marble against the blue sky, are a sight that cannot be imagined. . . . We went, too, to the ruins of Leonardo da Vinci's master-piece, "The Last Supper," and to the Picture Gallery in the Brera Palace.'

At length he reached the city that he had so desired to see from boyhood.

'Venice is the city of wonders, a living fairy-tale. In spite of all one has seen in pictures, or heard described, the reality surpasses everything. The Piazza of St. Mark, with its rich mosque-like church, enclosed within the rows of palaces, the countless lights above the deep-blue moonlit heavens, and a few paces off the deep-blue sea, with crowds of people as though it were a *festa*, all make up an indescribable picture. To-day and yesterday we went round with a great crowd to see all the wonders; but one becomes almost wearied with these impressions. The historical memories, the extraordinary wealth which Venice has harvested from half the earth, the art treasures, for the most part still in their pristine freshness of colour, cannot be overlooked. . . . In Germany we can only form a poor idea of Italian Art; here one can drink it in fully. I went alone to the Accademia, to enjoy the masterpieces to the full, and did not repent me, but found great satisfaction, such as one cannot obtain in Germany. It is a collection of the masterpieces of the Venetian school, including Titian's great "Assumption of the Virgin", which I knew already from engravings. But engravings are even a worse substitute for this than a piano score for a symphony, since the indescribable beauty of the work consists in its miraculous light and colour. I have never seen the like, nor can one imagine it till one has seen it, because this kind of beauty is of another order from our German pictures. Moreover this one work is unparalleled among the rest of the Italian paintings that I have seen here, although many give this feast of colour in an extraordinary degree, and one sees the greatest number of inspired and ideal heads that you could possibly imagine.

'When I had seen the Accademia, I wanted no more, but prepared for departure, strolled a little in the streets, heard the band in the evening on the Piazza of St. Mark, and then at 10 p.m. went off in a gondola to the steamboat. As we sailed away the moon had risen; we left the lights and palaces of beautiful Venice, and fared out through the openings of the canals in the Lagoon, to the still blue Adriatic.'

From Venice, Helmholtz went by Trieste to Vienna, attracted thither by his old friendship with Brücke, to whom he wished to bring the ophthalmoscope in person. 'We arrived so early that I went first with Herr R. to his hotel, washed, breakfasted, and then, about nine o'clock, went on to Brücke. He was much pleased to see me, and I at once took up my abode with him. Then directly after appeared Professor Wagner from Göttingen, and the next day Professor Bunsen from Breslau, one of our most gifted chemists, so that we are quite a learned society. Brücke is just the same: he looks rather better, and is as cheerful, calm, and friendly as usual; his wife is pretty, and has the same pleasing, cheerful manner. . . . As for Vienna, I have so far seen only scientific things because it is generally raining. On Friday, Brücke showed us his Physiological Institute first of all, and we admired living chameleons, strange creatures with strikingly Egyptian characteristics. In the afternoon we were able to take a short walk, and discussed how it would be possible to help du Bois, but could not hit off anything. In the evening, the ophthalmoscope for Brücke's benefit. On Saturday morning I went to the mortuary in the Hospital to see the celebrated pathological anatomist, Rokitansky. Brücke and Wagner had a competition with their splendid microscopes, and both won. Afterwards I demonstrated the ophthalmoscope to Wagner and his friends, and to Bunsen, and in the afternoon showed Brücke my induction work. In the evening there was company at the philosopher Lott's, where I found Wagner and many of the Vienna professors. The atmosphere was pleasant and cordial, but they told a good many rather trivial anecdotes.

'*Sunday*. In the morning Rokitansky demonstrated his splendid collection of specimens in pathological anatomy to us, and we saw the famous museum of wax models. In the afternoon a projected expedition to Schönbrunn was frustrated by the weather. Brücke, Wagner, and I therefore went to look at two famous statues by Canova—a monument of a princess in the Augustinian Church, and the statue of Theseus in the Public Gardens. Neither of them was the least comparable with what I had seen in Italy. Then we walked round the city on the walls, which are rather pretty, fled to Wagner's hotel in a storm, and had some wise talk with him.'

Apropos of this conversation he writes a few days later to Ludwig: 'Rudolph Wagner was there too, and wanted to know what we thought about the relation between soul and body, and other obscure points of physiology. He seems much concerned with these points, about which one can hardly say anything. Bunsen was also present, and urged me to go with him to Breslau.'

After fetching his family from Dahlem, Helmholtz returned refreshed in mind and body with them to Königsberg, and at once resumed his experiments on the excitation of nerve, the importance of which was being more and more recognized by physiologists. On his father's birthday he sends him the welcome news:—

'The French Académie inform me in a very courteous manner that they have appointed a Committee to draw up a report on my communications on the measurement of time-relations. For the moment the Committee will not be in a position to complete its report, since it will not be possible to repeat the experiments; but it shows that they are alive to the thing. My official relations here are unchanged. Only I hear privately, and beg you not to repeat, that my Faculty have petitioned the Ministry to make me Ordinary Professor. I hear no more of Heidelberg. A second paper on time-relations is ready. In the Christmas holidays I am to draw up a report on du Bois' work for the *Kieler Monatsschrift*.'

After sending the account of his experiments on the graphic record of the rate of nervous transmission in the frog to Johannes Müller for the *Archiv*, he employed the Christmas holidays, and the first weeks of the New Year, in writing a report (originally intended to be a popular lecture), at the request of Karsten, upon 'Recent Developments in Animal Electricity'. On February 2 he tells du Bois that in reading his book with the aim of summarizing the work on animal electricity, he has discovered a theorem which seems to him completely to resolve the difficulties as to the co-ordination of the different elements of a muscle; by a combination of the laws of electric potential and of the superposition of currents, he had succeeded in proving that when electromotive forces are distributed in any way in any conductor, all external action exerted by the conductor, i. e. all the derived currents which it excites in any linear or non-linear circuit, may be replaced by a distribution of electromotive forces upon its surface, just as the external action of a magnet can be stated in terms of the distribution of magnetic fluid upon its surface.

In the meantime the Prussian Ministry were not slow to accept the recommendation of the Medical Faculty, and to appoint Helmholtz, who was now recognized everywhere as a physiologist and physicist of the first rank, to be Ordinary Professor of Physiology, which he became by Royal Brevet on December 17, 1851.

While he was busying himself with the required Inaugural Dissertation, for the subject of which he turned to the Physiological Theory of Colour, Part II of his great work on the physiology of nerve and muscle appeared in *Müller's Archiv* under the title 'Measurements of the Rate at which Excitation is transmitted in Nerve'. In Part I he had already proved, by means of the electro-magnetic method of time-measurement, that the mechanical response of a muscle made its appearance later after excitation of the nerve, when the excitation had to travel through a longer portion of nerve before reaching the muscle, but the application of this method involved protracted experiments, and necessitated a favourable condition of the frog's tissues, on account of the long duration of the experiments. He now endeavoured, with a graphic method of time-measurement previously described in Part I—by which a contracting muscle records the magnitude of its twitch upon a travelling surface—to find a simpler method of confirming his determination of the rate of nervous transmission. After Ludwig, with the kymograph, had succeeded in recording the variations of blood-pressure in the vessels of a living animal, Helmholtz constructed his myograph for the graphic record of the contraction of a muscle—its principle being that a lever lifted by the twitching muscle traces a curve upon a surface moving at uniform speed, the vertical co-ordinates of which are proportional to the shortening of the muscle, the horizontal to the time. If two curves are recorded one after the other in such a way that the writing-point is always at the same place on the travelling surface at the moment of excitation, then both curves will start from the same point, and it can be seen from their congruence or non-congruence whether the different stages of the mechanical response of the muscle occur in both cases at the same interval after excitation. Two years later Helmholtz published important additions to these experiments on the frog, as recorded with the myograph.

Simultaneously with the above he published in the *Kieler Monatsschrift*, for April, 1852, the essay previously announced to du Bois on the 'Results of Recent Researches in Animal Electricity'. He gave a masterly sketch of the development of nerve physiology, and described the interest attaching to the 'investigation into the nature of the mysterious agent which, acting along barely visible nerve-threads, produces such fine gradations, such mighty energies, such complicated exchanges of sensation and motion—an agent that is the first link in the chain of processes which connect the mind that feels and wills with the material outer world, enabling it to receive and give out impressions'. As early as 1743 the Leipzig mathematician Hausen had expressed the opinion that this agent might be identical with electricity. Helmholtz now expounded the opposite theories of Galvani and Volta, the first of whom regarded animal electricity as the source of the electrical phenomena in all his experiments, while the latter by his theory of contact electricity, which led him to the most brilliant discoveries, had pushed the experiments relating to animal electricity proper completely into the background. He cites the long roll of Matteucci's painstaking experiments (to which he was obliged to return many years later in another connexion), and finally embarks upon a masterly exposition of du Bois-Reymond's discoveries: 'the fruits of assiduous study, and of ten years' labour consistently concentrated upon one aim, during which the frog and the divisions of the galvanometer were his world—a rare example of methodical observation, of rich knowledge, and of that perspicacity of conception which is learned in the school of mathematics.' After communicating the most important results of du Bois' investigations, experiments which he himself demonstrated to his audience by the now familiar method of throwing a beam of light from a mirror connected with an astatic system of magnets upon a graduated scale, he goes on to say that certain physiologists assume what is propagated in the nerve during excitation to be some definite form of motion like the undulations that are propagated as sound-waves in the air, and as light-waves in the ether. He submits that electrical phenomena also lead to the idea of such a motion, since the extraordinary rapidity of the variations of electromotive force, both in magnitude and direction, makes it probable that this force affects very mobile particles, and that the orientation of these particles is temporarily altered by excitation, from the excited point of the nerve onwards to the muscle, and within the muscle itself. He considers the unexpectedly low rate of propagation in nervous excitation as determined by himself to be incompatible with the older view of an immaterial or imponderable principle as the nervous agent, but quite in harmony with the theory of the motion of material particles in the nerve substance.

This publication concluded the series of the closely-connected physiological investigations which Helmholtz had begun immediately after the publication of his thesis, and he now turned to physiological optics. In this subject he worked out new physical principles, upon which, as physicist, physiologist, philosopher, and aesthetician, he erected a structure of such extent and security as had never been dreamed of, which to this day arouses wonder and astonishment.

He had already instituted comprehensive experiments on the law of colour-mixture, in order to correct an error of

Newton, which had been perpetuated in the following centuries; and had since his visit to Vienna been in correspondence with Brücke, who was much occupied with such investigations. On December 22, 1851, Brücke writes to Helmholtz: 'As you know, Goethe in his unfortunate theory of colours explains all colours by the overlapping of light and dark, basing his argument on the well-known fact that transparent media in front of a dark ground may look violet-grey, blue-grey, and blue, while in transmitted light they look brown, yellow, or red. I have also noticed in my experiments on chamaeleons, how often very distinct colours are produced in this way in the animal kingdom, and have not found this phenomenon explained by the undulatory theory, although the explanation seems obvious enough. . . . Pray tell me if the different colouration of the reflected and refracted rays has been considered in optics.'

Brücke had no idea that Helmholtz had already made fundamental discoveries in this direction, which were to astonish physicists and physiologists alike in the dissertation he was about to publish. His father, to whom Helmholtz made a short communication of the contents of the paper, writes to him enthusiastically on April 5: 'Your letter of the 21st gave us as much pleasure as all its predecessors, and there was the usual murmur of impatience till every one had read it. May God fulfil you ever more and more as a prophet of truth and fountain of wisdom, so that you may not have lived in vain for eternal Humanity, but may ever continue one of its corner-stones on earth; then I shall find consolation for the lack of results in my own life. God have your health in His keeping, and grant you increasingly such a position in externals that your intellectual life may find its full development. I am most curious about the interesting work that you have chosen for your thesis; you will clash with Goethe there!'

He is delighted when Helmholtz tells him that the coming summer may bring great changes in his external position :—

'There are three physiological vacancies in prospect. So there may be a regular migration, in which each must try for the best new place. Not that there are many candidates in the field, du Bois, Eduard Weber in Leipzig, and I being almost the only ones.'

While Helmholtz was engaged upon his inaugural dissertation (the scope of which grew wider and deeper, until it eventually took shape as a searching *critique* of Brewster's contributions to optics), du Bois-Reymond, who had lately returned in such good spirits from England that he warns Helmholtz 'not to go to England, it spoils one's taste for Germany', advises his friend on June 15, that he had told Sir David Brewster about the ophthalmoscope, and that if a copy of Helmholtz's paper on it were sent, Sir David would be responsible for an English translation. Helmholtz replies in a few days:—

'I should imagine that you would like England under such conditions. I can hardly avail myself of Brewster's proposal to assist in the preparation of an English translation of *The Ophthalmoscope*, because the second part of the essay on physiological optics which I intend to use for my dissertation, and which I shall give as a lecture, and then send to Poggendorff, is intended as a contradiction of Brewster's analysis of solar light, a theory which he has much at heart, and has defended with some heat. His observations on this subject are perfectly correct, but the alteration of the colours of the spectrum by absorbing media depends mostly upon subjective phenomena, contrast and the like, as may be proved convincingly. My treatise is of course written as cautiously as possible, but still I fear that Brewster may take it amiss.'

On June 28, 1852, Helmholtz delivered his Inaugural Lecture 'On the Nature of Human Sense-Perceptions', in which he not only displayed his unique gift for making the stiffest scientific problems intelligible by a lucid and exceptionally beautiful exposition, but once more opened up new fields of inquiry, lying 'nearer the limits of human knowledge'. It was not until a much later time, after the publication of his *Physiological Optics*, that the full import of the physical, physiological, and epistemological discoveries which he had even then made could be recognized. It was this lecture that at last won him the complete approval of his critical father:—

'Thanks for the Inaugural Lecture sent me by Dr. Friedländer, which pleased me greatly by its clearness and its unaffected popular style.   You make the conclusions of science comprehensible even to the laity, showing where the details are leading to, and what is the way and aim.   It almost seems to me that this mathematical-empirical method of investigation, when once it develops into a definite art, and no longer depends upon individual genius, may inaugurate a new, perhaps slow, but certain way to philosophy, which will at any rate define exactly the objective substratum of all knowledge, rendering its nature indubitably clear, and thus establishing the ego-doctrine of Fichte as the only possible mode of philosophical thought.'

In a letter written in September, to announce the birth of his son Richard, Helmholtz gratified his father by admitting that it had (as the latter surmised) been his intention in the lecture to give an empirical statement of Fichte's fundamental views of sense-perception, and expresses pleasure that his father is content with the form of the dissertation, and approves of his philosophical opinions.

His general philosophical and epistemological views were, however, quite unlike Fichte's, since they were based upon exact investigations, the results of which he set forth in the inaugural thesis 'On the Theory of Compound Colours', and in the paper published in *Poggendorff's Annalen*, 'On Sir David Brewster's New Analysis of Solar Light,' which laid the foundation of the whole of the modern theory of colour. After Newton's discovery of the composition of white light, he assumed the existence of seven principal colours in the spectrum, apparently taking this number from the analogy which he sought to establish between these colours and the intervals of the musical scale.   But while two tones of different vibration-frequency and musical pitch produce sensations of harmony or dissonance when struck together, but can still be distinguished separately by the ear, luminous rays of different wave-length and colour give rise to impressions which fuse into a single new colour-sensation. This combination is due to a purely physiological phenomenon involved in the specific mode of reaction of the optic nerve.   Before the discovery that white light is due to a mixture of coloured lights, the mixture of pigments had led to the theory of the three elementary colours, red, yellow, blue, from which all other colours must be derived by combination; Newton assumed (without proving it by any prolonged experiments) that the same results must obtain for the composition of coloured light also: and on this supposition of three primitive colours, Thomas Young built up his hypothesis that the particles which lie upon the surface of the retina are capable of specific vibrations; that, at any spot, particles of three different vibration-rates, corresponding with the oscillation-frequencies of the three primary colours, are in immediate juxtaposition; and that, lastly, mixed sensations are produced by excitation of the ends of the specifically reacting nerve-fibres. Helmholtz now discovered that the mixture of colouring substances gave quite different results from the blending of spectral colours. It is only when the two colours happen to lie near each other in the spectrum, that the fusion of coloured light yields almost the same results as the mixture of pigments, because the resulting colour then resembles the intermediate colour-tones of the spectrum; the disparity is most marked in the combination of blue and yellow, which yield green when pigments are mixed and white with the corresponding mixture of spectral colours. Now green is among the colours most imperfectly produced by the fusion of spectral colours; it was therefore necessary for Helmholtz, if the hypothesis of the composition of all colours out of three elementary colours was to be maintained, to select for these three primaries, not red, yellow, and blue, but red, green, and violet; by the mixture of these three all the weaker compound colours can be obtained, while if the saturated colours of the spectrum are to be imitated, at least five primaries, red, yellow, green, blue, and violet, are required. In order to settle, in the first place, whether there are three elementary colours, from which all possible colours are, or at any rate may be, built up, this hypothesis had to be tested upon the prismatic colours, as the purest and most saturated. By observing through a prism set vertically the spectra of the two limbs. of a ∨-shaped slit (letting the bands of colour run in the one from left above to right below, and in the other from right above to left below, so that each coloured band from the one spectrum intersected all the bands of the other in the common field), he obtained all the combinations which could be produced from any two simple colours. The relative intensity of the mixed colours could be altered by shifting the prism from its vertical position to one more or less oblique, and care was taken to examine the points of which the colour was to be determined through a small diaphragm (since it is impossible to judge the colour of the field so long as it is surrounded by equally saturated colours); thus all the combinations could be investigated at all degrees of their relative intensity by means of a telescope, the cross-wires of which were set parallel with the colour-bands of the spectra. Helmholtz then discovered the surprising fact that—contrary to the views hitherto entertained—there are only two among the colours of the spectrum, yellow and indigo-blue, which together yield pure white, that is, are complementary to each other, whereas their combination had always been supposed till then to produce green. The whole width of the spectrum is divided into three sections by the rays which produce white: the colours of the first and second sections combine to tones of yellow, with transitions to red, flesh-colour, white, and green; colours of the second and third to blue, with transitions to green, white, and violet; colours of the first and third to purple-red, with transitions to flesh-colour, rose, and violet. Now since the mixture of yellow and blue does not produce green, but at most a faint greenish-white, Helmholtz had to conclude that the hypothesis of the composition of all colours from red, yellow, and blue was erroneous. But he further investigated the composition of pigment colours, and was thereby enabled to explain the obtained results. If a yellow and a blue powder are mixed, the blue particles which lie upon the surface will yield blue, and the yellow particles on the surface yellow light, which combine to form white or greenish-white. From within the mixture, only such light will return as can penetrate the blue as well as the yellow particles, and since blue substances can only let green, blue, and violet light through, and yellow substances only red, yellow, and green light, green light alone is able to return from within the pigment; this combines with the whitish light reflected from the surface, so that green predominates. Thus Helmholtz established the composition of pigmentary colours on purely physical principles. If the theory of three elementary colours is to go. (Young proposed red, green, and violet), then Young's theory of the three fundamental colours as the three fundamental qualities of sensation must also be given up. For if e. g. the sensation of yellow is only aroused by the yellow rays of the spectrum because they simultaneously excite the sensations of red and green, which in combination give yellow, then it would follow that the same sensation must be excited by the simultaneous action of the red and green rays, which, however, never produce so bright and vivid a yellow as that due to the yellow rays.

Helmholtz was led to these investigations in following up the phenomena described by Brewster, which were in apparent contradiction with Newton's theory, and involved a more searching analysis of coloured light than had been made by Newton, Goethe, or Brewster. Brewster, like Goethe, had stated (and built up his entire theory of colour on that statement) that it was not the differing refrangibility of the rays that determined the colours of the prismatic image, but that there were three different kinds of light, red, yellow, and blue, exhibiting every degree of refrangibility, and so arranged that the red light contains a preponderance of rays of less refrangibility, the yellow more rays of mean refrangibility, and the blue more of greater refrangibility; hence the first predominates at the less refrangible end of the spectrum, the second in the middle, the third at the most refrangible end. The remaining colours of the spectrum would be produced by the mixture of the three primitive colours. The object of Helmholtz's inaugural dissertation was to prove this view untenable, but he now went farther. Brewster had recognized that if different coloured rays of equal refrangibility exist, the compound light formed by them must behave as simple light in prismatic analysis, but declared that such rays might be separated by taking advantage of their difference of absorption in coloured media; thus there would be rays of all three descriptions in all portions of the spectrum, and consequently the white light due to their union: this is in direct contradiction with Newton's theory, according to which homogeneous light passing through coloured media may indeed be weakened or extinguished, but can never exhibit changes of colour. In order to refute Brewster's theory, or to answer the question whether the colour of homogeneous light is altered by coloured media or no, the validity of his experiments had in the first instance to be tested. Helmholtz found that Brewster had overlooked the false light cast over the observer's field of vision by the slight turbidity inevitable in transparent bodies. He shows that the alterations of colour which Brewster had remarked are due partly to impurities in the glass of the prism and to irregularities in the polishing of its faces, partly to multiple reflections at the surfaces of the prism and of the coloured media, as well as to dispersion of light in the eye itself; further, such alterations of colour may depend on contrast effects, excited by the luminosity of the spectral colours; while, finally, the colours of the spectrum excite a different impression with different intensities of light. Thus he refuted the theories of Brewster by a long series of conclusive experiments.

These investigations were just concluded when Helmholtz delivered his Inaugural Lecture, for which he selected a subject standing in the closest relation with his previous work, namely, a general discussion of the mode in which our sense-perceptions correspond with the objects perceived: a question that led him far into problems of the theory of knowledge, and at the same time struck the note of his further researches in physiology and physics.

After a masterly exposition of the undulatory theory of sound and light, and a defence of Newton's theory of colour against that of Brewster on the grounds above stated, he emphasizes the simplicity and apparent unity of a compound colour-sensation. He refers the opposition of Goethe (and after him of the whole of the Hegelian school) to the idea of the composite nature of white light to the idiosyncracies of the poet-genius, who held it to be his highest function to insist on the adequacy of sense phenomena, and assumed that the same directness of perception should be possible in the intellectual world.

In order to obtain a less superficial view of optical phenomena, it is necessary to recognize the relation borne by luminous sensations to the objects sensed; and Helmholtz

discusses two propositions that were of great importance in
the development of the theory of knowledge, that, on the
one hand, all is not light that is perceived as light (a dictum
enforced by Johannes Müller), while on the other, there
is also light to which we are not sensible, i. e. invisible light,
such as the chemical rays, which exert a chemical action
beyond the visible spectrum. It is highly probable, he says,
that light-rays and heat-rays are identical within the luminous
portion of the spectrum, although the intensest heat lies beyond
the red end, so that radiant heat and light may be regarded
as identical; the reason that luminosity is confined to so
small a group of the long series of vibrations appears from
Brücke's theory that the transparent media of the eye admit
these only to the retina, while all the rest are excluded.
From the fact that sensibility to light and heat do not exactly
correspond in their limits, Johannes Müller had previously
concluded that the specific character of luminous sensation
is conditioned by the specific activity of the optic nerve,
which, excite it as you will, can only yield the one sensation
of light. The radiation which we term now light, now radiant
heat, impinges on two different kinds of nerve end-organs,
in the eye and in the skin, and the disparity in quality of
the sensation is due not to the nature of the object sensed,
but to the kind of nervous apparatus that is thrown into
activity.

From this simple and obvious truth, Helmholtz developed
his entire theory of knowledge. Which colour combinations
appear the same, depends only upon the physiological law
of their composition; equality of colour arising from different
mixtures of coloured light has only a subjective value, and the
groups of isochromic combinations of colour correspond with
no objective relations, independent of the nature of the seeing
eye. But if this be true for colour as a property of light, it
must necessarily be true for colour as a property of bodies
also. A body that only gives out orange light must have
a different internal structure from a body that gives out only
red and yellow, or a third which gives red, orange, and
yellow. Yet the colour of these three bodies during white
illumination must be the same ; the similarity has no
objective, but merely a subjective value. At the end of the

lecture, he gathers up all these propositions in a form that anticipates his later conclusions:—

'Sensations of light and colour are only symbols for relations of reality. They have as much and as little connexion or relation with it, as the name of a man, or the letters of his name, have to do with the man himself. They inform us by the equality or inequality of their appearance whether we are dealing with the same, or with different, objects and properties of objects ... beyond this they tell us nothing. As to the real nature of the external phenomena to which we refer them, we learn nothing, as little as we know of a man from his name.'

This lecture again attracted the attention of the philosophers to his views on physics and physiology, without, however, gaining their approval.

As soon as Helmholtz had finished his Inaugural Thesis he proceeded to develop the theorem of current distribution, previously communicated to du Bois-Reymond, of the importance of which he was well aware. At the end of April he writes to Ludwig: 'I had the luck to discover a mathematical theorem as to the distribution of current in bodies, which gave du Bois so much trouble; this greatly simplifies the matter, but involves a few minor alterations in the hypotheses he suggested.' In the middle of July, 1852, he sends du Bois a note for the Academy, entitled, 'A Theorem of the Distribution of Electrical Currents in Material Conductors,' while at the beginning of the following year, 1853, he sent the full exposition of the subject, 'Upon Certain Laws of the Distribution of Electrical Currents in Material Conductors, with Application to Experiments in Animal Electricity,' to Poggendorff for his journal. In this work Helmholtz for the first time enters the field of mathematical physics and physiology, with the full equipment of the higher mathematical analysis, of which he was the only master in its application to the latter science. Even here, and much more in his later works, we feel that, as he himself insists, his juvenile *penchant* for geometry had developed into a kind of special mechanical sense, 'by means of which I almost feel how the stress and strain are distributed in a mechanical contrivance': while, on the other hand, it is plain that he strives to make complex and important mechanical relations plain to himself and others by theoretical analysis. On July 22, du Bois-Reymond presented the abstract of the theorem to the Academy, and wrote on August 3 to Helmholtz: 'What a cornucopia of communications you shower on us; such fertility is unheard of. But your comparison with Gauss's law of the compensation of internal magnetic forces by surface-distribution does not please me: why should your theorem not appear *sui generis*? For the rest it consoles me that Kirchhoff, with whom I often discussed the problems that are so easily handled in the light of the new theorem, also failed to solve them. The theory of nerve and muscle currents is at last demonstrable, and that hideous Chapter III of my book can be reduced to a short and elegant exposition.'

But the elaboration of the memoir designed for Poggendorff involved many difficulties, since in addition to the theorem so greatly admired by du Bois, which was at least comprehensible without recourse to higher mathematics, it also comprised the deduction and application of the most difficult propositions of the Theory of Potential, of which almost all the German physicists of the day, with the exception of Neumann, Weber, and Kirchhoff, were ignorant.

In the middle of November Helmholtz writes to Kirchhoff: 'I have not yet elaborated my theory of current-distribution in regard to animal electricity, because new problems are perpetually cropping up. I am hampered by the want of Green's works, and by the fact that Neumann has not yet published anything on these questions. I cannot talk to him freely about it, because the propositions which I invent and use are either in his unpublished notes, or are so much like his, that after each discussion with him I am left doubting whether to publish any given point or no. Accordingly I am debarred from learning Green's theorems out of the notebooks of Neumann's pupils.'

Nor had the difficulties all been got over even by the end of January, 1853. Helmholtz tells du Bois that he has been unable to find a general proof of an important theorem which can be easily proved for conductors in which the resistance is equal in all parts, viz. that an electromotive force applied to any given surface-element a of a conductor will produce in any other given surface-element β the same component of current, normal to the surface, as that electromotive force applied to β would produce in a.

He expects that he will have to leave the proof of this theorem to the future, but at last he overcomes the difficulty, and is able to announce to Ludwig early in March, 1853: 'I have meantime discovered and worked out some new theorems on the distribution of galvanic currents in material conductors, by which the theory of currents of animal electricity can be demonstrated with strict accuracy, and by a very simple method, while du Bois-Reymond had to make shift with exceedingly complex approximations. My results of course agree in essentials with those of du Bois.'

Du Bois-Reymond himself affirmed at a later time that he had been helpless in face of these great difficulties until Helmholtz came to his aid with the conception of electromotive surfaces, and the theorem of the equal and opposite action of two electromotive surface-elements, by means of which the previously insuperable difficulties became almost elementary. This very interesting and fundamental work on the distribution of electrical currents in material conductors is purely mathematical in character, owing to Helmholtz's method of proving the theorems, which are intelligible enough from the physical point of view. It is essentially connected with the treatise on the Conservation of Energy, since Helmholtz merely substitutes for the expression 'free tension' there employed, the identical concept of Gauss's potential, or Green's potential function.

In his inquiry he starts from the three equations which Kirchhoff had laid down for dynamic equilibrium in the distribution of currents in systems of material conductors, and had shown to be necessary and adequate for the expression of potential as a function of the co-ordinates. He has no difficulty in devising a quite general proof of the law of the superposition of electrical currents, which had been already recognized as valid for individual cases. He expresses it very simply by saying, that if in any system of conductors constant electromotive forces are introduced at different points, the electrical potential at any point of the system will be equal to the algebraic sum of the potentials which are due to each of the forces independently of the others. With this he associates

the law of electromotive surfaces, which states that if electromotive forces existing anywhere within a conductor produce
certain currents in an attached conductor, it must be possible
to devise a distribution of electromotive forces on the surface
of the first conductor which would produce the same currents.
He arrives at the distribution on the surface by assuming
the conductor to be insulated and determining the electrical
potential at any point of its surface due to the currents excited
by the internal forces; the required surface electromotive force
(taken from within outwards) is then equal to this difference
of electrical potential. He terms the surface, thus conceived
as electromotive, the positive effective surface; and from these
two theorems (deduced by strict mathematics) derives a series
of important conclusions. These again yield the theorem that
the potentials within the attached conductor are equal to the
sum of the potentials existing in it antecedently, and of those
produced by the positive effective surface. It is obvious that
different modes of distribution of e. m. f. at the surface of
a conductor (if they are to give the same derived currents as
the internal electromotive forces) can only vary by a difference
of potential that is constant for all points of the surface; and
from equally simple considerations (based entirely on Ohm's
Law) results the general and important theorem, that when
any two points on the surface of an extended conductor containing constant forces are connected with a given system of
linear conductors, it is always possible to substitute for it
a linear conductor of definite e. m. f. and resistance, which
will give rise to precisely the same current in all linear conductors connected with it, as the material conductor. He
introduces the conception of electrical double layers, which
assumes that at opposite sides of a surface and at infinitesimal
distances from it, there will be exactly the same quantity of
positive electricity on the one side as there is of negative on
the other. By this device he transforms the Poisson-Gauss
equation for non-equilibrium states—on which Kirchhoff founded
his equation for equilibrium—so that the potential shall not (as
in that equation) be uniform, and the force components on
either side of the surface non-uniform, but conversely, with
uniformity of force the difference of potential function shall
be a quantity that is different from zero, which he terms the

electrical moment of the surface: he thus succeeds in reducing problems of current distribution to a question of the potential of electrical surfaces and bodies. Lastly, with the aid of Green's propositions, he develops the theorem communicated in January to du Bois-Reymond of the equal mutual action of two electromotive surface-elements, and thus clears the way for the experimental confirmation of the law and its important applications. For since each single element of an electromotive surface discharges as much electricity into a galvanometer circuit as would flow through itself if its e. m. f. were situated in the galvanometer circuit, the total effect of all the electromotive surface-elements must be equal to the whole current passing through the galvanometer. In all experiments on animal electricity, in which nerve and muscle represent extended material conductors, with electromotive forces distributed in them, it now becomes possible to test and correct the theoretical conclusions of du Bois-Reymond and other physiologists as to arrangement of electromotive elements within the nerve or muscle, by means of laws that have been ascertained empirically.

Meantime, the interest of the various medical and literary circles in Königsberg had been aroused by the effect of Helmholtz's Physiological Theory of Colour upon the scientific world; and he responded to their inquiries by giving a lecture on 'Goethe's Scientific Researches', delivered on January 18 (Coronation Day) to the Deutsche Gesellschaft.

Helmholtz had been induced by various considerations to protest against the attack made by Goethe upon the optical work of Newton, and he accordingly desired, in order to avert misunderstanding, to show that although Goethe's physical conclusions were often erroneous, he had done indisputable service in botany and osteology, and must always be reckoned among the great men of science. In his *Sketch of a General Introduction to Comparative Anatomy*, Goethe expresses the idea (which was never better nor more clearly stated, and has subsequently been but little altered) that all differences in the structure of animal species must be looked upon as variations of a common type, brought about by the coalescence, alteration, increase, atrophy or total loss of single parts. A similar analogy between the different parts of one and the same organism, as seen in animal species, exists in the manifold repetition of the same parts in plants, and again in the transition from the leaves of the stem to those of the calyx and petals—from which follows Goethe's theory of the 'Metamorphosis of Plants', which has been accepted, at any rate in its essential features, by the botanists. The repetition of homogeneous parts in animals, which Goethe noticed accidentally, led him to extend his doctrine to animals also, but in Helmholtz's opinion these osteological conclusions have been less favoured by science.

According to Helmholtz it was wonderful that Goethe should divine the existence of such a law, and follow out its indications so acutely, although he neither saw what law it was, nor even tried to find out; since he always held the view that 'Nature must yield up her own secrets, inasmuch as she is the transparent symbol of her ideal significance'.

But after emphasizing the great services which Goethe had rendered to the natural sciences, Helmholtz claimed the right of criticizing the physical conclusions arrived at by this great genius, and pointed out the errors into which Goethe fell, when he attempted to repeat Newton's experiments with the prism, in order to investigate the aesthetic laws of colour in painting. He was ignorant of the most elementary principles of optics, and held all Newton's facts and deductions to be an absurdity. Helmholtz discusses the very interesting question why this master-mind should have attacked Newton and the physicists in general with such unparalleled animosity, imputing nothing but ill will to his antagonists, and why this greatest of poets should have assumed his achievements in science to be far more valuable than all he had accomplished in poetry. Helm-holtz attacks his subject with a brilliancy of comprehension, a depth of aesthetic feeling, an appreciation of the poetic and scientific qualities of the man, and of the inductive and deductive methods of reasoning, possible only in a great and contemplative thinker, expressing himself in the language of inimitable charm and vigour that characterizes all his writings, and is unique as a model for the popular treatment of scientific problems.

For the poet, he says, as for every other artistic genius, an idea is not expressed as the product of a slowly matured intellectual concept, but the material of his art becomes the direct vehicle of the idea. With Goethe the phenomenal is the immediate expression of the ideal, in which he is the forerunner of Hegel's 'nature-philosophy', and he therefore appreciates experiments that can be carried out in clear sunshine, under the open heavens, in contrast to Newton's slits and glasses. Goethe could not and would not grasp the fact that the pure tone of white light is due to a fusion of colours; he endeavoured by a consistent observation of facts to determine their connexion, so as to discover the causes of the phenomena of nature, without trespassing into the realm of concepts: while the physicist denies all authority to sensation, and is increasingly aware that the nature of sense-perception depends less upon the properties of the objects perceived than upon those of the sense-organs by which he obtains his intelligence. All Goethe's conclusions and explanations are accordingly fallacious.

'Goethe is only content when he can stamp reality itself with poetry. In this lies the peculiar beauty of his poems, and it accounts for his resolute hostility to the mechanism that threatened to disturb his poetic repose, and his determination to attack the enemy in his own camp. Yet we cannot conquer the mechanical laws of matter by ignoring them: we can only subordinate them to the aims of moral intelligence. We must understand its levers and pulleys if we are to control them by our will, and herein lies the great significance, and full justification, of physical research in the advance of civilization.'

Forty years later, in a lecture given at Weimar to the Goethe-Gesellschaft, on 'Goethe's Anticipations of Coming Scientific Ideas', Helmholtz found a fresh opportunity of insisting on the great importance of Goethe's work for the general development of science. While his judgement of the optical part of it remained unshaken, he now interprets Goethe's errors and prejudices by his aversion to the abstractions of intangible concepts, in which the theoretical physics of the day was wont to reckon. He holds Goethe's protest against the abstractions of matter and force to be not unjustified, since 'though they were used by the great theoretical physicists of the seventeenth and eighteenth centuries in a coherent and definite sense, they contained the germs of the wildest misunderstandings, which now run riot in perverted and superstitious minds'. Helmholtz recognized that the seed which Goethe sowed in the field of natural science had developed in rich and full abundance, since Darwin's theory of the modifications of organic form rests confessedly upon those very analogies and homologies of structure in plants and animals which Goethe, the first discoverer, presented to his contemporaries in the form of anticipations only, while Darwin developed this poetic forecast into a mature concept. He finds the reign of law among physical phenomena, which Goethe sought to discover, expressed with the greatest precision and lucidity in Kirchhoff's lectures on mathematical physics, which enrolled mechanics among the 'descriptive sciences'. For Helmholtz, science and art are intimately connected, since both express and enunciate truth. The artist can only succeed in his work when he has a subtle knowledge of the natural relations of the phenomena which it expresses, and of their effect upon the auditor or spectator. 'When the task can be fulfilled by expression in the tangible images of poetic divination, the poet proves himself capable of the highest achievement; where the strict inductive method alone can avail, he founders. But again, where cardinal points of the relation between reason and empirical fact are involved, his firm grasp of reality preserves him from error, and gives him a sure insight which extends to the very limits of human understanding.'

The commencement of the New Year found Helmholtz in depressed conditions. It had been a sad Christmas, for his wife was ill of nervous gastritis, from which she only recovered after some weeks of unremitting attention from her mother and sister. His mother had been laid by with a serious operation. He himself was suffering from frequent attacks of migraine, which kept him in bed for days together. He proposed to take his wife to Marienbad on his way to England, but his father disapproved, on economical grounds, though this difficulty was partly removed by a rise of salary in April, 1853, which brought his income up to £150.

From the beginning of 1853 to the summer vacation, Helmholtz was engaged in the continuation of his measurements of the rate of transmission in nerve and muscle, which necessitated the contrivance of a special instrument for measuring the very small electrical currents which du Bois had observed in muscles. In addition to this he embarked on a protracted study of the adaptation of the eye for different distances, which was, however, interrupted by the discoveries of a young Dutch physiologist, Cramer. As early as January 23, Helmholtz sent du Bois a short preliminary notice for the Academy 'On a hitherto unknown Alteration in the Human Eye, during Altered Accommodation'. In this he describes an observation made as early as the winter of 1852, that in accommodation for near objects, the image reflected from the front surface of the lens is diminished to nearly half its size, a considerable alteration which cannot be explained by a change of position of the lens, but only on the supposition that there is an alteration of its form by the increased curvature of the anterior surface. He had previously determined by many exact observations that the edge of the pupil bulges outwards in near vision.

In March he joyfully communicates his 'little discovery in regard to the accommodation of the eye' to Ludwig, as published in the monthly reports. But on July 3 he informs him: 'Donders has written to tell me that a Dr. Cramer has been before me, his paper having been "crowned" in 1851 by the Haarlem Society, though it is only now being published: I shall receive a copy of it shortly. Lately there have been a good many coincidences between my work and that of others: (1) on Brewster's Theory; a portion of my results were also discovered by a young physicist, Felix Bernard, and published in the *Annales de Phys. et Chim.* in the same month in which mine appeared in *Poggendorff*, but he had communicated the work some time before to the French Faculty: (2) in January Gaugain brought out a tangent galvanometer, on the principle of the one I had made in 1849 for du Bois-Reymond's experiments; mine, however, is more convenient and better: (3) Foucault describes a method for the uniform lighting of large surfaces with homogeneous or mixed light; I received his paper after myself inventing and constructing the apparatus: (4) Cramer on Accommodation; I am most curious to see this paper.—Your textbook, so far as it goes at present, is my faithful friend when I am preparing my lectures.'

The promised copy of Cramer's paper was so long delayed

that Helmholtz writes to Donders after his autumn journey of 1853:—

'I have not yet received Dr. Cramer's treatise on the Accommodation of the Eye, and confess that I am very curious to see how much room he has left me for my own observations. Your letter was the first I had heard of his work, and though I regret the time lost on investigations that turn out to be the property of another, I am of course only too glad to clear the way as much as I can for a young man who makes his début in science with such a striking piece of work, and to help him towards recognition. I had equally arrived on theoretical grounds at the idea of a simultaneous tension of the radial and circular fibres of the iris, but am inclined to ascribe a considerable part to the *tensor choroidae* also.'

Helmholtz employed the enforced leisure of summer to continue his experiments on the mixture of homogeneous colours by other methods than those hitherto employed. He found, in agreement with Grassmann, that besides indigo-blue and yellow, another pair of complementary colours existed in the spectrum, although he had not previously been able to demonstrate them, and further, that all colours, with the exception of green, yield simple complementary colours. In order to determine the breadth of the colours in the spectrum, he defined white as the sensation due to the sum of the light-components simultaneously perceived by the eye, together with the vivid memory of such as were perceived immediately before.

He also carried on his experiments on the time-relations of excitation in man throughout the summer, arriving at the conclusion that the rate of the nervous impulse in man is about three times as great as in the frog. As regards the initiation of electrical processes during the excitation of nerve and muscle, he was able to determine 'that the electrotonic condition of the nerve begins with the entry of the primary current, whereas the negative variation of the muscle begins appreciably later than the excitation, but precedes the first trace of contraction'.

At the beginning of August, Helmholtz left Königsberg, and took his wife and the two children to his mother- and sister-in-law at Dahlem. Du Bois-Reymond was not in Berlin, but he had the satisfaction of seeing Johannes Müller, who was just starting for Sicily. He visited his parents in Potsdam, and found his father well and cheerful, but his mother greatly altered. At a dinner given by Magnus, at which H. Rose was also present, he met Tyndall, the English translator of his works: 'he is a very talented young man, and interested me more than any of the other strangers; unfortunately he will not be in England when I am there.' He also went to see Dr. Graefe, 'who was still attending to his clinique, and showed me some cases with the ophthalmoscope, and a mass of drawings made with the instrument, saying many kind things about the great utility of this invention.' After providing himself with letters of introduction from Magnus, Dove, and H. Rose, to distinguished men of science in England, and to the chemist Hofmann, Helmholtz went on to Bonn, where he had the pleasure of spending a few hours with Plücker. 'At first he seemed to me a little exclusive, like most of the Bonn professors, but afterwards he became quite genial, and commemorated my visit in a remarkably good bottle of wine.' Helmholtz crossed by Ostend to London, putting up at an hotel which Tyndall had recommended to him. He gave himself up entirely to English life, and sent daily letters to his wife with vigorous sketches of his varied and original observations. Space forbids the quotation of more than a few of these, which have special reference to the English scientists with whom Helmholtz now for the first time became acquainted, and with whom he formed a lifelong connexion.

'And now you shall hear about this great Babylon. Berlin, both in size and civilization, is a village compared to London. Everything here is on such a gigantic scale, that one ceases to wonder at anything. The disadvantages of an enormous city are pleasantly counterbalanced by the wonderful Parks within the town, and the green of its suburbs. But I had better go on with my diary, so as to tell you everything. . . . In the first place I went to Bence Jones, physician, physiologist, and chemist, hoping to get news of du Bois-Reymond, and of the chemist Hofmann. But he had gone off to du Bois' wedding. The Embassy was in the same direction, so I went there to present my letters to Bunsen. Bunsen was engaged, and invited me to visit him next day. This errand showed me something of the Park, which extends unbroken from the

West End nearly to the centre of London. In the afternoon
I explored it further; imagine enormous smooth spaces of
short, fine grass, dotted over with fine old trees or groups
of trees, a few paths cut through them which are only used
in wet weather (for when it is dry every one walks as he
pleases over the grass), and there is the ideal that you wanted
for our garden. Huge sheep, as fat as stuffed wool-sacks, graze
everywhere on the grass and keep it short. . . . The breakfast with Bunsen was just a way of receiving one's visit at a
leisure moment. Milady and two daughters, a Professor Larso
from Berlin, and Privatdocent Böttiger from Halle, both
Oriental scholars, were there too. The meal was refined
without being luxurious, but was swallowed post-haste. Each
helped himself as he pleased without waiting for the others.
I was last, because I had to talk so much. Bunsen somewhat
resembles S., interested in everything, lively, but a little con-
ceited. He was most affable and officious, and wrote me
a letter of introduction to the zoologist Richard Owen which
I did not want. For the rest, everything was on a very grand
scale in the house.—British Museum. Here were Layard's
monuments, Elgin's Marbles from the Parthenon, those from
the Lycian tombs, &c., all in real life. The Assyrian bulls
with human heads are enormous monsters. The reliefs are
far more vigorous than in the drawings; they are very clear
and sharply worked out, and parts of them look as if they were
quite new. In England they excite more interest than in other
places, because they are supposed to confirm certain passages
in the Old Testament. As regards style, they are infinitely
finer than anything in Egyptian art, and are parallel with the
best productions of the ancient Greeks. Bunsen tells me that
much progress has been made in deciphering the inscriptions.

'My attempts to see Professor Owen were in vain, but
I succeeded in finding the first physicist of England and
Europe, Faraday—perhaps, unfortunately, for the first and last
time, since he leaves town on Monday, and does not know
if he is coming to Hull. Those were splendid moments. He
is as simple, charming, and unaffected as a child; I have never
seen a man with such winning ways. He was, moreover,
extremely kind, and showed me all there was to see. That,
indeed, was little enough, for a few wires and some old

bits of wood and iron seem to serve him for the greatest discoveries.

'From there I went to the National Gallery. There are some beautiful Rembrandts, and fair examples of Rubens and the Italian masters, and two marvellous Murillos. In the afternoon I went by omnibus to Hammersmith, a suburb with villas on the Thames, to see Professor Wheatstone, the physicist, and inventor of the first practicable electrical telegraph. He had left, but they gave me hopes of finding him in Hull. In the evening dined at seven with Dr. Bence Jones: only he, du Bois and his wife, and I. Bence Jones is a charming man. Simple, harmless, cordial as a child, and extraordinarily kind to me. He appointed a second meeting for the next day, to see the ophthalmoscope, and took me to a mechanician where Faraday's instruments for the detection of table-turning are on view. On Thursday morning I worked at the lecture I am to give (" On the Mixture of Homogeneous Colours "). At noon, when I was going out for lunch, I met Professor Plücker from Bonn in the street, who joined me, and said that Professor Sommer from Königsberg was staying in the same house with him. Afterwards I went to Bence Jones, to keep my appointment.

'On Friday Airy invited me to go to Greenwich and dine with him. He had been rather stiff the first time, and can be very disagreeable, but on this occasion he was charming, and as I inspected all his appliances, praising much, and criticizing some things, he was quite unable to stop perambulating, so that I have probably seen more of the Observatory than any one else. Besides the regular observatory, of which I understood little, there are remarkably fine contrivances for magnetic and meteorological observations, in which the state of the instruments perpetually daguerreotypes itself, so that the series of observations is more exactly and completely recorded than it could be by the most accurate observer. Then we saw apparatus for the electro-magnetic measurement of time in star-transits, and electric clocks, which indicate the time simultaneously in London and at the mouth of the Thames, and at all the London railway stations. Airy's house and family life were arranged, as we should say, in style, but it is so with most of the English professors. His wife was rather formal, well preserved, with pleasant manners. The English ladies are all very interested in their husbands' work, and she was familiar with everything. He has a splendid position. What he writes goes out to the world not under his own name, but in that of Astronomer Royal, and he is superior to the rest from his training in methods: most of the English physicists do great things purely from instinct, not like the French from training in the best methods, so that their work is often spoiled by ignorance of the most ordinary matters. The afternoon at Greenwich was one of the most interesting and delightful of my journey.

'On Tuesday I looked up Wittich, and went about with him. In the morning we explored Westminster Abbey: its architecture is not nearly so beautiful as that of the best German cathedrals. It is too narrow, and the vaulting is not very intricate, but the array of monuments to the famous dead is extraordinarily imposing, and must stimulate the pride of Englishmen in the highest degree. To have had such men, and to see them so honoured, is grand. There lie professors of physics and chemistry between the kings, generals, and artists; even tragedians of the first rank have found their place and their monument here: Newton, James Watt, Humphry Davy, Thomas Young, Shakespeare, Milton, Garrick, Mrs. Siddons, Henry V, Richard II, Edward's sons, Warren Hastings, the two Pitts, Mary Stuart, and Elizabeth.

'On Wednesday I packed up, and went to Hull—by train of course, not steamer. I met Dr. Plücker at the station and travelled with him. The journey is uninteresting. Farther north, the country is not so exquisitely green as it is near London, and is mostly hilly. Here in Hull we are quartered on various people, I with a physician, Dr. Cooper, where I live "very fashionably", and am well taken care of. The foreigners (besides myself and Plücker there is only a Russian, du Hamel, here) are treated with exquisite courtesy. Yesterday evening at eight was the first General Meeting, when the President gave a survey of the progress of science during the last year: 600 persons were present, each of whom had paid at least £1, and 175 of them were ladies. We strangers were named in the report which the Secretary gave at the end; I was mentioned as Professor H. from Königsberg, who had contributed one of the most important advances in continental science. My 'Conservation of Energy' is better known here than in Germany, and more than my other works.

'Early this morning, Thursday, I was invited to breakfast by Mr. Frost, a wealthy private individual and a geologist. At his house I met Professor Stokes of Cambridge, a young but most distinguished man, whom I had not expected to see, because he had been in Switzerland. . . .

'The British Association at Hull was, as I have already told you, remarkably well attended; there were 850 members and 236 ladies. Here in England the ladies seem to be very well up in science, though of course many of them come to show themselves, or from curiosity, to listen to the discussions, and amuse themselves with them. Still on the whole they are attentive, and don't go to sleep, even under provocation. The six sections of the Society sit every day from eleven to three. From ten to eleven is occupied by the committees; I was taken to the committee of the Physics Section. The public generally wander from one section to another to hear the most distinguished speakers. The communications naturally varied greatly in quality: some were important scientific contributions, some the tomfoolery of crack-brained persons who imagine they have got hold of startling discoveries. But the presidents generally knew how to suppress these people. I was most interested in the arrangements for scientific investigations by committees, and the way in which the English attack these questions. Now, for instance, they are engaged upon a geological comparison of the surface of the earth with that of the moon, by means of their splendid telescopes, a number of astronomers and amateurs having joined together for this purpose. Further, they are preparing to send a gigantic telescope to the Southern Peninsula at Government cost, to explore the southern heavens. The most popular departments were geology, geography, and ethnology. These, too, attracted the most distinguished speakers; it is important to engage a great number of people upon common work in these departments, and the Association is very well adapted for this. On the other hand, many of the best chemists, physicists, and astronomers were absent, e. g. Airy, Faraday, Wheatstone. Others were there whom I much wanted to meet. Grove, a jurist and distinguished physicist from London, Andrews, Professor of Chemistry in Belfast, Stokes, a physicist from Cambridge; there was no one who could properly be called a physiologist. The clearest and most popular, as well as most valuable communications, were those of the geologists Phillips and Hopkins, and the ethnographer Dr. Latham, but many of them were tedious, and many to my surprise were mumbled, and so badly delivered that they were unintelligible. I joined in one discussion *ex tempore*, and explained a point in the optics of the eye that had been worked out in Germany. I got through all right, though I made plenty of mistakes, but the English people praised me, and said it was quite clear and easy to understand, although I used certain words in a different sense from that which they usually convey. I read my lecture on "The Mixture of Colours" aloud to Dr. Francis, who corrected the mistakes, and was much commended for it. The style of course was not entirely my own, but they were pleased with the delivery, and I received many compliments at the expense of Professor Plücker, who, considering how often he comes to England, speaks very badly.'

Helmholtz intended to visit Utrecht on the return journey, to make acquaintance in person with Donders, but was summoned home by his wife's illness. This time, however, she soon recovered from the attack of the malady to which she was becoming increasingly liable, and he was able to talk over his travelling experiences with her, invigorated in mind and body. This journey to England made a deep and abiding impression upon him, and he took every subsequent opportunity of revisiting his scientific friends there.

'England,' he writes to Ludwig, 'is a great country, and one feels what a splendid thing civilization is, when it penetrates into all the least relations of life. Berlin and Vienna are mere villages in comparison with London. London is quite indescribable; one must see its traffic with one's own eyes, before one can realize it; it is an event in one's life to see it; one learns to judge the ways of man by other standards.'

At length, in the middle of October, 1853, Helmholtz received Cramer's memoir for which he had been waiting so many months, and was enabled to continue the work on accommodation that had been interrupted by Donders's letter. After declining to write a textbook on Physiological Physics at the invitation of Vieweg, who in consequence gave the commission to Fick, Helmholtz, at Karsten's request, undertook the section on Physiological Optics in his great *Encyclopaedia of Physics* (a task which unexpectedly required ten years for its completion), and then busied himself in the first place with a new method of determining in the living eye the forms and distances of the refracting surfaces, the cornea and the anterior and posterior surfaces of the lens, in order to define the path of the rays of light in the eye. By April, 1854, he had got so far that after studying Cramer's paper, he could write to Donders hopefully of speedily determining the curvature of the iris and displacement of the border of the pupil as it occurs in adaptation :—

'I received Dr. Cramer's treatise directly after I had written my first letter to you. I have studied the book, for which again my best thanks, although I found it rather troublesome, as I first had to learn Dutch to read it. Happily your language is so much akin to ours that it is not difficult to understand. Dr. Cramer's work is interesting, and very satisfactory. I did not succeed in experimenting with fresh-killed eyes, because I used rabbits. Cramer's experiments on such eyes show that the iris is necessary to adaptation for near vision, as I had previously surmised. But it still seems to me doubtful whether the iris alone is involved. When the accommodation is for near vision, the edge of the pupil itself bulges forward, while a contraction of the iris alone, i.e. of its radial and circular fibres, which Cramer rightly assumes to occur, would be apt to produce the contrary effect.'

These difficult optical investigations were now pushed aside by another task, which was forced upon him by an unfortunate incident. At the close of 1853, Clausius published an unjustifiable attack in the *Annalen* upon Helmholtz's memoir on the Conservation of Energy, which was a source of great annoyance and distress to Helmholtz, since it emanated from a contemporary and distinguished member of the Physical Society, whom he had known intimately since 1848, and whom he had for a long time been in the habit of meeting almost daily. At the beginning of 1854, he refuted the attack in the same journal, under the title 'Reply to the Observations of Dr. Clausius', with such success that any doubt as to the correctness of his statements was henceforth impossible.

This assault might have been prejudicial to Helmholtz, inasmuch as it conveyed the impression to non-mathematical physicists that his conclusions were erroneous, and as he was not a professed mathematician, the allegations of Clausius might have been accepted. At the time when Helmholtz published 'The Conservation of Energy', he had already done a great deal of work in the direction of a mechanical theory of heat, but in the printed essay omitted everything that savoured of hypothesis, 'in order to facilitate the reception of the work by the physicists.' At a later period he had entirely left the matter aside, in the belief that the mechanical theory of heat could only be promoted by avoiding all presumptions as to the constitution of the molecules, and examining generally how the motions within the complex molecules affected the position of adjacent molecules. But he had been engaged on far wider problems prior to the publication of 'The Conservation of Energy'. When Carnot (on the presumption that heat was material, and as such could neither be destroyed nor added to) investigated the processes by which heat is able to perform mechanical work, he found that this can occur only when heat is passing from a warmer to a colder body. Perpetual motion would then be an impossibility only if the return of heat from the colder to the warmer body required an amount of work to be performed equal to that done by the previous and opposite process, besides which this expenditure of energy would have to be independent of the nature of the transmitting substance. Subsequent work upon the conservation of energy, however, made it impossible to maintain the material nature of heat, which had been an essential postulate in Carnot's deduction. Helmholtz had already attempted to formulate proofs, based on mechanical principles, for certain of Carnot's conclusions which seemed to him to hold good in the theory of heat, but he was forced for the time to leave over any decision as to the validity of these propositions. He had, therefore, gone much farther than Clausius had detected from the published memoir on the Conservation of Energy; farther indeed than Clausius himself had advanced at a much later period.

Clausius in the first instance attacked Helmholtz's derivation of the law of the development of heat in electrical discharges from the law of the conservation of energy. As stated in a letter to du Bois-Reymond, he had not noticed that the definition given by Helmholtz of the 'potential of a mass-in-itself' differed from the ordinary definitions. Helmholtz gives the particulars of this dispute some years later in a letter to Tait of March 17, 1867:—

'As to my discussion with Clausius, there was no essential difference between us as to the mechanical equivalent, except that Clausius takes the heat of the spark into account, while I believed it might be neglected, and that I took the potential of a body in itself as the sum of $m_a m_b / r_{ab}$ without excluding the repetitions of the indices (ab) and (ba), while Clausius followed the other mathematicians in excluding these repetitions, so that what he terms potential was only half as large as what I defined as such. Substantially both were equally correct.'

Helmholtz was able to refute the second objection raised to his work with equal ease, that, namely, criticizing the conclusions he deduced from the law of Riess, to the effect that with different charges, and a varying number of similar Leyden jars, the heat developed in each individual part of the wire closing the circuit must be proportional to the square of the quantity of electricity, and inversely proportional to the surface of the jars. This charge does not really touch Helmholtz, or the conclusions which he deduced under the assumption of this law, since Clausius attacked the correctness of the law of Riess in itself, and disputed its universal validity, while Helmholtz said in his paper that the law was in need of experimental confirmation. In regard to a misunderstanding of a passage in Holtzmann's book, Helmholtz candidly admitted his mistake, as appears from a letter to Ludwig. Clausius's main attack on the work of Helmholtz was directed against the proof of the proposition, that the principle of the conservation of *vis viva* holds good only where the working forces can be resolved into forces due to material points, acting in the direction of the lines joining the points, while their intensity depends solely upon the distance. Upon this Helmholtz founds a long and important argument with which his epoch-making thermodynamic work, the greatest achievement of the last decade of his life, is intimately connected, though the latter was of course considered from an altogether different point of view.

Helmholtz fully recognized the importance of an attack upon this particular part of his treatise on the Conservation of Energy, because this was his main advance on the investigations of Robert Mayer, and the chief significance of his own work rests upon the same considerations. Both engineers and physicists had for a long time defined the product of the mass of a weight raised, and the height it is raised to, as the measure of work done; this conception of quantity of work, as the product of force into a distance, had to be transferred from the case in which there is a force of constant magnitude acting in a constant direction, viz. gravitation, to the cases where a large or even infinite number of particles, acting upon each other, undergo relative displacement, so that work is done along the path of each individual particle by the forces exerted by the other particles.

Green had defined this amount of work as *potential*, for attractive and repulsive forces, the intensity of which is inversely proportional to the square of the distance of the interacting masses, and applied its mathematical properties to the explanation of electrical and magnetic phenomena. It was then seen that this same quantity of work, taken negatively, is a factor to be considered in all problems of mechanics and physics: it was named potential energy to distinguish it from the product of half the masses into the squares of the velocity, which was termed *vis viva*, or actual energy. By this conception Helmholtz was able to proceed from the earlier law of the 'Conservation of *Vis Viva*', as laid down in the mechanics of ponderable masses, to the great law of the 'Conservation of Energy', which, in addition to asserting that matter can neither be destroyed nor added to, affirms the constancy of energy as the sum of actual and potential energy. The old formula, the so-called 'law of the conservation of *vis viva*', only dealt with cases in which the potential energy was unchanged, and therefore disappeared in the final result.

Clausius protested against the derivation of the law of the 'conservation of *vis viva*', as given by Helmholtz in his memoir, where he takes it as the point of departure for his own great law. He objected that Helmholtz had, even in the simple case in which two particles act on one another, assumed, in addition to his assumption of the law of the conservation of *vis viva*, that the magnitude of the force was a function of the distance, concluding therefrom that the direction of the force coincided with the line connecting those points. Helmholtz showed this objection also to be ill-founded, and embraced the opportunity of giving a further and more complete discussion of this point, suggesting a new and interesting treatment of the subject. Starting with the definition that movable points have the same relative position to each other, whenever a system of co-ordinates can be constructed in which all the co-ordinates shall have relatively the same values, Helmholtz expresses the law of the conservation of *vis viva* in this form: 'When any number of particles in motion are only moving under the influence of such forces as they are themselves exerting upon one another, then the sum of the *vis viva* of all particles at any moment in which all the particles recover their same relative position, is constant whatever their direction and velocity at intermediate times'; and in virtue of this law he again refutes Clausius's objection that in certain cases the *vis viva* may be a purely arbitrary function of the co-ordinates of the system. He states expressly that he made the assumption in his treatise that the force exerted by one particle upon another is independent of any other forces that may be acting upon it, a principle which has always been accepted in mechanics. He concludes by saying that he had expected criticism from Clausius in regard to his Theory of Galvanism:—

'The chapter on electro-dynamics in my treatise was written under great difficulties. At that time I scarcely had access to any mathematical and physical literature, and was almost wholly confined to what I could discover for myself. It can only be a gain if the ideas which I endeavoured to bring forward in my paper at a time when they were finding little response from the physicists, are taken up afresh by another thinker, and handled with the same thorough criticism as Dr. Clausius has bestowed on other chapters of the Theory of the Conservation of Energy.'

He then enumerates the results obtained at a later period under more favourable circumstances, and lays down the principle, among others, that if a magnet is brought from infinity to a body magnetized by induction, mechanical work will be done, the value of which will eventually equal half the potential of the magnetized, in respect of the magnetizing body. But 'in order not to forestall Clausius', he did not cite all the results which he had already arrived at. At the time when he published the 'Conservation of Energy' he had access only to a few isolated portions (apart from their context) of the works of Poisson, Green, and Gauss, and therefore confined himself to the case in which the iron magnetized by induction was perfectly soft, and so offered no resistance to magnetization (the distribution of the magnetism thus being similar to that of electricity in conductors electrified by induction). It is, however, obvious from a fragmentary note that he had worked out the mathematical aspects of the problems involved, starting with the assumption that the magnetization of any element of a body is proportional to the magnetizing force.

The memoir thus designed by Helmholtz to refute the attacks of Clausius is of the greatest interest, since on the one hand it gives the first clear indication of the extent and depth of the work already accomplished by Helmholtz in mathematics and physics previous to his twenty-fourth year, and on the other it foreshadows the deductions of the marvellous achievements of his later life.

The most brilliant and the best known of Helmholtz's popular scientific lectures, i.e. that 'On the Interaction of Natural Forces, and recent Physical Discoveries bearing on the same', was written as the direct consequence of his renewed preoccupation with the Law of the Conservation of Energy after the appearance of Clausius's criticism, and of the demand that reached him on all sides in Königsberg for some more popular account of the great principle which was to underlie the science of the future. His stern father's opinion is interesting and characteristic :—

'It has given me the greatest pleasure, partly from its lucidity and wealth of facts, its easy wit, its hold on true science amid all the difficulties of interesting a non-scientific audience, partly from the high ideal relation it establishes between investigations that would otherwise appear totally independent of one another.

'The view that all phenomena of sensation, from the least of the infusoria to the most stupendous solar system, are transitory, follows of course from a philosophic conception of Time and Space, and of an eternally creating Idea; but I rejoice in this thought, already familiar to me in Müller's physiology, since even the much-abused natural science is finding its way by physical experiments to the same goal as that which the philosophical development of the idea has reached already; and thus to those for whom the reality of the spiritual has no meaning, the Eternal Idea is revealed in the external creation. It is only when we perceive that nature and history are the expressions of the divine life, objectively immovable, dependent on no subjectivity of the individual or epoch of development, laid down for each in every age as the sacred tables of revelation in imperishable bronze, that we enter upon the sure and never to be abandoned way that leads us to the knowledge of God.

'The only thing I do not like in your lecture, though I quite appreciate your motive, is the introduction of the Mosaic Creation. That is fundamentally untrue, and a weak concession of science which we should not make to our opponents, who are idly or childishly clinging to the letter of their beliefs. I found fault with Fichte for this when he sent me his last great philosophical work; he admitted my point, and promised not to do it again. No enemy is converted by it, while the weaker minds are confused, either as to the meaning of the Bible, or of the conclusions reached by Science.'

Even du Bois-Reymond, whose style is incomparable, writes to him about this lecture: 'I find it unique, especially at the beginning and close, and wonder at the way your style has developed. It has been welcomed in all quarters.' It did indeed fulfil all the conditions Helmholtz elsewhere laid down as essential to a popular treatment of science.

Nor did Helmholtz content himself with giving a masterly exposition of the Law of the Conservation of Energy, in a style that made it intelligible to all, along with the historical development of the mechanical principles involved in it, and a generous recognition of the fact that 'the first who conceived and stated this universal law of nature correctly was a German physician, J. R. Mayer, of Heilbronn, in 1842'. Taking his stand upon this great law (to which he leads his audience by comparing the development of energy in natural processes in relation to its utility to man, with the driving energy of machines), he proceeds to the question whether the total quantity of working energy, which cannot be augmented without a corresponding consumption, can be either lost or diminished, and replies that 'it certainly can for the purposes of our machines, but not for nature as a whole'. He then passes on to the Carnot-Clausius law, according to which heat can only be converted into mechanical work when it passes from a warmer to a cooler body,—even then its conversion is only partial, so that we cannot transform the heat of any body that cannot be further cooled into another form of energy, whether mechanical, electrical, or chemical—and develops the consequences of this law of nature for the universe: 'these physico-mechanical laws are, as it were, the telescopes of our spiritual eye, and penetrate into the farthest night of past and future'— thence deducing results which du Bois-Reymond aptly reckons among his 'most brilliant discoveries'.

If all bodies in nature had the same temperature, it would be impossible to convert any portion of their heat into mechanical work. The potential store of energy in the universe can thus be divided into two portions, one of which is heat and continues as such, while the other (to which a portion of the heat of the warmer bodies, and the total supply of chemical, electrical, and magnetic energy belong) is the source of all the countless interacting changes in Nature. Now since the heat of warmer bodies is perpetually striving to pass into those that are cooler, so as to establish an equilibrium of temperature, and since in every chemical or electrical process, and at each motion of a terrestrial body subject to collision or friction, a portion of the mechanical energy passes into heat, of which a part only can be reconverted, it follows that while the first portion of the store of energy (the unaltered heat) increases constantly in every natural process, the second portion, the mechanical, chemical, and electrical energies, is constantly diminished. And thus, as all the energy of the world must eventually be transformed into heat, and all heat will attain an equilibrium of temperature, there will come, as Lord Kelvin predicted, a total arrestation of all natural processes, and the universe will be condemned to a state of eternal rest.

But there remains the great mystery of the origin of the sun's heat, which keeps up the circulation of water on the earth by means of cloud, and rain, and streams, which governs all inorganic movement, and preserves the cycle of life by the metabolism of plant and animal. The actual heat of the sun, and the number of calories it gives out incessantly, could be computed, but there was no valid hypothesis as to the origin of this heat. Helmholtz set out from the Kant-Laplace hypothesis, that the materials now distributed in the sun and planets had originally occupied space in the form of a circulating nebula, which acquired the multiform aspect of the planetary system in virtue of its centrifugal and gravitational forces. He assumed that the density of the nebulous mass was at first a vanishing quantity in comparison with the present density of sun and planets, and then calculated how much work had been expended on this condensation, and how much of this work still exists in the form of mechanical energy, as the attraction of the planets towards the sun, and the *vis viva* of their motions, after which he estimated by means of the mechanical heat-equivalent, how much of that work has been converted into heat. Helmholtz found that only some 454th part of the original mechanical energy remains as such, while the remainder transformed into heat suffices to heat a mass of water equal to the mass of the sun and planets taken together to 28,611,000 degrees of the centigrade thermometer. 'The enormous quantity of heat lost from our planetary system without compensation is not, however, lost to the universe; it has radiated, and is daily radiating, into infinite space, and we know not whether the medium, through which the vibrations of light and heat are conducted, has any limits at which the rays are compelled to turn back, or whether they pursue their way for ever to Infinity.'

It follows from the conclusions of Helmholtz, that even the mighty primaeval dowry of the sun's heat, by whose shining and heat-giving rays the immense wealth of organic and inorganic processes upon the earth is constantly replenished, must one day be exhausted, and that Humanity is threatened with an eternal ice-age, even if, as Lord Kelvin suggests, the sun perpetually receives a certain increment of heat from the contraction incident on its cooling. This fundamental law of nature, indeed, leaves a long, but by no means an eternal existence to the human race: 'Just as the individual has to face the thought of death, so too the race; but it rises above the forms of life gone by, in having higher moral problems before it, in the consummation of which it finds its destiny.'

How great an effect, both ethical and scientific, this lecture produced in the scientific world, is shown by a letter of Ludwig to the Prussian Minister. Ludwig had embarked on a scientific dispute with Rudolph Wagner at Göttingen, which speedily degenerated, thanks to the retrograde party in science, into a war of religious views. 'What have you been up to in Göttingen with R. Wagner?' writes Helmholtz to Ludwig. 'Dark rumours have reached us here, which sound as though you, like Dr. Eck and Dr. Luther of yore, had held, or wanted to hold, a public disputation on the nature of the soul, in which Wagner of course would have fought with the Bible in his hand, and you with the weapons of the Devil, atheism and such like.'

At this time, notwithstanding the efforts of Helmholtz and du Bois-Reymond, Ludwig was in fact in no good odour in Prussia. When he was again passed over a year later on the occasion of a vacancy in the physiological chair at Bonn, although a long way senior to the other candidates, he addressed a letter to the Prussian Minister which was of real benefit from its distinguished sentiments, and in which, as the event was now past, and no unworthy motives could be ascribed to his communication, he pointed out the untenability of confusing scientific progress with religious principles. With reference to the foregoing lecture by Helmholtz, he says: 'How remote these religious ideas are from physical physiology is apparent from the fact that the physiologist Volkmann of Halle, a prominent supporter of the orthodox party, and our very dear friend, is not merely a stanch Christian, but has lately been busying himself in the attempt to deduce a proof for the personality of God from this very lecture of Helmholtz.'

On June 1, Helmholtz tells his father that a second edition of the lecture has already been asked for, adding: 'I have read several very flattering notices of it, but it was evident that the reviewers had no conception of the scientific point of view. The general trend of education in Germany is still quite aloof from natural science.'

The summer of 1854 brought Helmholtz many pleasant distractions: the best of all being a long-projected four weeks' visit from his father, whose dearest wish had been to see his son in his home life, and the distinguished scientist in the learned circles of Königsberg. With the latter the father also hoped to enter into relations, since he had been greatly pleased to learn from his son that the chief librarian and Orientalist Olshausen had come upon his treatise on Arabic literature in the library, and was much pleased with it, as he had long been engaged upon a similar subject. The King, too, came to the old Coronation city, and Helmholtz, as Dean of the Medical Faculty, had to appear 'three days running at Court in a scarlet mantle: at the reception, the banquet, and the departure'; while lastly, the second marriage of his widowed sister-in-law Betty took place at his house, so that during the summer months his time was fully occupied. Despite these interruptions he pursued his experiments on the excitatory process in nerve, together with some difficult optical problems, during the summer, and on July 3 sent du Bois a short notice for the Academy, 'On the Rate of Certain Processes in Muscle and Nerve,' recorded with his frog-tracing apparatus, or as he 'will pompously term it in future', the Myographion. The instrument, however, made its way slowly, and was little used in the physiological institutes; even du Bois did not venture, on account of its high price, to suggest to Joh. Müller to purchase one for the Anatomical Institute. Helmholtz had also constructed new appliances for time-measurements on man as early as the winter of 1853-4, but owing to the removal of the laboratory in the summer of 1854 to the anatomical buildings, was as yet unable to make any such experiments, using his spare time instead 'for some miscellaneous experiments in physiological optics, which have the advantage of not exceeding the comprehension of the scientific public, so that these worthies may perhaps be inclined to believe in my time-measurements, even if they cannot understand them'. After recalling the definition he had previously given—in which the period of latent excitation is that in which the mechanical properties of the muscle show no alteration, the period of rising energy that in which the tension of the muscle increases till it reaches a maximum, and, lastly, the period of falling energy that in which the tension falls rapidly at first, and afterwards very gradually, until finally the initial state of rest is re-established—he deduces a series of important theorems, by means of the myograph, by simple inspection of the fully or partially coinciding curves of contraction.   In these he states that the negative variation of the muscle current which induces secondary contraction appears before the contraction of the muscle, while the electrotonus of the nerve on the contrary coincides with the electrical current that excites it.   The most important result, however, was the proof that two instantaneous excitations produce the strongest contraction of the muscle when the interval between them is equal in length to the period of rising energy, while, on the contrary, two stimuli are not stronger than a single stimulus when the interval between them is so small that the first contraction has not reached any perceptible height before the second begins.   He notes provisionally a result to which he came back later, pointing out its importance for the mechanics of the spinal cord, since it is a means of distinguishing between direct and reflex twitches, viz. that the tracing of the contraction of the thigh-muscle in strychninized frogs excited from the sensory nerve shows that as compared with rate of propagation in the nerve, the reflex twitch is evoked after a comparatively long interval, and that in reflexes the passage of the excitation in the cord takes more than twelve times as long as its transmission in the afferent and efferent nerves.

Helmholtz now became more and more immersed in optical problems, and was hoping, after a number of publications on this subject in the journals during the summer of 1854, to finish his great work on Accommodation, when on October 1 he received the news of his mother's sudden death on September 30: the long distance made it impossible for him to arrive in time for her funeral.

'For the departed such a swift decease can only be regarded as a blessing,' he writes to his father; 'she had suffered enough, and more, in her lifetime for the readiness with which she ever sacrificed her health and energies to her dear ones. We can only take comfort in remembering that she spent the last years of her life in a comparatively peaceful if not too happy state, and was taken from us to her reward by a quick and painless death.'

The aged father, bereaved of his faithful companion, was left with two daughters and a son.

His eldest daughter, Marie, born on July 16, 1823, who was the more attractive, and intellectually the more gifted of the two sisters, gave promise of being a clever artist, but had to forgo the exercise of her undoubted talent on account of her eyesight. Her wish to make use of her talents led her at a later time to seek an independent sphere. She went to Russia with the family of Count Bareschnikow, and never returned to her own country. She died at Federowska in Smolensk, of a nervous fever, on December 17, 1867. The sunny charm of her personality was a sacred memory to her famous brother.

The younger daughter, Julie, born September 2, 1827, remained at Potsdam to take care of her father. In spite of much ill health she devoted her whole life to others with fidelity and self-sacrifice. The happiest times she knew, though they occurred at long intervals, of years sometimes, were spent in the house of her brother Hermann, sharing in the development of his richly gifted life. She died after much suffering from an attack of apoplexy on July 21, 1894.

The second son, Otto, born on January 27, 1834, was at the time of his mother's death attending the Industrial Institute in Berlin, where he had been since he left the Gymnasium at Potsdam, with the intention of becoming an engineer (sorely against the wish of his father and teachers, whose prejudices were very generally shared in those days, but with the full approval of his brother Hermann). His brother writes to him: 'As to the dispute about "trade" and "not trade", it is obvious from your accounts that you do not see the thing in such a light that I need enroll myself on the side of R. and his learned contempt for these low employments. The value of work depends not upon the material handled, whether in inorganic things or in mental products, but upon the amount of intellectual energy that is put into it, and on whether the work is merely a bread-earning industry, or a matter of independent intellectual interest. The man who only works on as he was taught by his teacher or master in bygone days, and merely cares to earn the means of his subsistence or pleasure, will be crushed by the mechanical side of his work, but any one who works from pleasure in the thing, and tries to help the subject forward, will be ennobled by his work, let it be what it may.'

Otto Helmholtz accordingly went into metallurgy, and soon became a distinguished engineer, the present Director of the great Rhenish Steel Works at Ruhrort. The brothers were united in the most intimate friendship until the death of the great scientist.

All the interests of the bereaved father now gravitated towards Königsberg. He was greatly pleased, and encouraged to look to the future without bitterness, and with confidence in his own powers, when his son Hermann (to whom he had sent some copies of the papers formerly published in the Reports of the Potsdam Gymnasium, for distribution among his friends) wrote: 'Lobeck told me the other day that he had been astonished to hear that the philologist Helmholtz was such a near relation of mine. It had not occurred to him to connect us, because our subjects are so very different.' He goes on, 'I wonder what you would have said if I had become a Peer of Prussia; as our two famous politicians Simson and Schubert declined, they asked me among others if I would not go up for election. Of course I refused decidedly, because that career needs quite a different sort of ambition from any I am prone to.'

The infirm old father heartily approved of his rejection of the membership of the Upper House, 'because your scientific work in science will be the most profitable to you.'

Five years of prolific academic work and splendid achievement in the different branches of science thus went by in Königsberg; Helmholtz and his wife were happy and settled there. Cheerful and contented, serious and industrious, averse to no social pleasures, they gradually formed an agreeable society of friends, who shared the interests of both wife and husband.

'When,' writes his sister-in-law, 'I look back at the style

of the domestic and social life of those days as compared with that at the close of Helmholtz's life, it makes me sad to think of the indescribable modesty of those earlier wants and pretensions, although my chief feeling is that never did he appear more truly great than at this time, when his marvellous genius was developing and growing, along with his sincere and noble nature. The man who ranked among the *élite* of the intellectual heroes of Europe, and was *fêted* by kings and princes, never seemed to me worthier of regard than the modest, indefatigable young investigator, who used to construct his bits of apparatus for optical experiments from his wife's reels, and his children's bricks, with ends of wax tapers and scraps of string.' This homely apparatus for his intricate and delicate experiments was, however, by no means a drawback in the eyes of Helmholtz. He was wont to say at a later time, when he had magnificent Institutes under his control, 'I was in the habit (and found the habit a very useful one) when I wanted to invent some totally new method, of making myself models of the required instruments, which although they were very fragile, and put together as a stop-gap out of the poorest materials, served me at least in so far that I could detect the first signs of the results expected, and learned the most important of the obstacles on which I might founder. This taught me by experience the difficulties which hamper the mechanician in such new experiments. And it was only when I had made my own theoretical conjectures and provisional experiments, that I took counsel with the mechanician who was to work out my models in brass and steel. And then the difficulties began.'

He often said in jest to his wife, 'Lend me your eyes for half an hour, and you'll be worth something in my optical experiments.' His wife was indeed all that he had hoped for and counted on, his faithful helpmeet and his true comrade. She worked and wrote for him; he read the lectures he was going to publish aloud to her before delivering them, that she might judge by her estimate how they would appeal to an educated audience.

But in the meanwhile her health, which had long been a cause of anxiety, was steadily growing worse, and the last visit to the sea, usually so productive of good, had failed in its effects: she had suffered from a cough since the birth of her children, and did not spare herself enough in her invincible loyalty to her duties. The doctors thought that the cold climate of Königsberg was one cause of her frequent illnesses, and when the physiological post in Bonn fell vacant, Helmholtz naturally endeavoured, if only in his wife's interests, to get himself transferred from Königsberg.

He took no steps, however, without ascertaining the wishes of his old friends Ludwig and du Bois-Reymond, in case the former wished to return to Germany, and the latter to become a regular professor at last. It was not until he heard that Ludwig's political attitude at Marburg, and the erroneous reports as to his atheism, gave him no prospect of a call to Prussia, and that du Bois hesitated to take this post because his appointment to the chair at Berlin was almost a certainty, that he wrote on November 5, 1854, from Königsberg to du Bois-Reymond:—

'If you have decided not to take the vacant post at Bonn, I should be obliged if you would let me hear definitely, because at an equivalent salary I should prefer the post at Bonn, and should like to approach the Ministry on the subject. My reasons are that I should have a wider circle of activity at Bonn, a slight though not at first important increase in fees, and, lastly, there is my wife's health, which seems to be seriously endangered in this climate. I myself lose no small portion of my energies for work through the inevitable chills. You see that my reasons are not so pressing as to prevent my leaving the post to you with the best possible grace, but I should grudge it to any one else.'

Du Bois did not reply till December 6, when he writes: 'I was unable to send a definite answer to your letter before, and cannot do so even now. Strictly speaking, I have never approached the subject of Bonn with the Ministry.... With the name you have made for yourself as a teacher you cannot fail to get another appointment before long. I shall probably keep out of the running. At present it makes me furious to see my neglected apparatus and manuscripts, and how you managed in your first years at Königsberg to make such colossal researches is a mystery to me. But, to be sure, *Du gleichst dem Geist, den Du begreifst.*'

Johannes Schulze of Bonn, whom Helmholtz consulted, replied that the Ministry intended to appoint an anatomist to Bonn, since the existing physiological lectures appeared to give satisfaction, but that Helmholtz should have his support if he would promise to give most of his time, for the present at any rate, to anatomy. His wife's health appeared to him such a serious consideration that he again expressed his wish to undertake the post on these terms, with certain reservations, but the answer was so long delayed that he gave up all hopes of the appointment.

During the summer of 1854, Helmholtz, who now devoted himself almost entirely to physiological optics, had sent a paper to *Poggendorff*, which was published in the following year with the title 'On the Composition of Spectral Colours'. In this he returns to the observation (erroneously stated in his earlier work on compound colours, and subsequently corrected) that indigo and yellow are the only complementary colours in the spectrum, an assertion legitimately attacked by Grassmann in favour of Newton's earlier theories of colour-mixture. The special physiological properties of the human eye, to which the erroneous conclusion was due, were now submitted by Helmholtz to a thorough analysis.

Owing to the dispersion of colours in the eye, it cannot be simultaneously accommodated for two kinds of rays; if a luminous point sends out red light and blue light at the same time, and if the eye is accommodated for the distance of the point with red illumination, blue light gives a diffusion-circle, and there is either a red point in a blue circle, or with reversed accomm dation a blue point in a red circle. The eye can indeed be accommodated so that red and blue light form diffusion-circles of equal magnitude, and there is a minute speck of the mixed colour, yet it is scarcely possible to fix this position of the eye when there is any considerable difference in the refrangibility of the two kinds of light; whereas in the complementary colours previously examined by Helmholtz the difference of refrangibility is minimal, and accommodation accordingly is more easily fixed. Finding that his earlier methods only resulted in a minute area covered with the mixed colour, he adopted an arrangement similar to that of Foucault, in which now one and now the

other of the two colours flashes out at the edge of the field,
while the remaining area (kept as large as possible) exhibits
the complementary colour. If a colour mixture is obtained that
can be taken as white, white daylight must be admitted from
some other part of the room, and allowed to fall on white
paper in order that its colour may be compared with that
of the mixed light. Helmholtz then found that the mixed
colour altered somewhat according to the position of the image
on the retina. When he combined red and greenish-blue, so
that the common field of illumination appeared as nearly white
as possible, with red predominating slightly, the image appeared
distinctly green on fixing a point on the paper lying near
the bright area; and the same occurred when the eye was
brought so near that the area of mixed colour covered a large
enough portion of the field of vision for many elements of
the retina, in addition to the yellow spot, to receive the
image.

After defining more precisely his use of the different names
of colours he succeeded, under the above conditions, in producing white from a mixture of indigo-blue and yellow, of
cyano-blue and golden-yellow, of violet and greenish-yellow,
and of greenish-blue and red. Green alone failed to give
any simple complementary colour; in order to produce white
it had to be mixed with purple, that is with at least two
other colours, red and violet. He then examined the sensibility of the eye for the individual elements of the violet
end of the spectrum, and found that the human eye could
detect all the refrangible rays of this region which were able
to pass through the prisms, and he accordingly altered the
name 'invisible rays' to that of 'ultra-violet rays'. The objective intensity of these is by no means a vanishing quantity,
as is apparent from the fact that while we perceive nothing
of the ultra-violet rays of a spectrum thrown on to a sheet
of plain white paper, because they are masked by the ordinary
diffuse light, the same parts of a spectrum thrown on to paper
soaked in quinine solution will, owing to the less refrangible
light from the fluorescing quinine, affect the retina with sufficient energy to be visible. The comparison of colour-tones
at different points of the ultra-violet spectrum implied the use
of equal light-intensities, since the colour-tone of this band

alters more rapidly with intensity of illumination than any other portion of the spectrum, and Helmholtz was able to detect a whole series of distinct tones of purple. He could not then extend his investigations of the sensibility of the retina to the ultra-violet rays, since the glass prisms he was using did not show sufficient of the ultra-violet spectrum. But he raised two other very interesting questions as to the relations of the wave-lengths of complementary colours, and the relations of intensity required if the mixture of simple complementary colours is to produce white. He succeeded in answering these questions quantitatively, and concluded on the ground of his measurements of the brightness of the colours whose mixture produces white, that there must be differences of saturation in the various simple colours, violet being the most, and yellow the least saturated. The treatise, which has been fundamental for all later work of the same kind, concludes with an inquiry into the validity of Newton's Colour Circle, which Helmholtz designates as one of the most brilliant inspirations of that great thinker.

After a long delay he received two rock-crystal prisms from Oertling in Berlin, which he had ordered through du Bois for his earlier experiments, and from which he obtained an ultra-violet spectrum, more than twice as long as that given by the glass prisms. In the paper which he sent immediately to *Poggendorff*, 'On the Sensibility of the Human Retina to the most Refrangible Rays of Solar Light,' he propounds the important, but highly complicated problem, whether the retina sees the ultra-violet rays directly, like the other colours of the spectrum, or fluoresces under their influence, and whether the blue colour of the ultra-violet rays is light of lower refrangibility, which is first developed in the retina under the influence of the violet rays. By varying the methods hitherto employed, he showed that the human retina is capable of directly perceiving all the rays of the sun's light, the re-frangibility of which exceeds that of the ultra-red rays; while further under the action of the ultra-violet rays the retinal substance scatters mixed light of lower refrangibility, the total colour of which is not pure white; and lastly, the fluorescence of the retina is inadequate to explain the perception of the ultra-violet rays in general. He found that the tolerably saturated blue colour of the ultra-violet rays was absolutely different from the almost totally white hue of the light dispersed by the dead retina. The wave-length of ultra-violet light was also measured by Esselbach in Helmholtz's laboratory at Königsberg, and under his supervision. This research was communicated by Magnus to the Berlin Academy in December, 1855, under the title, 'Measurement of the Wave-length of Ultra-violet Light, by E. Esselbach,' with an appendix by Helmholtz on the physiological-optical results of these measurements. He gives an extended comparison of the relations of the length of light-waves with that of musical intervals, according to which the entire visible portion of the solar spectrum comprises an octave and a fourth; his tables show how little analogy there is between sensations of tone and of colour, since the whole of the intermediate degrees between yellow and green are compressed into the breadth of a small semitone, while at the end of the spectrum there are intervals as large as a major or minor third, in which the eye is unable to perceive any alteration of colour-tone.

His great treatise on Accommodation was now approaching its conclusion. It was published in 1855, in *Graefe's Archiv f. Ophthalmologie*, and contributed an extraordinary mass of new points of view, methods, and results to physiological optics.

The priority of one fundamental discovery, as previously announced in the *Monatsberichte* of the Academy, had indeed to be forgone in favour of Cramer, i. e. that the lens in the resting condition of the eye, when it is accommodated for far vision, is not in its natural form, but is flattened by the surrounding structures, but that the pull of Brücke's muscle enables it to resume its natural form of marked curvature and greater thickness, in virtue of its elasticity—results which he obtained not by watching the alteration of form, or displacement of the media of the eye in accommodation, but by investigating the changes of the weak light-reflexes first observed by Sanson within the pupil, which take place at both surfaces of the crystalline lens, and are sufficient to account for accommodation. But many difficult questions still remained, which could only be solved by a gifted mathematical physicist. Such were the exact determination of the inner and outer surfaces

of the cornea, the alterations of the iris in accommodation, and lastly the curvature of the anterior and posterior
surfaces of the lens, which he determined with astonishing
perspicacity.

Starting from the presumption that a convex mirror-surface
gives smaller images of the surrounding objects in proportion
as its radius of curvature is smaller, so that the radius of
curvature may be calculated from the size of the images, he
attempts to measure the size of the minute image on the
cornea, but is at once pulled up by the difficulty that the living
eye cannot be fixed as immovably as such an exact measurement requires. In order to measure the free corneal image,
while the eye itself is in motion, he therefore applied the
principle of the heliometer (by which astronomers can estimate
the least distances of the stars in the moving heavens, notwithstanding their apparent motions, so exactly that they can plumb
the profundities of the firmament of the fixed stars), applying
it in an altered form to the moving eye. He constructed the
ophthalmometer, by which he succeeded in measuring the
curvature of the cornea and other phenomena of the living
eye with greater accuracy than had hitherto been possible on
the dead eye. The principle of the ophthalmometer, which was
to play so great a part in physiological optics, depends on
the fact that objects observed through a glass plate with perfectly even and parallel surfaces, held obliquely to the line
of vision, seem to be displaced laterally, and that this displacement increases with the increasing angle of incidence of
the rays of light upon the plate. When two plane-parallel
glass plates are rotated in opposite directions in front of a
telescope obliquely to its axis, two images of any object that
is within the field of the telescope appear simultaneously: if
the two glass plates are then rotated till the two images overlap,
Helmholtz showed that the size of the object observed can
be estimated from the magnitude of the angle of rotation, irre-
spective of the distance of the object from the telescope, because
the ophthalmometer shows the same linear displacement at all
distances. The limitations of the Institute compelled Helmholtz
to construct his telescope from materials which he happened to
possess, and the entire instrument, except the plane-parallel
glass plates, was made in Königsberg; but he soon suggested

to Donders a more practical construction, in order to obtain the maximum of brilliancy in the images.

When this instrument is used to measure the curvature of the cornea, the latter must reflect the image of some external object of known size and distance, and the magnitude of the image can then be measured in the ophthalmometer. Helmholtz made the important discovery that in all diseases of the eye that are associated with alterations of pressure in the fluid media, these changes can be detected on the cornea. His measurements of the radius of curvature at different points of the cornea showed that it corresponds in form with an ellipsoid, produced by the revolution of an ellipse about its major axis, so that the base of the cornea forms a plane vertical to the major axis of the ellipse, and the central point of the cornea coincides with the vertex of the ellipse. During accommodation there is not the slightest alteration of curvature in the cornea. This method could not be employed in determining the form of the inner surface of the cornea, because the image from the anterior corneal surface is so much stronger than that from the posterior that the latter cannot be observed, if the two occur very close together. Experiments with the cornea of dead eyes showed, however, that the thickness of the cornea scarcely alters at all in the two central quarters, but increases fairly rapidly towards the margin. From this it may be assumed, in calculating refraction of the eye, that the aqueous humour extends to the anterior surface of the cornea. And since the lens extends close to the iris, it is only necessary, in order to determine the distance of lens from cornea, to measure that of the pupillar border of the iris from the cornea, which Helmholtz again accomplished by means of the ophthalmometer. It was also shown by a series of extremely delicate observations that since the lens is always situated close to the pupillar border of the iris, while the form of the cornea and the volume of the aqueous humour are not altered in accommodation, displacement of the middle portion of the iris and lens cannot occur without such a backward movement of the iris at its periphery, that the anterior chamber gains as much in volume there as it loses in the centre.

The curvature of the anterior part of the lens cannot be measured directly by the images, because the reflected image is not sharp. The size of the image has to be compared with that of a corneal image close to it, by means of two reflected objects, one of which must be of varying magnitude, in order that the corneal image of one may be made equal to the Sanson's image of the other. It was then ascertained by means of the ophthalmometer that in near accommodation the anterior surface of the lens is more strongly curved, the radius of curvature is accordingly smaller, and its vertex is pushed forward. When Helmholtz applied the method to the posterior surface of the lens, he discovered, in determining the position of the latter, and the question whether cornea and crystalline lens are symmetrical to the same axis, that, in the eyes under examination, there was a slight but perceptible defect of centring, which produced the so-called astigmatism of the eye : the effect of which is that we cannot clearly see horizontal and vertical lines at the same distance simultaneously. This he characteristically expresses by saying that the eye, in spite of its wonderful powers, is an instrument so full of serious defects that if a mechanician turned out anything so imperfect he would show him to the door. In regard to the actual curvature of the posterior surface of the lens, he found that it became a little more convex during accommodation, and did not alter its position perceptibly. Lastly, in regard to the question how the observed changes of form in the lens are produced, he inclines to the view that the ciliary structures must be admitted to participate in some way or other in the movements of accommodation.

Writing before the publication of this work, Helmholtz informs du Bois that the article on Accommodation in *Graefe's Archiv für Ophthalmologie* is in the press, but not out yet :—

'I have determined the measurements of the curvature of the cornea and anterior and posterior surfaces of the lens, and their distances in the living eye, by new methods—not indeed with the greatest attainable accuracy, but only so as to show people that it can be done ; for I realized during the undertaking that it would be useless to expend great pains upon it. The human eye is not even properly centred, the magnitude of the corneal excentricity appears to be quite irregular and adventitious, and so on. You must judge the paper from these points of view, when you receive it, as should I think be the case shortly.' And du Bois-Reymond judged it as follows: 'Never had any one blended the fullest knowledge of physical and mathematical optics with such a vivid and exact idea of the anatomical conditions of vision as did Helmholtz.'

Just as Helmholtz's treatise on the Law of the Conservation of Energy had been epoch-making in the development of the physical sciences, so his experiments on Accommodation in conjunction with the Ophthalmoscope brought about a complete revolution in ophthalmology. As his great lecture on 'The Interaction of Natural Forces' had made the principles of the colossal work of his youth accessible to the scientific world as a whole, so now the opportunity presented itself of bringing the physiological-optical discoveries that had occupied him in the past year before wider circles. On February 27, 1855, at Königsberg, he gave a popular scientific lecture in aid of the Kant Memorial, which treated of the subjectivity of the sensations, and of their analogy with Kant's theory, and the psychical processes that underlie the interpretation of our sensations. 'Last Tuesday,' he writes to his father, 'I gave another lecture upon "Human Vision", in which I tried to put forward the correspondence between the empirical facts of the physiology of the sense-organs and the philosophical attitude of Kant, and also of Fichte, although I was somewhat hindered in my philosophical exposition by the need of making it popular.'

He sends Ludwig the following interesting account of the philosophical views which then prevailed in Königsberg :—

'In the early years of my stay, "nature-philosophy" was still rampant among the students, and the scientific circles of the city often took up the cudgels against my attitude. I never set myself aggressively in opposition to Rosenkrantz, who had once been the demi-god of the city, though now he has only a very limited and half-incredulous public; but left the weight of facts to speak for itself. ... The more intelligent portion of the scientific public will only attend, as a rule, to speculative investigations when they issue from men whose sound and original experimental work has proved them to be firmly grounded on the rock of facts.'

But while he believed that philosophy, when it has been

purged of metaphysics, will still remain as the vast field of knowledge of mental and psychical processes, and the laws that govern them, and that it alone can provide the scientific worker with the necessary insight into the potentialities of the instrument with which he works—the human mind—a letter written twenty years later to Fick shows that the development of philosophy, for which Helmholtz longed, and strove on the lines of his theory of knowledge, was slow to the last degree in its evolution:—

'I believe that philosophy will only be reinstated when it turns with zeal and energy to the investigation of epistemological processes and of scientific methods. There it has a real and a legitimate task. The construction of metaphysical hypotheses is vanity. Most essential of all in this critical investigation is the exact knowledge of the processes of sense-perception. . . . Philosophy has been at a standstill because it was exclusively in the hands of the philologists and theologians, and has so far imbibed no new life from the vigorous development of the natural sciences. Hence it has been almost entirely confined to the history of philosophy. I believe that any German University that had courage to appoint a scientific man with an inclination for philosophy to its Chair of Philosophy would confer a lasting benefit on German science.'

The lecture on 'The Interaction of Natural Forces' had not merely treated of the Law of the Conservation of Energy in a generally intelligible form, but had developed a series of totally new consequences for the constitution of the universe from this standpoint, so that it represented another distinct scientific achievement. In like manner the lecture on 'Human Vision', which set out with the review and interpretation of the laws he had discovered in physiological optics, went on, in bringing 'an offering of respect and veneration' to Kant, to develop the philosophical consequences of his discoveries, which were recognized ere long as the first principles of the modern theory of knowledge. Helmholtz's interest in epistemological questions had been awakened in early days, when his father, who had imbibed a deep impression of Fichte's idealism, held discussions upon the profoundest problems of speculative philosophy with his colleagues, who

venerated Kant or Hegel. He had long been convinced that
if the physicist tests the galvanometer and telescope he intends
to work with to the limits of their efficacy, it is no less in-
cumbent on a scientific man to include the intellect in the
sphere of his investigations, in order to ascertain what he can
arrive at by its means, and where it is likely to fail him. Helmholtz was fully aware that he had on the one hand 'all the
metaphysicians, including the materialists, and all minds with
lurking metaphysical tendencies', to reckon with, while on the
other, the scientific world would be impelled by the excrescences
of Hegel's 'nature-philosophy' to extreme suspicion of all
speculative explanations of natural phenomena, and would
extend this legitimate prejudice to the epistemological and
psychological investigations in which the attempt to penetrate
the laws of mental activity is both valid and necessary.

After pointing out in the lecture that physical science still
professes the principles of Kant (whose philosophy does not
add to the content of cognition by pure thought, but derives
all perception of reality from experience, and makes the
sources of our knowledge and the degree of its justification
the sole objects of investigation), he proposes the Theory of
Sense-Perception in man as the real theme of his lecture,
since it is here that philosophy and natural science are most
in touch. He inquires how the empirical data for the organ
of the eye stand in relation to the philosophical theory of
knowledge. After a full account of the construction of the
eye, and of his theory of accommodation, he gives an explanation of Joh. Müller's fundamental doctrine of specific senses,
'Light is only light when it falls on the seeing eye.' The
discussion of the theory of colours, the facts on which the
construction of the stereoscope is based, and other optical
phenomena, show us more and more plainly how little we
reflect in the daily, practical use of our sense-organs on the
part these have to play, how exclusively we interest ourselves
in such perceptions as bring us intelligence from the outer
world, and how little we attend to other perceptions not
adapted to this end. Now as consciousness (contrary to the
earlier theories) does not perceive sensations locally, at their
seat in the body, it can only know by unconscious inference
whatever we do not perceive directly. This inference is

mechanical in character, and comes under the category of involuntary combinations of ideas, arising when two percepts are frequently associated together. Thus in optical delusions, the mechanism of which is evident, we are aware that the idea called up by the sense-impression is false, but the idea nevertheless persists in full vigour. When, given a certain position of the eyes, any object excites a sensation of light in certain nerve-fibres of our two eyes, our past experience that it is necessary to stretch the arm out a certain distance, or to take a certain number of steps in order to reach it, has established an involuntary relation between the given visual impression and its distance and direction: the judgement of distance by the eyes is learned empirically. 'I distinctly remember the moment at which I became aware of the law of perspective, that distant objects look smaller. I was taken past a high tower, on the topmost gallery of which people were standing, and begged my mother to lift down the little puppets, as I quite thought she could reach the gallery of the tower by stretching out her arm. Afterwards I often looked up at the gallery of the same tower when people were standing on it, but nevermore to the eye of experience did they look like pretty dolls.' When once we have *learned* to see, i.e. to associate the idea of a certain object with certain sensations, which we perceive, the seat of the optical image upon the retina is a matter of indifference, since it is only the fibres of the optic nerve which are excited that are in question.

Helmholtz does not here attempt to decide the question of how far acquired associations of ideas, or such as are innate, i.e. implicate in the actual organization of man, are involved in the interpretation of our sense-organs. For him, sensations are mere signals to consciousness, the meaning of which we learn by a mental process, signals of the existence of changes in the external world, but not images of these changes except in so far as they represent the sequence of the same in time, and may therefore be considered to give us a direct representation of the temporal course of natural phenomena. It was only at a later time that he came forward as the champion of the empiricist, as against the nativistic theory, though he had already made a great stride in this direction.

Since we never can perceive the objects of the external world directly, but only from their action upon our nervous mechanism, the question obviously presents itself, how in the first instance we ever got into touch with the real world by means of our nervous sensations? We must postulate the presence of external objects as the cause of our nervous excitation, since there can be no effect without a cause: but this dictum can be no law of experience,—we already need it for the knowledge that there are any objects at all in the space around us. Yet it cannot come from the internal experience of our self-consciousness, since we regard the self-conscious acts of our will as free. Hence we must fall back on Kant's conclusion that all our thoughts and acts, the greatest as the least, are founded on our confidence in the unalterable uniformity of nature, and that the axiom, 'no effect without a cause,' is a law of our thought prior to all experience. Among the papers left by Helmholtz is the following interesting note on this subject:—

'The Law of Causation (the presupposed uniformity of nature) is a mere hypothesis, and not otherwise demonstrable. No previous uniformity can give proof of future uniformity. The sole test of any hypothesis is, try if it be so, and you will find out (best by experiment, where possible). In comparison with other hypotheses which enunciate special laws of nature, the Law of Causality is exceptional in the following ways: (1) all others presuppose it; (2) it gives us our sole possibility of knowing something we have not observed; (3) it is the necessary foundation of premeditated action; (4) we are reduced to it by the natural mechanics of our combinations of ideas. Hence we are induced by the strongest motives to *desire* its validity. It is the groundwork of all our thoughts and acts. Until we have it we cannot test it; therefore we can but *believe* in it, *act* upon it, and find it justified by fair tests. We must anticipate the consequences; then the consequences will be its confirmation. We must be aware that we anticipated the result; then we shall be aware of the law. *Thinking* means seeking for uniformity; *judging*, that we have found it. Hence, without the law of causation there can be no thought. No thought without acceptance of the law of causation is tautology; query, are we justified in thinking, and has our thought any meaning? this meaning can only be expressed in action (internal or external).'

The Bonn appointment had not yet been decided, although Helmholtz's call was rumoured in all the German papers. On March 15, 1855, du Bois-Reymond sends a few lines from a letter of von Humboldt: 'They beg me to bestir myself for Helmholtz, whom I love and esteem as much as you. I cannot say a word until I know your wishes. If you are not in haste, and can wait on, do not quit the capital, where you should have a great future,' adding that he had replied: 'I beg that you will exert yourself for Helmholtz as if there were no question of me.'

On March 24 Humboldt writes to Helmholtz:—

'Dear Professor, I was agitating on your behalf long before you honoured me with your confidence. The deplorable state of your wife's health makes a move from that raw climate most desirable. When Herr von L. first spoke to me of your fresh request, I ascertained from our mutual friend du Bois-Reymond that he did not wish to leave Berlin; so that my earlier friendship with du Bois does not prevent my having a free hand. Why should we seek abroad what lies so brilliantly to our hand? ... Any one who knows the history of science is aware that no individual, especially in the present state of knowledge, could possibly be equally strong in anatomy and in physiology, and the greater the renown of a man in one of these two branches, the more he is open to charges of weakness and negligence in the other. I have with great effort written a long and enthusiastic letter based on the materials you sent me, as I have only done once in my life before for Dr. Brugsch's Egyptian expedition, refuted the opinion of ——, without mentioning his name, and based my proposal on our friendship, your domestic trouble, your splendid talents, and extraordinary industry. I hope much good will come from this well-deliberated step. I am glad to have found an opportunity of offering you this poor proof of my sincere friendship.'

Humboldt had no doubt that the gifted investigator would soon rise to be a first-class teacher and authority in the ranks of the anatomists, for he was familiar with his admirable anatomical dissertation, and was interested in many of Helmholtz's anatomical observations as reported to him by du Bois. In Berlin, for instance, the young surgeon had amused himself, in the intervals of keen mental activity, by watching the movements of the people going in and out through the Brandenburg Gate, with a telescope, from his little laboratory in a tower at the corner of the Dorotheen-strasse and Sommer-strasse, comparing them with the descriptions and figures given by Weber in his work on the human locomotor apparatus. In this way he discovered, as du Bois relates, that there was an error of some practical importance in Weber's figures, in consequence of which thousands of recruits had been compelled into an unnatural position of the foot during their march on parade. His observations were long afterwards confirmed by instantaneous photography.

On March 27, his appointment as Professor of Anatomy and Physiology in Bonn, from Michaelmas, 1855, was announced.

During the summer Helmholtz devoted himself almost exclusively to his *Handbook of Physiological Optics*, which was to be given to the printers early in the winter, and he writes of the finished portion to Ludwig: ' The only really new bit of mathematics in Part I of *Physiological Optics* is the proof of Gauss's laws of principal points and nodal points by means of an accessory theorem (p. 50), which finds a useful application in the theory of the ophthalmoscope also.'

During his last days at Königsberg he received an invitation from William Thomson, now Lord Kelvin, from Kreuznach, to attend the British Association in September. Thomson wrote that his presence would be one of the most interesting events of the meeting, so that he hoped to see him on this ground, but also looked forward with the greatest pleasure to such an opportunity of making his acquaintance, as he had desired this ever since the ' Conservation of Energy ' had come into his hands ; he ended with expressing his deep regret that he had not been present at the Hull Meeting, having only heard later that Helmholtz had been there.

On July 29, Helmholtz left Königsberg, and went, after a short visit to his relations in Dahlem and Potsdam, to Bonn, where he found a suitable and healthy dwelling for his family in the building that had formerly been the summer residence of the Ecclesiastical Elector of Cologne, and was accordingly known as the Vinea Domini. He then proceeded by Bingen to Kreuznach, in order to make acquaintance with Thomson before his projected journey to England. He writes to his wife on August 6, 1855, that Thomson had made a deep impression on him:—

'I expected to find the man, who is one of the first mathematical physicists of Europe, somewhat older than myself, and was not a little astonished when a very juvenile and exceedingly fair youth, who looked quite girlish, came forward. He had taken a room for me close by, and made me fetch my things from the hotel, and put up there. He is at Kreuznach for his wife's health. She appeared for a short time in the evening, and is a charming and intellectual lady, but in very bad health. He far exceeds all the great men of science with whom I have made personal acquaintance, in intelligence and lucidity and mobility of thought, so that I felt quite wooden beside him sometimes. As we did not get through nearly all we wanted to say yesterday, I hope you will let me stay over to-day in Kreuznach.'

The closest friendship and mutual esteem connected these two great men for nearly forty years, until death separated them.

The last report from Königsberg, on 'Work bearing on the Theory of Heat in the year 1852,' had dealt with the famous publications of William Thomson, and these were now discussed by word of mouth at Kreuznach by the two great legislators in the field of science. Thomson, after establishing the already known law that the heat produced by animals, together with the work done by them, is equivalent to the chemical energies of their food and of the inspired oxygen, had arranged the different sources from which mechanical effect can be derived according to their origin, and came to the conclusion that the heat radiating from the sun, including its own light, is the principal source of all terrestrial processes, and that the motions of the earth, moon, sun, with their mutual attractions, are a potent source of kinetic energy, while an exceedingly small portion only is of purely terrestrial origin. The conclusion deduced by Thomson from Carnot's Law, to the effect that the heat of the coolest body in the universe will always persist as a work-equivalent, but cannot be reconverted into any other form of energy, had been briefly discussed by Helmholtz in the report, while he indicates the conclusions which follow from the considerations laid down by Thomson, and which he himself had developed so brilliantly in his lecture on 'The Interaction of Natural Forces'.

In the middle of September Helmholtz fetched his family from Dahlem, and settled them at Bonn, the move being accomplished without difficulty, as his wife was in fairly good health.

CHAPTER VII

PROFESSOR OF ANATOMY AND PHYSIOLOGY
AT BONN: 1855-1858

HELMHOLTZ soon accustomed himself to his new surroundings. He writes indeed to Donders in October: 'I could only take a very few of my instruments away from Königsberg as my own property, and find practically nothing here. It is a case of beginning over again to collect apparatus, and that with uncommonly small funds. Our Ministry still clings to the fiction that it will be involved in the war in the East, and declines to make any outlay of money.'

But in December he informs his father: 'All goes well here on the whole. While the thermometer in Königsberg was already below zero, and the freight wagons are crossing the Vistula on the ice, we have had alternately mild frost and wet weather, and are more inclined to moderate our stoves than to keep them up. The effect on Olga's health has been all one hoped; she has left off coughing since we arrived in Bonn. As regards my official position, the prospects for the winter are favourable. I have forty-five students at my lectures, and it is altogether quite different from Königsberg. The Anatomy Lectures are very troublesome this first time, especially in certain subjects, but it will go much better next year. I find anatomy more interesting too than I had expected, because the teaching of this science has hitherto conspicuously neglected the functions of the organs, so that interesting questions and points of view crop up on all sides as soon as one looks at them with the eyes of the physiologist. My success in physiology this summer is a little uncertain on account of the rivalry with Professor B.... The Faculty proposed that we should each give a course in physiology (instead of dividing it, and each taking a six hours' course, or half of it) after the Dean had asked me if I should not prefer that. I replied that I could not myself go back on my promise to B., but should be justified in breaking it, if the demand were made by the Faculty. B. himself did not seem to object.'

At first Helmholtz was fully occupied with his lectures in anatomy, and as the immediate result he made a short communication to the Nieder-Rheinische Gesellschaft on March 12, 1856, 'On the Movements of the Thorax,' in which he threw himself into a controversy as to the intercostal muscles. He concluded that the leverage of the upper ribs was the strongest, while it becomes weaker from above downwards, so that the thorax must be regarded as a basket of elastic hoops, each of which has its position of equilibrium, from which it is shifted during inspiration by the pull of the muscles, and which it recovers by its own elasticity in expiration, since expiration in quiet breathing seems to be effected merely by the relaxation of the inspiratory muscles.

He found great satisfaction in his scientific and pedagogic functions in this new field, and writes at the close of the first winter session, March 6, 1856, to his father :—

'All has gone well so far in my official relations. To-morrow will be the last of my lectures. The audience has kept fairly up to the mark, and the older students, who are taking Anatomy for the second time, have told me repeatedly that I have shown them and told them much that had escaped them before. So I am justified in hoping that I shall succeed with the Anatomy Lectures, and things will go better when I have got the Museum into order. It has been frightfully neglected.'

But while Helmholtz believed that he had been successful in the anatomy lectures, du Bois writes to him on April 27, 1856, on Lehnert's authority, that it had been reported to the Ministry that his lectures in anatomy were inadequate. Du Bois replied to Lehnert that while all things are possible, and stupidity probable, this was not only improbable, but also impossible; whereupon Lehnert, after giving him the source of the mischievous report, begged him 'to reassure the Minister personally, since he was suffering pangs of conscience for having made such bad provision for Anatomy at Bonn'. Helmholtz replies to du Bois on May 3 :—

'The report made to the Minister annoyed me, since it is not even an exaggeration of facts, but is a pure invention,

which shows up the intention of its author in no amiable light. . . .
I was told that people said I brought a good deal of physiology
and chemistry into my anatomy, which restricted the amount
of anatomy proper, and they made jokes at the introduction
of a cosine in physiological optics.   But I received many
indications of interest and appreciation of my lectures from
the older students, and from my colleagues also.'   At the close
of this letter Helmholtz sends heartiest congratulations 'to
the young sucking-philosopher, who has taken up his abode
with you, and is doubtless already occupied with such difficult
questions as the formation of concepts of time and space—of
which he knows more now than all the learned physiologists
in the world'.

Nor was it as a teacher alone that Helmholtz had found
a congenial sphere of activity. He sought to acquaint the medical
world of Bonn, who were somewhat remote from his standpoint, with his nerve-work, by reading a paper on the 'Contraction Curves of the Muscles of the Frog' recorded with the
myograph, to the Nieder-Rheinische Gesellschaft on May 14.
He also endeavoured, while preparing his *Physiological Optics*,
to interest his scientific colleagues in these new and difficult
investigations.

On March 6 he made a short, but important and interesting
communication to the same Society 'On the Explanation of
Lustre'.   Helmholtz started from the fact that in looking at
dull surfaces, they appear equally illuminated, and equally
coloured, to both eyes, while for shining surfaces the contrary
is the case, since one eye may be affected by the more or
less regularly reflected light from the smooth surface, and
the other not. The surfaces then appear brighter to the one
eye, and if the reflected light differs in colour from that of
the surfaces, of a different colour also, although these differences of colour as presented in daily experience to both eyes
by shining surfaces are usually insignificant. Now if the
observer looks with the stereoscope at any surface that appears
brighter or somewhat differently coloured to one eye than
to the other, he will conclude from the analogy of everyday
experience that this surface is lustrous, a phenomenon that
had long been known, but had found no adequate explanation.
With greater differences of colour, empirical analogy is totally

wanting, and different persons form a different judgement, some seeing a mixed colour, others irregular specks of colour. From this Helmholtz deduces the all-important conclusion that the sensation from each eye comes separately to consciousness, so that simple vision with both eyes is not the consequence of an anatomical junction of the nerve-fibres, but the result of an act of judgement.

In September, 1854, Helmholtz writes from Königsberg to A. Fick:—

' I have been busy for some time over my *Physiological Optics.* I cannot make it all as popular as the doctors would like, but I have tried to arrange so that what they do not care for is put together, leaving the rest for them.   I have not covered much of the ground yet, because I began with the hardest parts, refraction, accommodation, &c., and was tempted into making new and systematic measurements on the living eye, which have only resulted in the conclusion that the human eye is so irregular that exact measurements do not repay one. I have also made a number of experiments on colour.... There are so many vexed questions in physiological optics that can be settled by a couple of accurate experiments, that one is ashamed to bandy words about them, without making the experiments, so that I really see no prospect of getting on any faster.'

Part I of the *Handbook* appeared in 1856.   Meantime, with a view of establishing the subjectivity of sensation for the other senses also, and of determining the psychical processes by which we understand these sensations, Helmholtz had been turning his attention to physiological acoustics, in which he again opened up an entirely new field of physiological discovery, and in which his results were as admirable as those he obtained in physiological optics.

On May 21 he writes to Wittich :—

' During the winter I reinvestigated the connexions of the auditory ossicles, and worked at Tartini's tones.   I am so far ready that I have sent a *résumé* to the Academy at Berlin, and am now working at the longer paper.   I hope to derive the whole theory of harmony from the fundamental fact that the ear perceives movements that are *regularly* repeated at given intervals as a continuous sensation of tone, and that a continuous sensation of tone is felt to be a consonance, a discontinuous sensation to be a dissonance. Tell Richelot that I am now endeavouring to establish thorough bass upon an integration of partial differential equations of the second order and second degree. I hope this may interest him more than the subjects of my earlier work.'

On June 18, he writes to William Thomson: 'I have busied myself with certain observations in acoustics during the winter, especially on combination tones, which have shown me that these tones, which have hitherto always been supposed to originate within the ear, can arise externally to it also, whenever the vibrations of the air or of any other elastic body, including the tympanum of the ear, are so strong that the second power of the elongation has influence on the motion, so that the law of the superposition of small vibrations ceases to be valid. If m and n are the vibration numbers of two simultaneously sounding tones, I have, in addition to the long-recognized tone of $(m-n)$ beats, discovered another tone of $(m+n)$ beats.'

His paper on Combination Tones appeared the same year in *Poggendorff's Annalen*. It was known that there is on the one hand undisturbed superposition of various sound-waves in the air, and that on the other the ear, when simultaneously affected by several such waves of sound, has the power of perceiving and recognizing each of them separately. But in such cases the ear not only hears the different tones excited by the resonant bodies, but other additional, if feebler, tones, the combinational tones, which are not primarily produced by one of the sounding bodies, but are of secondary origin from the concurrence of two primary tones. These were formerly held to be subjective phenomena, dependent on the special nature of the sensation of the vibrations of sound through the auditory nerve. Helmholtz, however, submitted this question, as well as the possible existence of other than the known combinational tones, to a searching examination, supplemented by mathematical analysis.

He names any oscillation of an elastic body, in which the distance of each vibrating particle from the position of equilibrium can be represented as a simple sine-function, with a constant factor, of a linear expression of time, a simple vibratory motion ; if the oscillations are transmitted through an elastic medium, a simple wave-motion ; he calls all other oscillations that can be expressed, as was already known, as a sum of such sine-functions with arguments, which again are linear functions of time, a compound vibratory or wave motion. Starting with the fact that wherever investigation by mathematics and mechanics establishes the existence of compound wave-movements, the trained ear is able to distinguish tones which correspond with the simple wave-movements contained in them, he next propounds the same question for simple wave-motions, and tries to discover means of producing simple wave-motions in the air. But since all resonant elastic bodies assume various vibrational forms in which they can give out tones of different pitch, Helmholtz selected a tone-producer, which imparts its vibrations as little as possible to the air, while another, the resonator, was so arranged that it was set in sympathetic vibration with the first, and gave out its vibrations easily and forcibly to the air. If the prime tone of the two bodies is exactly the same, while all the higher partial tones of the one are different from those of the other, the resonator will only be excited by the prime tone, and will only give out the vibrations of the prime tone to the air. Helmholtz chose a tuning-fork, and as resonator took the string of a monochord, or an air-chamber formed of cylindrical tubes made of pasteboard, closed at both ends with a round opening in the centre of one end. With the help of this arrangement it was found that simple tones, as Helmholtz calls tones produced by simple vibrations, on the analogy of the simple colours of the spectrum, only give out clearly such deeper combination tones as have a vibration number equal to the difference of the vibrational numbers of the generating tones, and that when combination tones of another order exist along with these, they are too weak to be audible with generating tones of moderate strength. When, therefore, combination tones of the higher order are very perceptible in compound tones, they must be the combination tones of the higher partials. Helmholtz also finds a second class of combination tones, the vibration frequency of which is equal to the sum of the generating tones, which he calls summational tones, while he designates the others as differential.

Starting with the assumption made by Ohm in 1843, that in auditory sensation the ear analyses the motions of the air into simple vibrations, in the same way that Fourier's series for each periodic function is composed of the sum of periodic sine-functions, or that any wave-form may be composed of a number of simple waves of different length, of which the longest has the same length as the given wave-form, while the others are a half, a third, or a fourth, &c. of this length, Helmholtz gives the name of *compound tone* (*Klang*) to the composite tone of a musical instrument, while he confines the term *tone* to simple tones. A compound tone is really a chord with a predominating prime tone; its strength will be the sum of the strengths of the individual tones which it contains, its pitch the pitch of its prime tone. The ear analyses all sound-waves according to Fourier's theorem, by resolving the wave-form into a sum of simple waves. It perceives the proper tone of each simple wave, whether the waves in the first instance issued as such from the source of tone, or have united together on the way, and by listening attentively it is possible to detect the over-tones corresponding to the separate simple waves.

These considerations reinforced the views which Helmholtz deduced from optics in regard to our sensations. A certain compound tone is the adequate sensuous token of the presence of a certain resonating body. In analysing this sound, we must give the same artificial support to our attention before we can perceive the over-tones, as is required in the case of double images and the blind spot, just as we do not normally realize that the sensuous apperception of an object corporeally extended in space is built up from the two distinct retinal images of our two eyes. Helmholtz further determined that combination tones appear only with strong generating tones, that their intensity grows much faster than that of the prime tones, and that the latter may almost entirely disappear when the intensity is very great.

He now proceeded to attack the problem as a whole from its mathematical aspects. He found the generally accepted view of the simple superposition without mutual disturbance of a system of tone-waves excited simultaneously in the air, to be contrary to the laws of mechanics, and proved by strict mathematical deduction that the different simple oscillatory motions of an elastic body are superposed without disturbance, as long as the amplitude of the oscillations is so small that the motive forces excited by the displacements are sensibly proportional to the latter. When, however, the amplitude of the vibrations is so great that the squares of the displacements exert a perceptible influence on the magnitude of the motive forces, new systems of simple oscillatory motions arise, the vibration-period of which corresponds with that of the combinational tones. The vibratory motions of the air, produced by various sources of sound in simultaneous action, correspond with the exact sum of the motions produced by the separate sources of sound only when the vibrations are infinitesimal, i. e. when the alterations of density are so small that they do not come into play as compared with the total density, and when therefore the displacements of the oscillating particles are vanishingly small in comparison with the dimensions of the entire mass; if the law does not hold good, combination tones are produced. It followed from these considerations that the origin of combinational tones is not necessarily dependent on the sensations of the auditory nerve. With two simultaneous tones of the right strength, the combination tones may correspond with actual vibrations of the tympanum and auditory ossicles, received by the nervous apparatus in the usual way. But, as Helmholtz pointed out, conditions similar to those affecting the movements of the apparatus of the tympanic cavity may also occur outside the ear, so that vibrations corresponding to combination tones may be produced quite independent of the human ear, and external to it, and he made experiments to prove the objective existence of combination tones. The nature of combination tones has therefore nothing to do with the marvellous property by which the ear analyses a confused group of sound-waves into the single tones of which it is made up, and distinguishes the voices of separate individuals, and the quality of the different musical instruments. In regard to the origin of this property of analysing the aerial motion produced by the joint effect of a number of resonant bodies into the elements corresponding with the particular effects, Helmholtz had indeed formed a special hypothesis, but felt it necessary to test it upon the various phenomena.

Hence, while still immersed in the preparation of *Physiological Optics*, Helmholtz was planning his great work on the Theory of the Sensations of Tone, busying himself in the first place with the physiological questions it involved, the interest of which is increased 'by the antiquity they have attained, unsolved', and with their significance for music and phonetics.

Before setting out on his summer journey, he was gratified by a visit from Donders, and then left for Schwalbach on August 15, 'in order,' as he writes to his father, 'to meet Prof. Thomson from Glasgow, whom I visited last year in Kreuznach, and who has principally concerned himself with the Theory of the Conservation of Energy in England. He is certainly one of the first mathematical physicists of the day, with powers of rapid invention such as I have seen in no other man.'

After spending a day there, and the next morning trying some new experiments with the siren, which had occurred to Thomson in the night, and which 'if they succeed must yield the most striking results', he joined his travelling companion for Switzerland, Dr. Otto Weber, Privatdocent of surgery in Bonn, 'a talented young man who had previously done a good deal of work in geology,' in Frankfurt. From Heidelberg, where he 'found Kirchhoff already gone, and Bunsen packing', he went to Basle, whence he sent his wife an enthusiastic description of the Holbein drawings: 'They are marvellously finished; it is rare to find such a combination of force, character, and dramatic vigour, though there is little grace.'

From there he went to Chamounix, and made several long excursions on the mountains and glaciers, the beauties and dangers of which he describes to his wife in glowing colours. Fatigue and longing for work, however, took the 'thirty-five year old dotard' back to Bonn by September 1. A few days later he received specimen copies of the first edition of the *Handbook of Physiological Optics*, in which he gathers the results of years of work into a harmonious whole.

Besides the papers on physiological optics which have already been mentioned, and an admirable review of all previous work comprised under this heading, the book contained a store of new and most important results, which provided a firm mathematical basis for the whole structure of physiological optics. After a masterly anatomical description of the eye, Helmholtz divides the theory of visual sensation into three sections, dealing with the path of light in the eye, the sensations of the optic nerve, and the interpretation of visual sensations or visual perception. In the part first published, he is principally concerned with the problem of the refraction of the light-rays, or the dioptrics of the eye. He begins with a simpler and more comprehensive account of refraction in centric systems of refracting and reflecting spherical surfaces, than that given by Gauss, and then applies the theorems to the refraction of light-rays in the media of the eye, where he makes the interesting point that the distance between the principal points in the crystalline lens is less than it would be in a lens of the same form with the refrangibility of the nucleus : at the same time he is led by measurements carried out upon the living eye, to doubt whether the form and focal length of a dead lens are the same as in the living eye accommodated for far vision. He examines the different reduction methods of Listing, and, after defining accommodation, discusses its mechanism, and the theory of diffusion-images upon the retina, with the aid of all the measurements previously made by others and by himself with different optometers. He makes some excellent observations on astigmatism and the entoptic phenomena of the eye, but in this first section touches the question of colour only in so far as it relates to the dispersion of colours in the eye. His estimation of brightness in the diffusion-area produced by dispersion of a single luminous point, as also at the edge of an evenly illuminated surface, is interesting, and he goes on to explain why the chromatic dispersion of images in the eye interferes so little with the acuteness of vision; a combination of lenses designed to make the eye achromatic had no perceptible effect on the clearness of vision. Lastly, he works out the refraction at the vertex of an ellipsoid with unequal axes, and investigates pencils of rays falling obliquely upon a spherical surface.

In order to establish the mathematical theory of the luminosity of the eye, and of the ophthalmoscope, Helmholtz develops some more general theorems than those already published in his work on the ophthalmoscope, the following of which may be cited: (1) when two rays of light pass in opposite directions through any number of simple refracting media, and coincide in one of these media in a straight line, they must coincide in all; (2) if the pupil of the observed eye is to be luminous, the image of the source of light on its retina must wholly or partially coincide with the image of the observer's pupil; (3) if in a centric system of refracting spherical surfaces, the refractive index of the first refracting medium be n_1, and that of the last n_2, and there be in the first, vertical to the axis of the system, and close to the axis, a surface-element a, and in the last a similar element β, then when a has the illumination n_1^2 . H, and β has the illumination n_2^2 . H, as much light falls from a upon β as from β upon a; this law, applied to the problem of luminosity in the eye, tells us that the quantity of light which falls from any surface-element of the retina of the observed eye into the eye of the observer is equal to the illumination of the retinal element by the source of light, multiplied by the quantity of light that would fall upon that retinal element from the pupil of the observer, if its illumination were unity. By these laws he succeeded in establishing a general method for determining the illumination of any spot of the observed retina, as seen by the observer with the ophthalmoscope, and on this again he founds his comparison of the various forms of the ophthalmoscope. The historical evolution is everywhere traced out in its smallest details, with a careful summary of the literature of the subject.

Meantime his acoustic observations widened in import, and a most valuable series of physiological discoveries in optics and acoustics followed in quick succession.

On May 18, 1857, he writes to du Bois:—

'I have gradually accumulated a considerable amount of material for the reform of physiological acoustics, and am waiting for instruments to carry it out. I will mention one fact that has interesting bearings on nerve physiology, i. e. that the fibres of *N. acusticus*, which perceive the higher tones, must be capable of distinguishing as many as 150 alternations of rest and excitation (150 vibrations) per second from a continuous excitation, whereas in the optic nerve and in muscle, a rhythm of 10–15 per second acts as a continuous excitation. This agrees with the rapid alternations of electrical distribution in nerve, and it looks as if the lag in the above effects must occur in the fibres of the muscle and the portions of the retina that are sensitive to light.'

By the end of the year his Theory of Vowel Tones, with which he had been occupied for months, was so far advanced that he was able on November 4, 1857, to tell Donders that they were distinguished by the higher partial tones which accompany the prime tone. By singing into a piano, it is easy in pronouncing *a, o, e* to set the strings corresponding to the upper partial tones into vibration; it is only necessary to sing the tone exactly, and keep it on; the experiment succeeds best with practised singers, 'with my wife better than myself.' If the fundamental tone is called the first tone, and the higher partials, with two, three, four, &c. times as many vibrations, are termed the second, third, fourth, &c., then when *a* is sung the third and fifth tones are heard plainly with the first, while the second, fourth, and seventh are weaker; with *o* the third is rather weaker than with *a*, while the second and fifth are very feeble; with *u* the prime is almost the only tone audible, the third is weak; with *e* the second is very marked, the upper tones are scarcely audible; and with *i* the clear character of the vowel seems to depend on second and third tones preponderating over the weak ground-tone, while the fifth is heard feebly.

There were still, however, great difficulties to overcome before the Vowel Theory could be completely established, and Helmholtz was occupied with these till the beginning of 1859. 'In the next place I must attack the problems relating to the origin of timbre (*Klangfarbe*), since these will solve the fundamental problem of physiological acoustics discussed by Ohm and Seebeck: what kind of vibration corresponds with a *single* audible tone? I believe Ohm to be right in his view that the ear analyses and hears the motions of the air in exact correspondence with Fourier's theorem,' he writes to Donders in the letter above quoted.

It was many years since Helmholtz had discussed his philosophical position with his father. On December 17, he writes:—

'All goes well here, we are all flourishing. My official

position has improved since Prof. Budge went to Greifswald.
I am now the only official representative of Physiology, and
the Ministry can no longer come down on me for comparative
and microscopic anatomy, for which I might have been held
responsible.   For if I lecture on human anatomy in the winter,
and take physiology as my principal subject in the summer,
my time is full, and no one can reasonably expect more
of me.'

He then supplements these few lines, on December 31, by
a long letter, in reply to one received from his father with
the news that he had retired from his post at the Gymnasium :—

'I am delighted at what you write about your present life ;
I think you will be more and more interested in philosophy,
the more you give yourself up to it.   It seems to me a favourable moment for voices of the old school of Kant and the
elder Fichte to obtain a hearing once more.   The philosophical
vapouring and consequent hysteria of the "nature-systems" of
Hegel and Schelling seem to have exploded, and people are
beginning to interest themselves in philosophy again.   I have
only read a little of the *Anthropologie* of the younger Fichte ;
I found much that was interesting, but as a whole the book
gave me the impression of a series of plausible but unfounded
hypotheses, and I laid it aside, as I saw that one would have
to discover his main argument from his other writings.   The
younger Fichte, indeed, appears to me not to be free from the
reproach which has brought philosophy into disrepute, thanks
to Hegel and Schelling.   He introduces a number of matters
into his discussion, which he thinks he is obliged to talk about,
though they do not really belong to philosophy at all, but either
come into the scope of experimental science, or are matters of
purely religious faith.   Philosophy finds its great significance
among the sciences as the theory of the source and functions
of knowledge, in the sense in which Kant, and, so far as
I have understood him, the elder Fichte, took it.   Hegel, however, wanted it to replace all the other sciences, and to find
out by its means what is perhaps denied to man, by which he
diverted philosophy from its proper scope, and gave it tasks
it can never accomplish.   The majority of educated men at
first believed in him, and then rejected philosophy altogether,
seeing that nothing came of it.   The popularity of Schopen-

hauer at the present time seems really to be due to the fact that he goes back to the sound old Kantian standpoint.'

And on March 4 (after a long letter from his father) he resumes :—

'We who approach natural science from the mathematical point of view are disciplined to a painful exactitude in the testing of facts and consequences, and compel each other to proceed by very short and safe steps in the hypotheses with which we endeavour to sound what is still an unexplored ocean, so that we are perhaps too much afraid of a bolder application of the facts of science, which may very well be justified upon other occasions.

'Your letter implies that you suspect me of believing in the trivial tirades of Vogt and Moleschott. Not in the very least. And I must protest vigorously against your taking these two men as representatives of natural science. Neither has so far shown by any special scientific achievement that he possesses either the respect for facts, or the discretion in accepting conclusions, that is acquired in the discipline of science. A sober investigator knows right well that the fact of his having gained a little insight into the complexities of natural processes in no way justifies him in concluding more than other men as to the nature of the soul. And for this reason I do not think you are right in supposing the majority of sober men of science to be inimical to philosophy. Indifferent indeed they are, but that I put down solely to the exaggerations of Hegel and Schelling, who have been presented to them as typical philosophers. Lotze, for instance, has a fair following among the naturalists. Personally I get no satisfaction out of him. He is not clear or strict enough for me. I feel the crying want of a special treatment of certain questions, which have not, so far as I know, been attacked by any modern philosopher, and which lie wholly within the field of à *priori* concepts which Kant investigated, e. g. the derivation of the principles of geometry and mechanics, the reason why we are logically bound to reduce reality to two abstractions—matter and energy, &c., or again, the laws of the unconscious arguments from analogy, by which we pass from sensations to sense-perceptions. I see plainly that these can only be solved by philosophical investigation, and are resolvable by it, so that

I feel the need of more profound philosophical knowledge. Schopenhauer I deliver over to you; I disliked what I have read of him.'

Helmholtz had hardly settled down at Bonn, when proposals were made to him to move to another sphere of action. In April, 1857, Bunsen tells him 'the Baden Ministry are willing to make considerable sacrifices, in order to attract a good physiologist to Heidelberg'. The selected candidates were all of first rank; Brücke, Ludwig, du Bois-Reymond, Helmholtz. The Faculty desired one of the two last, and as a member of the Senate Bunsen invited Helmholtz to state his present income, and the conditions on which he would consent to be called to Heidelberg. In his reply, dated May 16, 1857, Helmholtz points out that for the time being he is under certain obligations of personal gratitude to the Prussian Ministry for sending him to Bonn on account of his wife's health, and that the situation at Bonn is at present so little developed that its temporary disadvantages would not justify him in disregarding these obligations. Helmholtz also believed that du Bois-Reymond was almost certain to accept the Chair at Heidelberg, which was an additional reason to him for refusing to consider it.

On June 20, Kirchhoff writes to his old friend Helmholtz, to the effect that he was the only candidate selected by the Faculty, and begging him, if he really declined it, to recommend the appointment of du Bois to the Ministry. On July 14, Helmholtz informs du Bois that after putting the case to the Prussian Ministry, he had been promised an increase of £60 salary, with fresh promises of reconstruction of the Anatomy Buildings, so that he had decided definitely to remain at Bonn.

In July, Helmholtz had the satisfaction of receiving a visit from his father and his sister Julie, after which he went off for several weeks to Switzerland, his farthest point being the Gornergrat. His letters to his wife are as usual filled with beautiful and enthusiastic descriptions, but by the end of August he is back at Bonn, to make the necessary preparations for the Congress of Natural Science to be held there at the end of September, which he describes to his father as follows on October 3:—

'We were all rather upset till the day before yesterday. People have been here without intermission ever since you left, all expecting to see more or less of us, and we had no peace. The Congress itself was very successful (about 1,000 members), and there were many interesting and distinguished visitors—although the most important did not turn up—more in fact than one could profit by, so that I did not see a good many I wanted to forgather with. The meeting was very interesting, but a fearful rush for me, and I avoided most of the social things. Olga was quite upset, because she had to receive a number of visits in my absence. Only two of our rooms were occupied. Prof. Dove of Berlin and v. Wittich from Königsberg came to us. They were both out all day like myself. Wittich and I usually came in for meals. I could not have stood public dinners on the top of the mental excitement. I did go to the first, but it upset me for the whole of the next day. We did not entertain much either, only having a few men to tea one evening.

'I gave an address on the Telestereoscope at a general meeting in the Riding School, and put up two different instruments first in the Hall, then in the Anatomy School, and eventually in my own house, and had enough to do in demonstrating them to every one. At the Anatomical Section, which was well arranged, and well attended, I put up and demonstrated experiments with the myograph on Time Measurements in Nerve, because these experiments have been too little seen and repeated. I also gave a short lecture on the movement of the auditory ossicles, illustrated by a few preparations.

'In the Physical Section I spoke on Combination Tones. Besides this I joined in the debate on Expenditure, in which I was in the minority, as you will have seen by the papers, but my minority had the most authority all the same. And I had another unexpected pleasure. I received a letter immediately after from Munich, from the King of Bavaria, who is willing to apply a considerable annual sum to the very objects I proposed to the Congress, i.e. to endow such scientific undertakings as exceed the powers of private persons, and asks my advice as to expenditure. Of the social things I only took the expedition to Coblentz, and went to the concert with Olga. It was given by the city of Bonn, and crowned the functions. Beethoven's works alone were given.'

Helmholtz's experiment in Acoustics had been reported to

the King of Bavaria, and he was invited to draw up a brief report on the result of his discoveries in the Theory of Tone for the King's edification. On April 15, 1858, he writes to du Bois-Reymond:—

'I have now put together a complicated apparatus at the King of Bavaria's expense, by which one is able to control the vibrations of a tuning-fork at will by an electro-magnet, with complete command of intensity and difference of phase. This is in order to regulate the production of *timbre* (*Klangfarbe*).' The cost of this apparatus was 400 *gulden*, paid by the King.

After he had commenced his lectures and scientific work for the winter session, Bunsen again approached him on December 15, 1857, stating that the Baden Ministry had not given up hopes of persuading Helmholtz to come to Heidelberg, since the postponement of the building of a new Institute at Bonn seemed to cancel some of his reasons for refusing, and that they had therefore taken no steps as yet in other directions.

Helmholtz consulted his father, who urged him strongly to go to Heidelberg: 'Your scientific life and satisfaction in your official career will have widely different prospects in Heidelberg as compared with Bonn; the mere fact of your being able to confine yourself to physiology will be valuable to your own scientific projects. Your obligations to science are greater than to the State.'

Helmholtz finally accepted the invitation from Heidelberg; and on February 27, 1858, Kirchhoff writes to him: 'All Heidelberg is rejoicing at your decision, and I hope you will find a congenial atmosphere here.' On March 5, Helmholtz informs du Bois that he had forwarded his resignation to v. Raumer, as the Senate and Ministry had taken no steps since his first refusal of the call to Heidelberg to carry out their promises. On the same day he writes to his father:—

'At last I have accepted the call to Heidelberg. I have already sent in my resignation to the Minister, v. Raumer. The correspondence over the rebuilding of the Anatomy Department was left four months before the Prussian Ministry attended to it, at the end of which time an undecided, procrastinating answer was sent, and the feeling of the Academic Senate, who were to cover a portion of the cost by selling some of the land belonging to the University, is quite uncertain, so that while there is some probability of the construction of the Anatomical Buildings, nothing is decided. In Heidelberg, on the other hand, I have a position that is in every way convenient for my scientific enterprises. I went to Heidelberg myself, at Carnival time, when they take a few days' holiday here upon the Rhine, to inspect the situation, and also to Carlsruhe. The present accommodation in Heidelberg is impossible, and I was obliged to ask for a new Physiological Institute, to which the Minister agreed without much difficulty.'

His father replies with great satisfaction on March 9:—

'I am rejoiced at your good fortune, and that you have made a reputation which secures you a most distinguished position—and an academic position—while you are still so young. I told you before that the post at Heidelberg was, in my opinion, in every way more profitable to you than the Chair at Bonn, where I was little pleased with the temper of the learned gentlemen, and thought it very unlike Königsberg. The proximity of the Court and the fashionable world is not good for men of letters, who are too prone to idealism from their preoccupation with science, and too little versed in worldly matters. I was grieved to hear of your beloved Olga's illness. Doubtless the first days of summer will relieve her of her suffering, which one may hope will not return in the more southern and much milder climate of Heidelberg, with its sunny valleys, near to so many famous health resorts. You must work harder than ever in the future, to live up to your great renown, and overcome all envy at your appointment.'

But as Helmholtz had not obtained his discharge from the Prussian Government by April, he was obliged to postpone his departure for Heidelberg till the autumn. On April 28, on his return from a visit to Donders at Utrecht, he received a letter from du Bois-Reymond announcing the death of Johannes Müller, with the information on good authority that the Prince of Prussia had made very sharp inquiries into the reasons for Helmholtz's departure from Bonn, and had declared his intention of going himself to Baden, to release Helmholtz in person from his contract, and set him at liberty to enter into new relations with the Prussian Government. Helmholtz accordingly writes to Donders:—

'The Prince of Prussia, who is at present carrying on the

Government, had already expressed his displeasure at the way the Prussian Government have subordinated scientific interests to those of Church and State on several occasions, when my resignation was laid before him. He took this opportunity of once more fulminating against the Minister, and proposed to settle the matter in person with the Grand Duke of Baden. The Minister did not at first agree to this, as it was a reproach to himself. Finally, when J. Müller was dead, and there was a want of good candidates, came a request from the Ministry that I would remain here under the same conditions as were offered me at Heidelberg.'

He gives the following account of these negotiations to his father :—

'I now know from reliable sources that the negotiations of which Olga has told you were really undertaken in consequence of the Prince of Prussia's action, although this has since been expressly denied. I had already promised the Baden Government to accept the post in Heidelberg, and had no very pressing interest to make me give Bonn the preference. Although, generally speaking, it is my rule to stay where I am well off in many respects, and not to exchange what is known and endurable for the unknown, because it has a more seductive aspect, and though Olga's health makes a move undesirable, and the pecuniary emoluments may, at the outset, be larger here than in Heidelberg—still it must be admitted that the people there seem most anxious to do whatever is necessary, in order to promote the scientific success of the position offered me. In Prussia they are promising me what I asked, only for personal reasons, and would probably carry it out literally, refusing later on what would by then be absolutely necessary, in the way they always stint everything connected with the University. So that I really had no reason for pulling the chestnuts out of the fire, and compromising myself with the Baden Government for the sake of Prussia.

'At first they simply tried to make me break my word, and quoted a string of stories about other Professors who had broken theirs. I declined firmly. Next they wanted me to appeal to the Prussian Government to back up a petition to Baden to absolve me from my promise; a statement to this effect was laid before me which I was to sign there and then, as it had to be telegraphed to Berlin in a desperate hurry (which turned out to be mere invention). I rejected this and drew up another document, which I signed, in which everything relating to my own wishes was left out, and it was thrown entirely on the Government to work Baden so that I should be released from my promise. Then, I said, I was prepared to remain in Bonn. So that I made my position circumstantially plain. I did not for a moment suppose that any one would negotiate, and openly expressed my conviction that I could not see why the Baden Ministry should consent; but our Prussian officials have far too high an opinion of the importance of their Ministers not to think that one of the lesser German States would not at once acquiesce in their wishes.'

The negotiations dragged on for some time, as the Prussian Government gave it to be understood that Helmholtz wished to be released from the appointment at Heidelberg, and he was obliged to circulate the drafts of his letters to prove that he was not playing fast and loose with Baden. Finally, he received his *congé*, and, after three years' connexion, was free to depart from Bonn.

'These three years,' says his sister-in-law, 'were a continuation of the life at Königsberg, save that external relations had broadened, and that the indescribable charm of the landscape made a most poetic background for their daily life. The two children were growing in mind and body, and Helmholtz was a devoted father. They had plenty of friends and social intercourse. Their circle included the families of Heine, Busch, Naumann, Otto Jahn, the biographer of Mozart, the elder Arndt, who was particularly attached to Olga, the surgeon Weber, several English families, and for a short and much appreciated time, Prof. Donders from Utrecht, who was a great friend of both Hermann and Olga. The old terrace on the Rhine, with its view of the Drachenfels, where they lived in the ancient Vinea Domini, has seen many a gathering of clever and congenial people, and when the garden was illuminated in Donders's honour with coloured lamps, and the children ran about in their merry play, it gladdened one's heart to see this sunny family happiness.'

Frau Geheimrath Busch, who was a daughter of Mitscherlich,

writes that 'after forty years the impression made on me by
that noble head, with its deep clear gaze, its classic and
dignified expression, is indelible. Helmholtz was generally
cheerful and sympathetic, even playful, and delighted of an
evening in reading plays aloud; he preferred a character-part
in Shakespeare, or some other classic. It was an intimate
little circle in which the Helmholtz couple took the lead.
Often enough Helmholtz would sit still, plunged in his own
thoughts, but I never saw him out of temper, or anything but
cordial'.

The last year of Helmholtz's stay at Bonn was marked by
a series of important publications. The complexities of
acoustics had induced him two years previously to occupy
himself with the application of Green's Theorems to hydrodynamic and aerodynamic problems. In 1857, in a work of
genius that proved him to be a mathematician of first rank,
'On the Integrals of the Hydrodynamic Equations which
express Vortex-motion' (published in *Crelle's Journal f. reine
u. angew. Mathematik*), he gave the solution of some extremely difficult hydrodynamical problems. He rejected the
earlier hypotheses, and followed up the analogies between the
motion of fluids and the electromagnetic action of electrical
currents, which were of so much importance for his subsequent
work on the Theory of Electricity and Magnetism. Up to that
time the integrals of hydrodynamic equations had been determined almost exclusively on the assumption that the rectangular
components of the velocity of each element of the fluid are
the differential co-efficients, with reference to the co-ordinates,
of a certain function, which Helmholtz termed the *velocity-
potential*—an assumption which was lawful so long as the
motion of the fluid resulted from the action of forces which
had a potential of their own. Helmholtz abolished this limitation, and took into account the friction between the elements
of the fluid, and against fixed bodies, the effect of which on
fluids had not till then been defined mathematically, and
endeavoured to determine the forms of the motion which
friction produces in fluids. Starting with the equations of
motion for the interior particles of a liquid, he pictures the
changes undergone by an indefinitely small volume of the
fluid in an indefinite fraction of time as composed of three

separate motions : a translation of the element of the fluid through space, an expansion or contraction of the elements in three principal directions of dilatation (in which any rectangular parallelepiped, whose edges are parallel with the principal directions of dilatation, remains rectangular), and, lastly, a revolution round some instantaneous axis of rotation in any direction. In the first place he proves by rigid mathematical deductions that the existence of a velocity-potential is incompatible with the existence of a rotation of the fluid elements, but when there is no velocity-potential some fluid elements at least can rotate. On the assumption that all forces acting on these fluids have a 'force-potential', it follows necessarily that such particles of water as have no initial rotary motion cannot be thrown into rotation at a later period. If lines drawn through the fluid so that their direction coincides everywhere with the direction of the instantaneous axis of rotation of the element of fluid lying there, are termed *vortex-lines*, it follows again from the equations of hydrodynamics that each vortex-line remains permanently composed of the same elements of fluid, and swims along with them in the fluid. Helmholtz terms a filament of the fluid with an indefinitely small cross-section, a *vortex-filament*, when it is produced by drawing vortex-lines through every point in the circumference of any indefinitely small surface. Since, further, the expressions for rotary velocity show that the magnitude of the latter varies in any given element, in the same proportion as the distance between this element and its neighbours on the axis of rotation, it follows that the product of the angular velocity and the cross-section in any portion of a vortex-filament containing the same particles of fluid remains constant during the motion of the filament, and further that this product does not vary throughout the whole length of any given vortex-filament. The vortex-filaments must accordingly return upon themselves within the fluid, or end at its boundaries. But from this it follows directly, that if the motion of the vortex-filaments in the fluid can be determined, the velocity of rotation can be ascertained, and that the velocities of the elements of the fluid are determined for any given moment of time, when the angular velocities are given, with the exception of an arbitrary function, which covers the limiting conditions. This determination of velocities connotes the important law that each rotating element of fluid implies in every other element of the same fluid mass a velocity whose direction is perpendicular to the plane through the second and the rotation axis of the first element. The magnitude of this velocity is directly proportional to the volume of the first particle, its angular velocity, and the sine of the angle between the line that unites the two elements and that axis of rotation, and inversely proportional to the square of the distance between the two elements. But since the same law holds for the force exerted by an electrical current in the first element, parallel with its axis of rotation, upon a magnetic particle in the second element, Helmholtz, by means of the definition of n-dimensional space (i. e. one which can be traversed by $n-1$, but not more, surfaces, without being separated into two detached portions), formulates a law that has acquired great importance in electrical theory. When, that is, a velocity-potential exists in a simply connected space full of moving fluid, the velocities of the fluid elements are equal to, and in the same direction as, the forces exerted on a magnetic particle in the interior of the space by a certain distribution of magnetic masses at its surface. But if vortex-filaments exist in such a space, the velocities of the fluid elements are represented by the forces exerted on a magnetic particle by closed electrical currents, which flow partly through the vortex-filaments in the interior of the fluid mass, partly on its surface, their intensity being proportional to the product of the cross-section of the vortex-filament and the angular velocity. Since the first motion implies a velocity-potential with only one value, while the second in the non-rotating particles of water implies a velocity-potential with more values than one, it is sufficient in hydrodynamic integrals of the first class to know the motion of the surface ; in those of the second class, we must further determine the motion of the vortex-filaments in the interior of the fluid, with reference to their mutual action, and having regard to the limiting conditions. Helmholtz succeeded in doing this for certain simple cases, in which the rotation of the elements occurs only in given lines or surfaces, and the form of these lines or areas remains unaltered during motion, e. g. in straight, parallel, or circular vortex-filaments—which theorems and conclusions, taken as pure mathematics, are fundamental laws of the modern Theory of Functions. His conclusions for ring-shaped vortex-filaments are very interesting. When two such rings of small section have the same axis and the same direction of rotation, they travel in the same direction; the first ring widens and travels more slowly, the second shrinks and travels faster, till finally, if their velocities are not too different, it overtakes the first and penetrates it,— the same process is then repeated for the next ring, and so on. An analogous statement holds good when the directions of rotation are opposite.

When Tait, some ten years later, proposed to translate the work of Helmholtz on Vortex-Motion, and wrote to him on the subject, Helmholtz replied: 'If you find quaternions useful in this connexion, it would be highly desirable to draw up a brief introductory explanation of them, so far as is necessary in order to make their application to vortex-motion intelligible. Up to the present time I have found no mathematician, in Germany at any rate, who was able to state what quaternions are, and personally I must confess that I have always been too lazy to form a connected idea of them from Hamilton's innumerable little notes on the subject.'

In 1868 Bertrand published some criticisms in regard to the universality of Helmholtz's methods. Helmholtz had assumed (as above) that the motion of an indefinitely small volume of water is due to the propagation of an element of fluid through a space, the expansion or contraction of the element in three principal directions of dilatation (so that a rectangular parallelepiped constructed of water, whose sides are parallel with the principal directions of dilatation, remains rectangular, while its sides alter in length, but remain parallel with their previous direction), and to revolution round a definite instantaneous axis of rotation. Bertrand contended that in a great number of cases oblique parallelepipeds might also be constructed with an arbitrary direction of the edges, which could be transformed into other parallelepipeds, whose edges should remain parallel with those of the former. Helmholtz replied in three Notes published in the *Comptes Rendus* for 1868, 'Sur le mouvement le plus général d'un fluide,' 'Sur le mouvement des fluides,' and 'Réponse à la note de M. J.

Bertrand du 19 octobre,' in which he showed that the motion defined by Bertrand can be due to the combination of a rotation and three rectangular dilatations, and that 'he did not by dilatations mean translations'.

Lord Kelvin has associated his Theory of the Constitution of Matter with Helmholtz's law that a vortex in a frictionless fluid persists as an invariable quantity. Kelvin sees a fundamental analogy between the indestructibility of the vortex and the indestructibility of matter. He conceives an atom as a whirl or vortex in the ether, and accounts for the chemical disparity of the atoms on the supposition that we have in them different combinations of vortex rings.

After Helmholtz had finished this paper, which was intelligible in the first instance only to mathematical physicists, and which, with that on Aerial Vibrations in Tubes, published the following year, was always regarded by Kirchhoff as the author's most important contribution to the subject of mathematical physics, he busied himself in the remaining months of his residence at Bonn with optical and acoustic investigations.

On July 3, 1858, he read a paper to the Nieder.-Rhein. Gesellschaft, 'On Subjective After-Images of the Eye,' which was subsequently extended in *Physiological Optics*. He had already, in his previous work on Colour-Mixture (undertaken in support of Young's theory of the red-, green-, and violet-perceiving elements of the fibres of the optic nerve) come to the conclusion that the spectral colours are not the most saturated that can occur in visual sensation. In order to settle this last fact he first of all examined Fechner's theory of the subjective after-images of the eye. After looking at a bright object, and then exposing the eye to complete darkness, a positive after-image first appears, i. e. the bright parts of the object appear bright, and the dark are dark; with uniformly illuminated surfaces, on the contrary, the after-image is mostly negative, i. e. the bright spots of the image appear dark, and the dark, bright. Fechner's explanation is that positive after-images result from persistent excitation of the points of the retina that had been excited by light, negative after-images from fatigue of the same points rendering them less sensitive to new impacts of light; the strength of illumination of any surface required in order to turn the positive after-image that appears on a dark ground into a negative image, diminishes with the time.

After confirming Fechner's theory in detail, Helmholtz produced after-images of pure prismatic colours in his eye, observed them upon a field covered with another prismatic colour, and found that the phenomena in no way differed from those which arise on regarding the colours of natural bodies and pigments. There was, however, one interesting case, in which he looked at a round spot brightly illuminated by a spectral colour, then observed its after-image upon a field covered with the complementary colour, and completely purified from diffuse white light. The complementary colour then appeared purer and more saturated within the after-image, than around it. Helmholtz thence concluded that although the prismatic colours are the purest and most saturated, that is the most free from a mixture of white, presented to us in nature, yet, by the above means, the sensation of even more highly saturated colours may be excited, in comparison with which the purest prismatic colours will appear whitish.

Towards the end of August Helmholtz moved with his family to Heidelberg, where he received a great ovation. The newly-formed Ophthalmological Society presented him with a cup, inscribed 'To the Creator of Modern Science, the Benefactor of Mankind, in grateful remembrance of the discovery of the Ophthalmoscope.'

In September he attended the meeting of the British Association at Aberdeen, and the Naturforscher-Versammlung at Carlsruhe, the capital of the State to which he was to consecrate his mighty energies for the next thirteen years. His address 'On After-Images' gave a summary of the experiments and conclusions described above, and another discourse 'On the Physical Causes of Harmony and Dissonance' was the epitome of a lecture on 'The Physiological Causes of Harmony in Music', delivered to a large and enthusiastic audience the year before at Bonn—Beethoven's birthplace.

'Of all the subjects at which I have worked,' he says forty years later, 'I have chiefly felt myself a dilettante in Music. Art and Science are essentially distinct in their external aspects and technique; but I am none the less convinced of the profound internal relations between them. Art, too, strives to acquaint us with reality, with psychological truths, though it expresses them in the wholly different form of sensual manifestation, and not in that of concepts. Eventually, however, the complete phenomenon connotes the conceptual idea, and the two are ultimately united in the whole.'

Such was the standpoint from which Helmholtz connected physical and physiological optics with aesthetics, in a form that was epoch-making for future generations.

Starting from the well-known observation that we can feel the vibrations of the air in deep tones through our skin, he shows in his lecture how the aerial vibrations first become sound, when they impinge on the hearing ear, and then develops his views as already enunciated upon the correspondence of quality of tone (*timbre—Klangfarbe*) and wave-form. He discusses his theory of prime tones and over-tones, and suggests that the over-tones give rise to the indefinable peculiarity of tone that is known as timbre. And thus, as the existence of over-tones depends on wave-form, he identifies timbre with wave-form. Since the cochlea of the ear is separated by membranes into three chambers, the middle one containing innumerable microscopic lamellae, which lie in regular apposition like the keys of a piano, and are connected at one end with the fibres of the auditory nerve, and at the other with the extended membrane, and since elastic appendages to the end of the nerves had been discovered in the form of stiff hairs, Helmholtz regards it as probable that each of these appendages is tuned like the strings of the piano to a single tone, and that each tone which reaches the ear not only sets the lamella in the organ of Corti that corresponds with its prime tone in sympathetic vibration, with excitation of its associated nerve-fibres, but affects the lamellae corresponding with the upper partials also, so that the over-tones are perceived as well as the prime tone. Strictly speaking, therefore, in relation to sensation, the tones of musical instruments may all be looked on as chords with a predominating fundamental tone. It is true that a certain measure of attention is needed in order to detect the over-tones, but Helmholtz succeeded in hearing the partials of the human voice, and in making other people recognize them.

The discovery made by Pythagoras, that vibrations which bear to each other simple ratios of number, e. g. the octave, fifth, twelfth, major third, produce a pleasing impression, while tones with more complex ratios of vibration-frequency are dissonant, had not been adequately explained by the assumption that the contemplation of simple ratios of vibration affords a pleasurable sensation to the mind.

' Mathematics and music, the sharpest antithesis of intellectual activity that can be found, are yet interrelated, mutually helpful, as if to show the secret consistency that is implicated in all the activities of our mind, and which leads us to surmise unconscious expressions of a mysterious law of reason in the revelations of artistic genius.'

It had been proved in the earlier acoustic work of Helmholtz and others, that when two tones have only an approximately equal vibration-period, and their crests coincide at the outset, so as to reinforce each other, the undulations of the one will gradually outrun those of the other, and produce an alternating ebb and flow in the tone, which are known as beats, and which, if they become more rapid, are converted into a continuous tone-sensation. When the ratio of the prime tones is 2 to 3, the two over-tones of six vibrations (whose existence was previously ascertained) are exactly equal, and do not disturb the harmony of the fundamentals, but when the ratio is only approximately that of 2 to 3, the two partials are not exactly equal, but produce beats with one another, and the tone becomes harsh. Consonance and dissonance are therefore distinguished by the even flow of tones in the former, as undisturbed as if each tone were sounding alone, while in dissonance there is an incompatibility, and the tones are broken up by their mutual action into separate impacts, which disturb the listener and make him wish for harmony. In conclusion, Helmholtz drew a contrast between eye and ear, pointing out that the eye cannot analyse a compound system of light waves, i. e. composite colours, and is indifferent, in a mixed colour, whether the component colours are or are not in simple ratios of vibration-frequency. The eye has no harmony in the same sense as the ear; it has no music. 'The phenomena of purely sensual harmony are indeed only the lowest grade of musical beauty. Consonance and dissonance are but the means, albeit an essential and powerful means, to the higher and more spiritual beauties of music.'

At the end of September, 1858, Helmholtz took up his abode in beautiful Heidelberg, and there with Bunsen and Kirchhoff inaugurated an era of brilliancy, 'such as has seldom existed for any University, and will not readily be seen again.'

CHAPTER VIII

PROFESSOR OF PHYSIOLOGY AT HEIDELBERG:
1858–1871

THE move to Heidelberg involved a temporary interruption of Helmholtz's important experimental researches. While waiting eagerly in the hope that the new Institute might be ready for his apparatus by the beginning of the session, he occupied himself in endeavouring to finish Part II of *Physiological Optics* by the middle of October. He writes to Wittich that he is 'sticking over the after-images, and cannot get to the end of them'; while after commencing his lectures he was 'experimenting in acoustics on Sundays, and in spare moments'.

He soon settled down at Heidelberg with his family, and writes on December 11 to his father: 'So far all goes well with my official concerns in Heidelberg. I have as large an audience, in spite of the reduced numbers of the medical students, as I had in Bonn for physiology. Indeed, the number of students is too large for the place, and we are rather crowded; but the plans for a new building are to be made out at once, and then we can arrange ourselves better.

'In November I was elected a corresponding member of the Academy of Sciences at Munich, and have to-day received my first Order, from Holland, of the Dutch Lion. Prof. Donders writes from Utrecht that a new hospital for diseases of the eye has been founded there under his direction, and opened with much ceremony, on which occasion they thought it becoming to celebrate the discovery of the ophthalmoscope in this way. You see Heidelberg is bringing me luck as regards outside recognition.'

The father's answer expresses a lively satisfaction at the happiness of his children. It was the last letter written by the old man (now an invalid of sixty-seven) to his son; and he ends with a vigorous criticism of a new work on the nature of the soul by his friend Fichte, offering at the same time to draw up his own solution of the problem:—

'For although your task be the rigid investigation of the physical, its coherence, and the significance of particulars in and for the body, it seems to me that this necessarily involves some conception of what the body is and means for the soul, and of the life that develops in it. Both Anthropology and Psychology may suggest much that would be of value to your material researches.'

At the close of the winter session Helmholtz went to the Festival of the Bavarian Academy, at Munich, in March, 1859, and on the 30th describes it as follows to his wife:—

'I have been getting on famously. Early on Sunday Eisenlohr appeared with Jolly, the physicist here, to fetch me. After writing our names down at the Academy, Jolly took us to Kaulbach's studio, which was filled with an enormous picture of the Battle of Salamis, a powerful and impressive work. Kaulbach himself, whom I met again at the first banquet, is a most charming and refined artist, with a keen interest in everything that has even the remotest bearing on art. He is justly beloved by every one here. . . . Afterwards we wandered about a little in the streets, and paid visits to a few of the Academicians: both midday and evening I was bidden to Jolly's. His wife comes from Heidelberg, and is a sister-in-law of Weber. . . . Monday was the great function. At 9 a.m., Service with a good solid sermon in the Protestant church; at 11, the meeting, at which King Ludwig appeared, and presentations were made. At the meeting, an Old-Bavarian Catholic, an Orientalist named Müller, made a speech on the history of the Academy, in which he let out with such bitterness against the Jesuits that I could hardly believe my ears. As we dined later, I breakfasted with many others on a glass of beer, which as a matter of fact far surpasses all foreign imitations of Bavarian beer. At three there was a great banquet, here at the Bayrischer Hof. I sat between Schönbein and Bischoff, opposite Liebig and Kaulbach; it was very amusing. In the evening one of Terence's plays was given in the small theatre.

'Yesterday, early, I went with Eisenlohr to the optical works of Steinheil outside the city, and saw much that was excellent. Then a rather dull sitting with speeches, more Bavarian beer, and a rest at mid-day. Then dinner with His Majesty, preceded by a very long and elaborate reception. The King is very friendly, and talks sensibly, but seems to have inherited his father's bad constitution. He congratulated himself on making personal acquaintance with me; I thanked him for graciously permitting me to do so. He hoped that I would make some acoustic discoveries that would benefit the architecture of public halls; but I could hold out small prospect of that. The banquet in the Barbarossa Hall was most brilliant: the food very delicate and not substantial, as I like it. Subsequently *Oedipus Colonus* at the Theatre, with Mendelssohn's music, but it is less inspired than his *Antigone*.

'To-day the saloons of the Castle are thrown open to us; in the evening a great May Festival at the Rathhaus, when the beer is tapped solemnly. . . . I must conclude, for R. Wagner has just come to fetch me.'

During this Academic Festival, Helmholtz gave a lecture on April 2, 'On the Quality of Vowel Sounds'; the important parts of it were subsequently published in *Poggendorff*, after the Vowel Theory had been completed by verbal and written discussion with Donders.

On June 13, 1859, he writes to Ludwig that the necessary preliminary study of the motion of air in tubes had led him to a definite theory of timbre (*Klangfarbe*). His detailed explanation shows how chords of different timbre and equal pitch of fundamental tone are distinguished by the ear because of the different frequencies and strengths of the harmonic over-tones, i.e. timbre results from the combination of the prime tone with different intensities of over-tones. He defines as the musical quality of tone that part of it which is independent of the irregular murmur that cannot properly be reckoned with the musical constituents of the tone, e.g. the scraping of the violin bow, the whistling of the stream of air blown over a flute, the varying intermittency of the expired breath in the pronunciation of consonants; and then proceeds to the question of whether the distinction of musical timbre depends only on the perception of over-tones of different intensity, or whether the ear can distinguish differences of phase also. Quite different wave-forms obtain for a wave composed of a prime tone and its first higher octave, according to whether the condensation-maximum of the fundamental coincides with that of the octave or not. Helmholtz endeavoured to decide these questions by building up tones of different timbre by the direct combination of simple tones produced according to his own method with a tuning-fork. He selected the different vowels of the human speech as a suitable object for imitation because these can be produced as evenly sustained musical tones. He had characterized these vowels (in writing to Donders) as sounds in which it is not the fundamental tone, but one of the over-tones that is the strongest. He now adds the more exact determination that *o* arises when the fundamental is strongly accompanied by the higher octave, a weak accompaniment of the second and third tones producing an improvement in the sound, while *e* is characterized by the third tone, with moderate strength of the second, and the transition of *o* to *e* is produced by diminishing the second tone, and letting the third swell out, so that when both partials mentioned are given strongly, *o* modified (*ö*) arises. Thus he shows that the results produced with the tuning-fork are confirmed by the investigations of the tones of the human voice, at least when the vowels are sung to a definite note. Since the vowel, as pronounced, is a sound produced by the vibration of the vocal cords, and the mouth, according to Helmholtz's theory, acts as a resonator, which intensifies a given over-tone, corresponding with a given vowel-sound, alteration in the position of the mouth will produce given vowel-sounds from the same musical sound. In order to demonstrate his vowel theory, Helmholtz constructed little glass bulbs as resonators with two openings, one of which was prolonged into a short funnel-shaped neck to be inserted into the ear. Then, on sounding the proper tone outside, the mass of air within the sphere vibrated in sympathy, and thus acted on the ear. With these resonators it was easy not only to demonstrate most of the acoustic phenomena, such as objective combinational tones, over-tones, and their beats, but also to establish the accuracy of the vowel theory. Further, it was proved that musical timbre depends solely on the presence and intensity of the partial tones contained in the musical tone, and not in their different phases, although this is only certain where the investigation extends to the sixth or eighth partial tone. By establishing this last theorem, that difference of phase does not come into the question, Helmholtz confirmed his previous assumption that our sensation of different qualities of tone is reduced to the fact that other nerve-fibres, corresponding with the partials, are simultaneously excited along with the fibres that respond to the fundamental tone. This simple explanation would not suffice, if the difference in phase of the deeper harmonics had to be considered.

Helmholtz gave an enlarged account of his work in the following year to the Nat. Hist. Med. Verein, at Heidelberg, in a lecture 'On Timbre'. He removed the restriction that the vowel-sounds should be sung upon a single note (that of a man's voice at B), and investigated all pitches of sung vowels, finding that certain vowels are characterized by still higher over-tones.

In the paper laid before the Bavarian Academy, Helmholtz refers to the great work, which he had termed a preliminary study, published that year in the *Reine u. Angew. Mathematik* —'The Theory of Aerial Vibrations in Tubes with Open Ends,' the contents of which he had already communicated to the above Society at Heidelberg on March 15. This research, with that mentioned above on Vortex Motion, must be reckoned among the most brilliant of Helmholtz's mathematical achievements, only rivalled, and perhaps surpassed, by the work of the last ten years of his life.

'In 1891,' he writes, 'I have been able to solve a few problems in mathematics and physics, including some that the great mathematicians had puzzled over in vain from Euler onwards: e. g. the question of vortex motion, and the discontinuity of motions in fluids, that of the motions of sound at the open ends of organ pipes, &c. But any pride I might have felt in my conclusions was perceptibly lessened by the fact that I knew that the solution of these problems had almost always come to me as the gradual generalization of favourable examples, by a series of fortunate conjectures, after many errors. I am fain to compare myself with a wanderer on the mountains, who, not knowing the path, climbs slowly and painfully upwards, and often has to retrace his steps because he can go no farther—then, whether by taking thought or from luck, discovers a new track that leads him on a little, till at length when he reaches the summit he finds to his shame that there is a royal way, by which he might have ascended, had he only had the wits to find the right approach to it. In my works I naturally said nothing about my mistakes to the reader, but only described the made track by which he may now reach the same heights without difficulty.'

The Theory of Organ Pipes had till then been treated on the assumption that the motion of the aerial particles within the tubes was everywhere parallel to their axis, and that both velocity and pressure were equal at all points of the same cross-section of the tube, a view that was valid for the parts of a cylindrical or prismatic tube more remote from the open ends, but was inadmissible near the open ends where the waves which are plane in the tube spread out from it in the form of spherical waves ; for such a transition could not come about suddenly. The view of Bernouilli, Euler, and Lagrange that the condensation of the air at the open end of the tube was *nil* was equally inaccurate, since the density there cannot be taken as equal to that of the undisturbed air, but only to the altered density of the adjacent air that is itself thrown into vibration in the free space. Helmholtz followed up his earlier work in acoustics by an exact theoretical inquiry into the question as to the manner in which plane sound-waves, produced in the depth of a cylindrical tube, behave on their escape into free space. He settled this very difficult problem mathematically, without resort to hypothesis, by setting himself to discover what form of vibration is permanently set up, when the cause of the vibrations is allowed to act continuously and uninterruptedly. In accordance with his earlier theory, he assumed that the vibrations correspond with those of a simple tone, since all complex vibrational forms can be considered as due to the summation of a number of such simple tones.

After applying the most important general laws of the Functions of Electrical Potential to the Theory of Sound-waves, he goes on to his particular problem of determining the motions of air at the open end of a cylindrical tube, when plane waves, corresponding to a simple tone, are produced within the tube from any cause, and communicate their motion from the mouth of the tube to the external air when it is affected by no other

sound-producing agency. By means of the repeated application of Green's theorem to four distinct spaces, he was enabled,
under certain assumptions as to the magnitudes involved, without knowing the special form of opening or the motion of the
air within the opening, to deduce certain relations between
the plane and the hemispherical waves that spread out into
the remoter space; and thus the unsolved problem of the influence of the open end upon plane waves was determined.

In the first place it was found for the form of the waves
in the tube, that the maxima and minima of the vibrations,
i. e. their nodes and internodes, occurred at quarter wave-
lengths from each other, and that the phases of motion differed
by a quarter of a period at the maximal and minimal points.
Helmholtz termed the distance of the cross-section from a
point on the axis at a given definite distance from the mouth,
the reduced length of the tube, and found that the maxima
of vibration occurred throughout where the reduced length
was equal to an even multiple of the quarter wave-length,
while the surfaces of least motion, or nodal surfaces, occurred
on the contrary wherever the reduced length of the tube
equalled an uneven multiple of the quarter wave-length.

After deducing this general law, by which the problem is
referred to the determination of the reduced length in the
different forms of tube, Helmholtz next proposes to discover
in what forms of tubes the aerial motion at the mouth, and the
reduced length, may be fully determined for sound-waves of
such great wave-length, that the dimensions of the opening
of the tube, its cross-section, and that of the part of the tube
that deviates from the cylindrical, vanish.

Helmholtz contributed a supplement to these inquiries in the
lecture given on Feb. 27, 1863, to the Nat. Hist. Med. Verein,
'On the Influence of Friction in the Air upon the Motions
of Sound.' He returns in this to the theoretical differences
between real and reduced lengths in particular forms of the
mouth of tubes, since the theory for narrow tubes shows far
smaller differences than are actually found by experiment;
the correspondence was much closer when the friction of the
air is taken into consideration, which Helmholtz was able to do
on the basis of Stokes's investigations, as he had previously in
the case of fluids.

The universal recognition of Helmholtz's acoustic achievements by the scientific world, and his election to the Corresponding Membership of the Academy at Vienna, and the Scientific Society at Erlangen, had filled his aged father with pride and delight, and as the old man 'had felt much better of late, and the indications of brain trouble were quite insignificant', it was an unexpected shock to Helmholtz to receive the news on June 4 that his father had had a stroke, and lay at death's door. He started at once for Potsdam, leaving his sick wife with a heavy heart, but his father died before his arrival. 'The circumstances,' he writes to his wife, 'were much the same as in my mother's case, only the stroke was less rapidly fatal.'

Helmholtz returned from the funeral to find little comfort in his own house; his wife's health was failing irrevocably, slowly at first, but afterwards very rapidly. 'Nothing did good,' writes her sister, 'and at length we gave up all hope; Heidelberg knew only the shadow of her former self.' Helmholtz suffered severely from all this agitation; his frequent migraines, which were becoming more frequent and serious, obliged him at the doctor's orders to go off to Switzerland at the beginning of the autumn holidays, a change that was always beneficial. But he was shortly recalled to Heidelberg by disquieting news of his wife's health, and came back to sad and heavy months, in which his only comfort lay in the severest intellectual discipline.

At the outset he went on with the work commenced during the previous summer, on friction in fluids : ' I have just begun some work on friction in fluids with Piotrowski, in which he will do the experimental part. I hope we shall get the fundamental hydrodynamic equations in reference to friction out of it. After that, any special work on the motion of fluids would be reduced to a mathematical problem, although it would only be resolvable in a very few cases.'

But this most arduous mathematical work, which required the greatest mental concentration, proved impossible in his perpetual preoccupation and anxiety over his wife's illness, and he turned for distraction to easier experimental questions in optics and acoustics, as an appendix to his earlier work.

On Nov. 11, 1859, he gave a lecture to the Nat. Hist. Med. Verein, on ' Colour-Blindness ', which led on from his lecture at Carlsbad on 'After-Images' (September, 1858), part of which had already been given to the Nieder-Rheinische Gesellschaft. He pointed out in the first place that the Theory of the Three Fundamental Colours could not be retained, in the sense of deriving all actual objective colours from any given three such objective colours, since it is impossible, if we select any three spectral colours (as the most saturated colour we know), to derive all remaining spectral colours from them, as the resulting mixture is always more or less white. Young's theory is, however, independent of this, when it states that there are three principal colour sensations, distributed to three systems of nerve fibres, which can be excited collectively, but in different degrees of intensity, by all kinds of light, so that they yield qualitatively different sensations; here the choice of fundamental colours is arbitrary, to a certain extent. In any case spectral colours will not excite the separate fundamental colour sensations pure, and distinct from the other two; this would agree with the view of Helmholtz set forth in his Theory of After-Images, that there are more highly saturated sensations of colour than those which are aroused by spectral colours. In support of Young's hypothesis, Helmholtz examined a colour-blind subject with the help of Clerk Maxwell's colour-tops (which in sound eyes produce any given colour by the mixture of three suitable fundamental colours, with the addition of white, exhibited on sectors of variable breadth), and found Maxwell's results confirmed, since his patient could match all colours by mixtures of yellow and blue; thus for his colour-blind eyes one of the fundamental sensations was wanting. He found the colours which the colour-blind confuse with neutral grey to be red and green-blue, the red of which appeared to them dark-grey, and the complementary greenish-blue a very light grey, since the colour-blind eye was found to be very insensitive to red. By this means red was proved to be one of the fundamental colours. Helmholtz gives the name of red-blindness to this kind of colour-blindness, in which, according to Young's theory, there is a paralysis of the red-perceiving sensory nerves. He regarded it as probable that the other class hitherto denoted as colour-blind are green-blind, although the experiments had not at that time been carried out, which, by the aid of Maxwell's tops, establish in the case of colours which appear approximately the same to the colour-blind, whether the difference lies in the tone of colour or the degree of saturation.

Helmholtz's working capacity, however, became gradually exhausted, since the condition of his beloved wife was growing more and more serious; her relatives took charge of the family, and gave ceaseless attention to the invalid and care to her children. 'It was my privilege,' writes her sister, 'to be with her to the end. She died conscious, in simple strength as she had lived, fearless, with her friend beside her, ever turning towards the highest, on Dec. 28, 1859.'

Her husband wrote of her: 'I enjoyed the purest and highest happiness that marriage can give one; it was too beautiful for this world.'

A simple stone marks the grave in Heidelberg churchyard, with the inscription, 'Blessed be the rich seed that Love scatters round it.'

For many months Helmholtz was totally incapacitated for work by the heavy blow that had befallen him. On April 9, 1860, he writes to Donders: 'My warmest thanks to you and yours for your sympathy with my heavy loss. I have been unable to write before, because I have been ill for some time. I had got into a state of nervous irritation from the disturbed nights and agitation of the last few months, so that I could not do any continuous writing without severe headache or attacks of fever. It has been a sad time. In not being able to work, I lost the best means of defence against the feeling that one is alone and has no interests in the world. And I spent two months thus in sleepless nights and weary days. Since the beginning of March I have been able to get a little comfort in work.'

The fainting fits to which he had been subject of late years increased in consequence of all this trouble. 'Before Whitsuntide,' he writes on June 27, 'the attacks came on sometimes twice a day; now they are less frequent and severe, so that I can hold up against them if needs be.' But he constrained himself to work, since that alone could fortify him. During March he concluded the paper which he had announced to Ludwig and Thomson the previous summer, in co-operation with

Piotrowski, the latter having done the experimental work under Helmholtz's direction, and presented it on April 12, 1860, under the title, 'The Friction of Liquids,' to the Academy of Vienna.

The equations of motion within a non-viscous fluid mass subject to friction had been developed earlier by Poisson, Navier, and Stokes, and confirmed by experiments conducted in very long, narrow tubes, but it had proved impracticable to reconcile theory with experiment when the tubes were wide. Helmholtz now undertook to investigate a second case of motion in fluids (the theory of which can be derived completely from the hydrodynamic equations for fluids exerting friction), in order to obtain a new determination of the constant for the internal friction of water, so far derived only from Poiseuille's observations, and to compare the same with the observations. He succeeded in proving this for the movement of water in a sphere, polished and gilded inside, by throwing the spherical vessel into vibration, round a perpendicular axis, by means of a special apparatus, while the lag in the vibrations in the fluid was measured with a reflecting mirror and telescope. In this case, the force exerted by the fluid within the vessel upon its walls was experimentally determined, and compared with the force calculated from the mathematical theory of the motions of fluids.

He simplified the hydrodynamic equations by making the vibrations of the sphere so small that the squares of the velocity vanished as compared with its first power, and thereby succeeded, on the assumption that gravity was the sole external force, in finding particular integral equations, by which the components of the velocity at any moment of the water, present at a given point, could be expressed as the product of the co-ordinates, multiplied by a function of the time and of the distance of the point from the origin of the co-ordinates. This function satisfies a differential equation, analogous to the known potential equation of a sphere, which here contains a further factor, involving the friction-constant for the interior of the fluid; the form of the motion corresponding with this integral equation may be described by saying that the mass of water splits into concentric spherical layers, each of which performs a rotary movement like that of a thin hollow sphere round the direction of gravity. He analyses this function, which characterizes the angular velocity of the rotation, into an exponential function lineally dependent upon the time, and another that depends only upon the distance, and is independent of the time, and thence deduces the general integral of the normal differential equation, characteristic of this second factor; after this it is a simple matter to determine the integrals of the equations of motion for a fluid mass, subject to friction, within a hollow sphere. Since it was assumed that no force, beyond gravity, was acting inside the mass of water, the forces which set it in motion can only act upon the outermost layer, and this is actually set in motion by the friction of the vessel with which it is in contact. It does not adhere to the inner wall of the vessel, but glides along it.

As the analytical function for the components of the force with which a fluid in motion acts upon a superficial layer was known, it was evident that the force which the moving water exerts upon its outermost layer must be balanced by the force exerted by the wall of the vessel on the outermost layer of water; hence it appeared in the first place that the motion in the vessel described by the integrals arrived at fulfilled the conditions of Piotrowski's experiments. Helmholtz was next able, by comparison of these experiments and the theoretical functions, to calculate the constants for the internal friction of different fluids, their value differing according to the nature of the fluid and its temperature. The experiments, however, presented great difficulties, since they seemed to show that the chemical composition of the wall of the tube was not in every case without influence upon the motion of the fluids.

Immediately after this, Helmholtz gave a lecture to the Med. Nat. Hist. Verein, on 'Contrast Phenomena in the Eye', in which he endeavoured to distinguish contrast phenomena from after-images, and to demonstrate a method by which the true simultaneous contrast-images could be investigated apart from after-images. In trying to determine the most favourable conditions for the appearance of the familiar phenomena of contrast, he finds that all the conditions are fulfilled in the phenomenon of coloured shadows. When these are observed through a blackened tube, the eye retains an impression of a colour once established, even when the conditions which produced it are removed; in homogeneous red illumination the parts that are poorly lighted take on the complementary green in consequence of retinal fatigue. Helmholtz conjectured that the appearance of true contrast phenomena depends upon an error of judgement: we can compare correctly when the points to be compared are adjacent in the field of vision; spatial separation and succession in time on the contrary weaken the positiveness of the impression. He opposes this view to the earlier explanations which assumed actual alteration of the nervous excitation.

Starting from Fechner's Theory of After-Images, which only fails to give a positive explanation of phenomena in cases where the circumstances are very complicated, Helmholtz attempts to give a theoretical exposition of the temporal sequence of visual impressions. Since Fechner gives two grounds of explanation, to which he refers the complexity of the phenomena relating to this subject, i. e. survival of excitation, and fatigue of the nervous mechanism of the eye owing to previous excitation, it is obvious that in the colour phenomena of after-images, each of these processes must come into play for each of the three kinds of nerve-fibres assumed by Young's Colour Theory. Accordingly there must be six quantities of alterable magnitude, on which depend the brilliancy and colour of the after-image observed under certain given external conditions of illumination. As an after-image is positive when the after-excitation more than counteracts the fatigue, negative in the opposite case, an explanation of the complex processes with several colours is only possible under definite quantitative assumptions as to the time phenomena of excitation and fatigue in the nerve apparatus. As at the time of his investigation there were very few real quantitative determinations, Helmholtz confined himself to finding the mathematical functions, the variation of which with time corresponds, at least in direction, with the course of the phenomena, even if no exact correspondence of actually measured magnitudes be demonstrable.

'We find,' he says in a note on these observations, 'that two kinds of alterations are brought about in the living eye by light, apart from any distinctions of colours, i. e. excitation and fatigue. Neither of these processes is in its time-relations directly conditioned by the action of light. For when the light is cut off, excitation of the points of the retina previously stimulated still persists for a recognizable time in the dark field, and on testing with renewed and equal illumination of the field traces of fatigue are visible for a long time as negative after-images. We can also see how these conditions gradually disappear while the eye is resting in the dark, when they decline very fast and perceptibly at the outset, but the residue subsequently vanishes very slowly. As a rule, indeed, excitation dies out more quickly than fatigue. My conclusion is that persistent processes obtain in the living eye, even during the action of light, which tend to abolish both excitation and fatigue; the simplest mathematical expression of this fact is that the velocity with which the excitation s disappears, or, if the time be denoted t, the negative differential quotient of s with respect to the time, is proportional to the total strength of excitation at the moment, provided there be no simultaneous action of light. In the same way I assume for the alteration of fatigue f, that so long as there is no augmentation by simultaneous excitation we have a differential equation of the same form between f and t. On the other hand, the sensation may of course be reinforced by a new impression of light. This increase as a rule is not sudden, since the fresh exciting impression is added at each moment to the residue of the previous excitation. We may take the consequent increment of excitation as proportional to the luminous intensity of the impression. Further, this rise of excitation is conditioned by the concomitant fatigue, and the increment is less in proportion as the fatigue is greater. If we take $f = 1$ as the maximum value of the fatigue when the new impression fails to produce any effect, we may take that portion of the differential quotient of s with respect to t, produced by the new light of intensity i, as $mi(1-f)$, so that this differential quotient $= -as + mi(1-f)$. Fatigue is correspondingly augmented by excitation in proportion to the magnitude of stimulus, and this increment may be taken as proportional to the excitation; hence the complete expression of the alteration of fatigue will be the differential quotient of f with respect to t, viz. $-bf + ns$. The two equations then exactly determine the course of the two processes. Since the four constants a, b, m, and n can only be determined from the results of the experiments, and the values f and s are constantly changing, it is certain that within narrow limits of the values f and s, the above equations must be correct. Whether they hold good for wider limits, or whether the four quantities here given as constants are really independent of s and f, can at present be determined only by experiment, i. e. comparison of the results of our equations with experience.

Taking the intensity i of the light that impinges on the eye during the observed time as a constant, and forming the universal integrals of the two linear differential equations for f and s with constant co-efficients, Helmholtz finds the value to which the magnitude of excitation approximates increasingly with protracted illumination i, and thence deduces the maximal value of the persistent illumination of the eye as the quantity $\frac{b}{n}$. If F and S be taken as the limits to which the magnitude of fatigue or of excitation approximates gradually with long illumination i, it follows from the given integral functions that, if s and f are both at the outset larger or smaller than the values F and S, which they finally arrive at, s must at first exceed or fall short of S, then reach a maximum or minimum, and finally rise or fall once more to the value S, while f constantly rises or falls to the value F; and the same is true whether at the outset $s > S, f < F$ or $s < S, f > F$.

The first case explains directly 'the alternation of positive and negative after-images, when the eye looks steadily at a constantly illuminated field, or even at the retinal field illuminated with its intrinsic light, on which a lighter or darker object has become temporarily visible, and then disappeared. In the former case excitation and fatigue are simultaneously augmented at the point on the retina that is covered by the image of this object; in the latter they are simultaneously diminished. Upon the disappearance of the object, excitation and fatigue of the spots involved return gradually to their final value, at which the other parts of the retina have remained. The positive after-image corresponds with the period at which the excitation has not yet reached this final value, the negative with the period when it has been exceeded, as always occurs in this case. The moment of alternation between negative and positive images is found by determining that value of t, at which s exceeds S. The greater the excitation, and the less the fatigue deviates from its final value, the longer will be the duration of the positive image. A very brief period of excitation favours this. Further, with otherwise similar conditions, it is favourable to the duration t of the positive image that the magnitude of intensity of the persistent illumination shall be low, as is actually seen in experiments in which the positive image is visible for the greatest length of time upon the perfectly dark field. The longer the time t, the smaller'—as follows from the exponential quantities of the integrals—'will be the intensity of the negative image. In a wholly darkened field of vision, where the retina is excited only by entoptic stimulation, the negative image is only visible when the ratio between the final and initial value of f and the final value has become fairly large in consequence of very strong illumination, or its prolonged action. If we neglect the feeble intrinsic light of the retina the course of the excitation will be quite independent of the concomitant fatigue.'

Helmholtz only began to develop the 'rise of excitation in the recuperated eye' from the integral formulae. The application of the relations found to the problem of intermittent illumination leads to an expression for the strength of excitation with persistent illumination of a given intensity, from which Helmholtz concludes that the hypothesis made in framing the differential equations is in agreement with the well-known law, 'by which the apparently uniform brilliancy of a periodically alternating illumination is equal to that which would be obtained if the whole quantity of light in each period were evenly distributed over the entire period.'

During the summer, Part II of the *Textbook of Physiological Optics* appeared. It was indeed ready before the death of his wife, and on August 6 he sent a copy to Fechner, with the following words :—

'You will find the same subjects in this second part that you have dealt with lately in your own work. I had written the chapter on Intensity of Light, in all essentials, before I received your treatise on it. I therefore introduced some modifications afterwards. In the After-images, as you will see, I have modelled myself on you throughout. Contrast gave me the most trouble; I have tried to clear up this chapter, but have not yet got it right.'

Part II of *Physiological Optics* deals with the Theory of Visual Sensation, and treats in the first place of the various forms of stimulation of the optic nerve, and then of its excitation by light in particular, after which Helmholtz gives a connected development of the theories previously published by himself and others on simple and compound colours. In connexion with the intensity and duration of visual sensation, he gives a number of experimental methods and results, some of which, e. g. the Psycho-Physical Law of Fechner, are substantially completed by some of his own later works, and lastly he deals with the Theory of After-Images and Contrast Phenomena, on the lines indicated above, and illustrated by new and interesting experiments.

Two points may be selected from the wealth of new results that had not previously appeared, either in his earlier works or in the long series of profound theoretical deductions and delicate experiments which combined his own with the work of other investigators.

For the purposes of physiological investigation it was necessary to make a much more precise analysis of simple light than was required by physical work in general, and in the first place to investigate the theory of refraction in prisms, in so far as this is essential to the production of pure spectra. While formerly only the refraction of single rays of light in prisms, not the position and character of the prismatic images, had been determined, Helmholtz now investigated the prismatic images formed by any kind of homogeneous light, when the eye looks through a prism, or examines the light issuing from a prism with lens or telescope, since these images must be regarded as objects for the further optical images produced by the media and lenses of the eye.

If a ray is passed through different refractive media, and the length of its path in each medium multiplied by the refractive index of that medium, the sum of all these particular quantities being termed the optical length of the ray, then the optical length is proportional to the time in which the light traverses the length of the ray, and equal to the distance which the light would have traversed in the same time in empty space.   The law of refraction of light-rays may accordingly be expressed by saying that the optic length of the ray between given points in the first and last medium must be a limiting value (maximal or minimal) when the refracting media are limited by surfaces of continuous curvature.   In following up the analogy with the potential function, Helmholtz finds that if the rays have started from any point, and are broken by an indefinite number of surfaces of continuous curvature, they will after the last refraction be perpendicular to that curved surface for the points of which collectively the optical length of the ray is of constant value.   This surface contains all points at which the same phase of ether vibration occurs, and is accordingly a wave surface.   After laying down this theorem he applies the known properties of the normal and of the curvature of a surface to the determination of the course of the rays in an infinitesimally thin bundle of rays.   But this further gives the laws of the refraction of bundles of rays in prisms.   Helmholtz finds that an infinitesimally thin bundle of homocentric rays, starting from a point at infinite distance, will only remain homocentric after its passage through a prism if it has passed through at an angle of minimal deviation, i.e. if it is in a plane perpendicular to the refracting edge, and makes an equal angle with both surfaces of the prism.   Since a luminous point can only form a clear image when the refracted light is homocentric, the accuracy of the image of a line of light is evidently not affected by deviations of the rays, provided they lie in the direction of its image.   From this he arrives at the images of luminous objects, when these consist of vertical bright lines of different, monochromatic lights ; and is able to determine the brilliancy of the spectrum, and to prove that its brightness, apart from loss by reflection and absorption, is directly proportional to the brightness of the spectral colours involved, and the apparent breadth of the slit inversely proportional to the apparent length of the part of the spectrum that is in question.

Meantime Helmholtz had determined, while still engaged on his *Physiological Optics*, to write a similar work on Sensations of Tone, in consequence of the radical discoveries he was making. In 1860 he writes to Donders: 'I have decided to put my acoustic work together in a book. It will be a small volume, as popular in style as possible, so as to make it available to lovers of music. I think I shall be able to expound the physico-physiological basis of the theory of harmony.'

Helmholtz sought comfort and distraction in hard mental work: his home, despite the devoted and tender ministration of his mother-in-law, who looked after the two little children, was empty and desolate. All the external honours that poured in on him—his appointment as Corresponding Member of the Academy of Göttingen, the Sömmering Prize given him by the Senkenberg Naturforschende Gesellschaft at Frankfurt-a.-M., and so on—affected him little, though in former days he would have welcomed them for the pleasure they gave his father and his beloved wife. In the summer of 1860 he betook his sorrow, and the fatigue engendered by the term's work and his ceaseless study of the deepest problems of human knowledge, to his friend W. Thomson (Lord Kelvin) in the island of Arran, returning after some weeks, refreshed in body and mind, *via* Edinburgh and Hamburg, to Heidelberg.

He now occupied himself almost exclusively with acoustics, and writes to his brother Otto:—

'The physiological basis of consonance and dissonance may be thus simply expressed: consonance is a continuous sensation of tone, dissonance is discontinuous. Two tones that are near each other give coincident beats, i. e. intermittent excitation of the nerve. The whole theory of Harmony, and of our modern System of Tone, follows directly from the beats of harmonic over-tones, combinational tones, &c.'

On Nov. 23 he gave a lecture to the Nat. Hist. Med. Verein on 'Musical Temperament', in which he dealt with the disadvantages of tempered intonation for various instruments, and in which the breadth of his historical studies, which in itself makes his later theory of the sensations of tone such a marvellous achievement, is obvious. In any given major scale, the major third and the fifth are always tuned so that their vibration numbers are as $4:5$ and $2:3$; the three chords contained in the scale are then pure. On passing into another key, the new chord of the final tone now gives a fifth, which is no longer identical with the third of the original key; hence in keyed instruments it is usual to substitute for these two slightly different tones (one of which is the third of the original tonic), one single tone, since an impure fifth is more readily perceived than an impure third. On further progression by fifths the tonic is not recovered; in order to distribute the error evenly, all the fifths must be slightly altered; the deviation of the fifths in the now general system of intonation will however be exceedingly small, since the ratio of the pure to the tempered fifths will be as $886:885$. But since this produces errors in the thirds, and modern music is harmonic throughout, the discord of the false intervals of intonation makes itself unpleasantly heard in the beats of their combination tones and harmonic over-tones. In the instruments best adapted for artistic music, the disadvantage of tempered music is least felt, because the singing voice is independent of it, while the harshness can be modified on bowed instruments, and the piano, the tones of which soon die away, does not favour dissonances. The want of true intonation is, on the other hand, apparent in all long-sustained tones, particularly in the harmonium, where the beats are too obvious when the instrument is played slowly, and the difference between pure and tempered chords is so marked, that the latter sound like dissonances in contrast with the former. In order to obtain pure harmony, Helmholtz gives two distinct values to each note of the scale, according as it is the third or fifth, in relation to the tonic of a major chord, and gives the series of major chords which satisfy the conditions. In practice, either two keyboards must be introduced, or the instrument tuned correctly for each key that occurs in the course of the piece, by arranging the notes in eight groups, and providing all the notes of each group with a separate supply of wind from the bellows, when almost pure intervals can be obtained.

In this connexion we may refer to a later work of Helmholtz. Starting from the view that scales originated in the desire to distinguish single tones clearly and sharply from one another (whole tones only being recognized by the unpractised ear of uncivilized peoples to this day), and that semitones were only introduced into music as the ear became gradually developed, Helmholtz thought it well to undertake historical studies of the development of the scale in different nations, our major and minor scales having been developed very late. In July, 1862, he read a paper on 'The Persian and Arabian Scales' to the Nat. Hist. Med. Verein. In the system he proposes for the construction and tuning of musical instruments, in which all the keys can be played in pure consonant chords, twice as many intervals were required as usual. These historical studies led him to the conclusion that in Greek scales, the fifth fifth from C upwards was used as the third of C, from which it differs only by the minute interval 81/80; while if eight fifths are taken downwards from C the tone F flat is reached, which only differs from the third of C by something like the tenth part of the interval 81/80, so that it can be substituted for it. The musicians of Persia and Arabia took advantage of these substitutions to obtain pure natural scales; their system was one of seventeen fifths, from which scales with Pythagorean, or natural, thirds and sixths were derived. Helmholtz followed a common physical principle throughout, i. e. that of the relationship of musical tones. The definition chosen by him, according to which two compound tones are related when they have some common over-tones, shows that the notes most nearly related to the fundamental are the octave, and then the fifth and fourth; these related musical tones occur in all 'modes'.

After Helmholtz had ascertained from his experiments on timbre that differences in quality of musical tone depend principally upon the number and strength of the harmonic partials that accompany the prime tone, he next had to investigate the forms of the elastic vibrations executed by variously sounding bodies. He published his observations on the vibrations in strings produced by the bow of a violin, in the *Proceedings of the Glasgow Philosophical Society*, on December 19, 1860, with the title 'On the Motion of the Strings of a Violin'. It was at once obvious that the string set in motion by the bow can only vibrate in the same plane as the string and the hair of the bow. He powdered the string of a fine instrument with starch, illuminated it strongly, and examined its motions by means of a vibration microscope constructed for the purpose, the object-glass of which was

carried by a tuning-fork which vibrated under the influence of
an electro-magnet once to four vibrations of the string. In
this way he discovered that the starch granules described a
shining curve, the horizontal abscissae of which corresponded
with the displacements of the tuning-fork, and the vertical
ordinates with the displacements of the string. This motion
may therefore be imagined as consisting of two different kinds
of vibration, the first of which greatly preponderates in regard
to amplitude, while its period corresponds with the period of
the fundamental tone of the strings, independent of the point
to which the bow is applied; the second weaker motion, on the
contrary, makes very minute deflexions in the curve, since its
vibration-period corresponds with one of the higher partials of
the string; at all nodes of the partial the principal motion alone
appears. Experiment showed in regard to the principal motion
that every point of it first advances with constant velocity in
one direction, and then returns to its first position with another
constant velocity, from which, in view of the fact that the
vibrations of a string occur in a plane, the analytic expression
of the displacement of any point may be stated with the aid of
Fourier's series as a function of the distance of the point
from one end of the string, and of the time. Along with this
principal form of vibration, other lesser vibrations, which
may be expressed in precisely the same way, are produced
if the bow touches any point of which the distance from the
nearest end of the string is the reciprocal value of a whole
number of lengths of the string; in such a case the
over-tones (on the analogy of Young's investigations for the
strings of a harp) of which the multiples correspond to that
whole number will not be heard, although the ear can plainly
distinguish all other over-tones. Helmholtz concludes from the
simple analytical consideration of this combination, that during
the motion of the string the base of the abscissa of its point
of greatest displacement moves to and fro along the line of
equilibrium with constant velocity, while the apex itself
describes two parabolic curves that run above and below the
position of equilibrium and through the ends of the string, and
the actual form of the string at any instant is given by the two
straight lines that join a point on the parabolic curves with the
ends of the string.

A year of work and of the richest scientific discoveries lay
behind him—of sad memories also. At the Christmas season
of 1859, the beloved wife lay dying, who had watched him
grow up from the modest assistant-physician at Potsdam into
the most famous physicist and physiologist of the day, and who
had beautified his home and life with the most self-sacrificing
love and discerning judgement. And now the Christmas of
1860 found him weary in body, overtasked in mind, desolate
in his affections. Notwithstanding the love and devotion of
his mother-in-law, he felt that the education of his two little
children could never be all that he and his wife had planned,
and further, that his deep interest in science and art, and
the love of aesthetics which had never been eclipsed by his
profoundest abstractions, were in danger of atrophy, whereby
he would lose the marvellous fertility and productivity that
elevated him above all the other scientific men of his day.

On February 13, 1861, he writes to Lord Kelvin:—

'On this account I had seriously to think of introducing
a new order of things, and if this had to be done, it was better
on all accounts that it should come soon. At the end it did
come about more rapidly than I had expected, for when love
has once obtained permission to germinate, it grows without
further appeal to reason. My *fiancée* is a gifted maiden, young
in comparison with myself, and is I think one of the beauties
of Heidelberg. She is very keen-witted and intelligent, accustomed to society, as she received a good deal of her education
in Paris and London, in the charge of an English lady, the
wife of her uncle Dr. Mohl, Professor of Persian at the Collège
de France, in Paris. She therefore speaks French fluently,
and is decidedly better than I in English. For the rest her
"fashionable" (*sic*) education has in no way interfered with
her straightforward, simple nature.'

Du Bois writes to inquire further details, since all that
concerned Helmholtz had a lively interest for him.

'My bride-elect,' replies Helmholtz on March 2, 1861, 'is
the daughter of Robert v. Mohl; she appealed to me from
the outset of my life here as a most intelligent young lady,
but I saw very little of her. She was away for a long time
in Paris, staying with her uncle Julius v. Mohl, Professor of
Persian at the Collège de France. His wife is an English-

woman, and Anna went to her several times for long visits to Paris and England, where she imbibed the best sides of French and English manners and customs. I must confess that I rather avoided than sought Anna v. Mohl last summer, for I felt that a girl like her would be dangerous for me, and I should never have presumed, as a widower with two children, and no longer in my first youth, to seek the hand of so young a lady, who had every qualification for playing a prominent part in society. However, it all came about very quickly, and now I can once more face the future happily. The wedding is to be at Whitsuntide.'

In the Easter vacation Helmholtz went to England to give two lectures on 'The Physiological Theory of Music', but found he had to deliver a third without any preparation, since Bence Jones and Faraday insisted on his giving an evening discourse on the Conservation of Energy. In this lecture, delivered April 12, 1861, 'On the Application of the Law of the Conservation of Force to Organic Nature,' he first, as in all his earlier lectures, gives an account of the principle of the conservation of force, which, with Rankine, he prefers (since it bears no relation to amount of force) to term the conservation of *energy*, and which he designates as the most important advance of science in the century because it embraces all laws of physics and chemistry. He now proceeds to apply this law to organic nature; he points out that continuation of life is bound up with continued supply of means of sustenance, which after complete digestion pass into the blood, are slowly consumed in the lungs, and finally produce almost the same compounds with the oxygen of the air, as those which would be produced by burning the food in an open fire. Now since the amount of heat produced by oxidation is independent of the time occupied in consumption and of the intermediate stages, it can be calculated from the mass of the materials consumed, how much heat, or its equivalent work, can be produced by any animal body— experiments that involve great difficulties. On a later occasion, when a criticism of some scientific book was demanded from him, he pointed out that the difficulty which arises in considering these very important and very recondite physiological problems (the question of heat production in animal bodies, and its connexion with metabolism) is principally due to the fact that the heat to be measured is not evolved suddenly, but in the course of hours, so that it cannot be even approximately collected in an apparatus, while further a considerable quantity of air has to be led through such an apparatus, which carries off a good portion of the heat produced, apart from the augmentation of work consequent on the necessary size of the apparatus. Within limits, however, experiment shows that the heat actually produced in animal bodies corresponds with that given off in chemical processes. He makes it intelligible that the animal body does not differ from a steam-engine in the way in which it obtains warmth and energy, but only in the objects, and the way and means, for which and by which it uses the acquired energy. In conclusion he points out how the hypothesis of a vital energy has been gradually eliminated by all these experiments, so that the younger scientific workers, who are seeking the true causes for all these processes, no longer admit any distinction in chemical and mechanical work within and without the living body. The law of the conservation of energy points the way in which these fundamental questions, which have given rise to so many speculations, can be really and adequately solved by experiment.

On May 16, 1861, Helmholtz was married to Fräulein Anna von Mohl. 'Even Helmholtz's closest friends,' writes the sister of his first wife, 'found it difficult to reconcile themselves to his marrying again after only one year. After the ideal happiness of the former marriage such a step, taken so quickly, appeared almost inconceivable. They did him injustice. He did not really lose his wife at the time of her bodily death . . . she had gone from him before, owing to the terrible nature of her illness. For more than a year, her inner life had been dying out step by step, paralysing all her interests and sympathies. Only in death did she regain her old intellectual and moral eminence. Thus Helmholtz had long been a solitary man when she died, and the outlook for the future with two small children and their grandmother, who in spite of all devotion and self-sacrifice was an old woman, was a sad one. For Helmholtz, who was accustomed to the most active mental companionship, it was absolutely impossible. He chose a wife who responded to all his needs. Anna von Mohl, a person of great force of character, talented, with wide views and high aspirations, clever in society, and brought up in a circle in which intelligence and character were equally well developed, was to the time of his death an admirable companion, while her judgement was always a law to him.'

CHAPTER IX

HELMHOLTZ AS PROFESSOR OF PHYSIOLOGY AT HEIDELBERG: 1858-1871 (*continued*).

AFTER a few days' absence at Whitsuntide, Helmholtz returned to Heidelberg with his young wife. 'To the end of her life she spoke with emotion of this first journey from Baden to Schloss Eberstein with her husband, whose eminence and noble character were just dawning on her.' On reaching home, he found warm congratulations from his old friend Ludwig, who at the same time expressed 'unbounded astonishment at the increasing significance of the discoveries made by Helmholtz'—receiving the modest answer:—

'I wish you did not think so disproportionately well of my work, and so little of your own. We all have our special capacities, and I know very well that I could not have discovered the dependence of the salivary secretions upon nervous control, or carried out any of your other investigations.'

Under these altered conditions Helmholtz appeared in a new light; the dark shadows that had saddened his life for so many years were dispersed, and his home was brightened by the charming and universally popular wife, who shed sunshine around her.

He had already become recognized as the first authority in the scientific world, where he was looked up to on all sides with admiration and astonishment, while his work in optics and acoustics had attracted the attention of the world of art as well; and now his influence extended still further, among other ranks of educated society. In Königsberg and Bonn his public lectures had introduced his vast and comprehensive scientific views to the wider circles of the world of science: at Heidelberg, though his circumstances were naturally somewhat restricted, his house became the centre of scientific and artistic activity, to a degree which ordinarily is only possible under more favourable conditions.

'Journeys to England,' writes his sister-in-law, Freifrau v. Schmidt-Zabiérow, the elder daughter of Robert v. Mohl, 'as well as long and frequent visits to our relatives in Paris, where the intellectual atmosphere of our aunt's *salon* at 120 Rue du Bac, which was the focus of the best society, had developed my sister's rich gifts to the utmost, and made it a necessity for her to live in intercourse with distinguished people. She had ample opportunities of forming such connexions, both in our parents' house, and among the many intellectual foreigners of good social standing who were at that time living in Heidelberg. A widened outlook on life and greater demands upon it were the natural result of these international relations. My sister had as perfect command of French and English as of her mother tongue, and all restriction to any particular set of society was abhorrent to her from her earliest youth. Her fresh and merry temperament, her sense of humour, her rapid grasp of things and people, may have had a directly beneficial influence upon Helmholtz.'

In spite, however, of these extended social relations, Helmholtz's intellectual and thoroughly genial life expended itself mostly in his own house, where his incomparable wife succeeded in maintaining her environment at an unusually high level, and in respecting the limits enforced by her husband's ceaseless activity in work and thought. Order now began to reign in his library and workroom, of which she had written a few months before their marriage : ' How I shall have to struggle with myself and subdue my natural inclinations before I can become a really useful wife ! Do not lose patience with me, Hermann, I am easily discouraged ; but I must tell you that your writing table is frightfully untidy. If I were not far too well brought up in regard to learned confusion, I should take the liberty of sorting out all the written papers from the blank sheets, with energetic hand, and putting away all the letters in a drawer—*N.B.* unread—and then go over everything with a damp cloth, on Miss Nightingale's principle. But as it is I must leave things as they are, and am only thankful to have discovered one human failing in you.'

His correspondence with his scientific friends at this time was even more extensive than before. If there was less science in his letters to du Bois-Reymond, because Helmholtz was now working at subjects with which du Bois was not much concerned, this was replaced by an increasingly intimate correspondence by word and letter with W. Thomson (Lord Kelvin), in which they not only discussed the epoch-making work they were themselves engaged upon, but communicated to one another the most important researches and discoveries of other observers during the long period of nearly fifty years. In this way Helmholtz was the first to inform Lord Kelvin of Kirchhoff's discovery of metals in the solar atmosphere. Although the letter in question can no longer be found by Lord Kelvin, he addressed the following very interesting lines to the author on September 26, 1902 :—

'There should be several others between that date and 1856, when I first had the great pleasure of making personal acquaintance with Helmholtz in Kreutznach when he came to see me, and in Bonn where I returned his visit.

'There should be a letter of November or December, 1859, telling me of Kirchhoff's discovery of metals in the solar atmosphere by spectrum analysis. You may possibly find my answer which I wrote immediately on receiving it, telling him that as chanced two or three days before, I had, in a lecture to my students in Glasgow University, told them that I had learned from Stokes that the double dark line D in the spectrum of sunlight proves that there is sodium vapour in the sun's atmosphere, and that other metals might be found there by the comparison of the Fraunhofer dark lines in the solar spectrum with the dark lines produced in flames by metals. I am sure I must also have told him that I had been giving this doctrine regularly in my lectures for several years.

'I well remember that at that time I was making " Properties of Matter" the subject of my Friday morning lecture. On one Friday morning I had been telling my students that we must expect the definite discovery of other metals in the sun besides sodium by the comparison of Fraunhofer's solar dark lines with artificial bright lines. The next Friday morning I brought Helmholtz's letter with me into my lecture and read it, by which they were told that the thing had actually been done with splendid success by Kirchhoff.'

After the publication of the Second Part of *Physiological*

Optics Helmholtz had devoted all his energies to the preparation of his great work on Acoustics, and by the beginning of 1861 was feeling that after years of preparation he might soon hope to lay the results of his profound discoveries in acoustics and the art of music before the educated world. Soon after the heavy misfortune that befell Lord Kelvin, Helmholtz wrote on January 16, 1861, to Thomson's wife :—

'I have been working all the winter at my physiological theory of music, and have only two chapters left to write ; then the first draft of it will be ready, though much will doubtless have to be worked up in detail, and improved. I hope to give the book to the printers after Easter. Mr. Thomson will find a great deal that is new since we discussed it last summer, which I have put in while I was working out the details. I have penetrated a long way into the Theory of Music with my physical theories, much farther than I dared to hope at the outset, and the work has amused me considerably. In developing the consequences of any valid general principle in individual cases, one constantly comes on new and quite unexpected surprises. And as the consequences are not arbitrary, and contingent on the caprice of the author, but develop according to their own laws, I often have the impression that it is not my own work that I am writing out, but some one else's. Mr. Thomson must have found the same thing in his own work on the mechanical theory of heat. I have also had to look through a great deal of music, and to study the history of music. The Scotch Ballads have been of great use for this, as they have preserved many of the ancient forms.'

A paper on 'The Theory of Reed Pipes' (July, 1861) concluded the publication of Helmholtz's detailed acoustic observations, and he went on to formulate a physiological acoustic as previously announced to Thomson.

General happiness, and satisfaction with his new circumstances, had restored his mental energy and inexhaustible powers of work, and with these he had recovered his old delight in art and nature, and conceived the notion of building the bridge to lead from physics and physiology to aesthetics.

At the close of the session, after making a cure at Kissingen, he took a long journey in Switzerland and Italy with his young wife, returning with restored health and rejuvenated mind and body. He was now able to participate cheerfully in all that life offered him in the beautiful city on the Neckar, where for the first time he felt himself at home. In September he brought his children Käthe and Richard (who since April had been at Dahlem with their grandmother) to Heidelberg, where he now had a commodious dwelling on the Anlage which he shared with Frau von Velten.

Helmholtz took up his book on Acoustics with fresh energy, plunged into arduous optical problems (the solution of which was to form Part III of the *Physiological Optics*), elaborated the structure and detail of his Theory of Knowledge, and at the same time continued the electrical investigations to which he had been led by du Bois-Reymond and by his own physiological researches.

In a lecture given to the Nat. Hist. Med. Verein at Heidelberg (December 8, 1861) on 'A Universal Method of the Transformation of Problems of Electrical Distribution' a number of interesting and important propositions were brought forward by Helmholtz, who was not acquainted with the work done by others in this department.

Immediately after the publication of this paper, he was informed that its essential results were already contained in two letters from W. Thomson to Liouville, and at once acknowledged this in the *Heidelberg Transactions* of May 30, 1862. He also wrote on May 27 to W. Thomson :—

'I have to beg you to answer a scientific question. Last autumn I fell back on potential functions again. I was troubled by the difficulties that remained unsolved in my work on sound vibrations in an open cylindrical tube. The difficulty of attacking the question lay in the fact that the aerial motions are discontinuous at the edge of the open end of the tube. This led me to investigate the distribution of electricity at a circular edge. I found that I could derive this in certain cases from the distribution along the straight edge in which two infinite planes intersect one another, and I solved the problem for this case. Afterwards, however, I noticed that you had already stated in the *Cambridge Math. Journ.* that you had solved this question, and I want to know whether you have published the solution, or intend to publish it, in which case it is not worth my while to work out my own solution for the press. The principle of reflection from a spherical surface, by which a straight edge can be converted into a circular one, was also discovered (as he supposed) by another and very capable young mathematician, Lipschitz, but happily we came on it in time in your previous work. Unfortunately I have already published it in a short Note in the *Transactions* of our own Scientific Society, for which I must beg your pardon; but in its fuller exposition by Lipschitz, the priority will be given to you.'

Thomson at once gave him full information upon these mathemical points.

Meantime, the great work on Acoustics was nearing its completion; on April 29, 1862, Helmholtz writes to Donders (after telling him that a son had been born on March 3, who received the names of Robert Julius, and whose life nearly cost that of his mother):—

'As to my work on acoustics, *A Physiological Basis for the Theory of Music*, the blocks are made, the text is being set up, and two-thirds of the manuscript have been sent off: there is a good deal still to alter and patch up in the last third, but the most important parts are already written. I shall be thankful when I have finished the last words of this long-winded undertaking, for I have been working on it for seven years, which certainly won't be seen from the size of the book. And then very likely the philosophers and musicians will regard it as trespassing on their domain, while there are not many musical people like yourself, for instance, among the physicists and physiologists. You will be my most intelligent critic, and I shall be very curious to hear whether my bold attempt to bring scientific methods into aesthetics will meet with your approval.'

The busiest and most productive period of Helmholtz's life in Heidelberg opened with the year 1862. His *Theory of the Sensations of Tone* and *Physiological Optics* were both near their completion; his epistemological views were shaping themselves into a consistent system of philosophy; he was incessantly occupied with problems in hydrodynamics and electrodynamics, and his thoughts were already turning to the investigations of the axioms of geometry, which in a few years' time were to reveal the depth of his mathematical and philosophical conceptions to the scientific world. During the next ten years, Helmholtz displayed an illumination in his view of scientific problems, an elevation of philosophical conception, a purposeful attitude in regard to the riddles and mysteries of Nature, a grasp of all the resources of thought and feeling available for the investigation of the whole field of human knowledge, such as are seldom met with in the history of the sciences, and can only be appreciated in their full extent and significance by those who had the privilege of personal contact with this extraordinary genius.

In his youth his friends du Bois-Reymond, Brücke and Ludwig had applauded his marvellous discoveries, and now it was Bunsen and Kirchhoff who were amazed at his scientific achievements. Long after Kirchhoff had won immortal fame by his discovery of spectrum analysis, he used to say, modestly indeed, but none the less truly, 'I am content if I can even understand a single work of Helmholtz, but there are still many points in his great book on acoustics that I cannot unravel.'

It was to this time of intellectual activity that Helmholtz referred when he said thirty years later in his celebrated speech on the commemoration of his 70th birthday, November 2, 1891:—

'There are many narrow-minded people who admire themselves enormously if they have one stroke of luck, or think that they have had one. A pioneer in science, or an artist, who has a repeated run of happy accidents, is indubitably a privileged character, and is recognized as a benefactor of mankind. But who can count or weigh such lightning flashes of the mind? Who can trace out the secret threads by which our conceptions are united? For

> Was vom Menschen nicht gewusst,
> Oder nicht bedacht,
> Durch das Labyrinth der Brust
> Wandelt in der Nacht.

'I must confess that the departments in which one has not to trust to lucky accidents and inspirations have always had the greatest attraction for me. Yet as I have often been in the predicament of having to wait on inspiration, I have had some few experiences as to when or how it came to me, which may perhaps be of use to others. Often enough it steals quietly into one's thoughts and at first one does not appreciate its significance; it is only sometimes that another fortuitous circumstance helps one to recognize when, and under what conditions, it occurred to one; otherwise it is there, one knows not whence. In other cases it comes quite suddenly, without effort, like a flash of thought. So far as my experience goes it never comes to a wearied brain, or at the writing-table. I must first have turned my problem over and over in all directions, till I can see its twists and windings in my mind's eye, and run through it freely, without writing it down; and it is never possible to get to this point without a long period of preliminary work. And then, when the consequent fatigue has been recovered from, there must be an hour of perfect bodily recuperation and peaceful comfort, before the kindly inspiration rewards one. Often it comes in the morning on waking up, according to the lines I have quoted from Goethe (as Gauss also noticed, *Works*, v. p. 609: Law of Induction discovered January 23, 1835, at 7 a.m. before rising). It came most readily, as I experienced at Heidelberg, when I went out to climb the wooded hills in sunny weather. The least trace of alcohol, however, sufficed to banish it. Such moments of fertile thought were truly gratifying, but the obverse was less pleasant when the inspiration would not come. Then I might worry at my problem for weeks and months, till I felt like the creature on the barren heath

> Von einem bösen Geist im Kreis herumgeführt,
> Und ringsumher ist schöne grüne Weide.

Sometimes nothing but a severe attack of headache could release me from my spell, and set me free again for other interests.'

To all these great scientific labours and projects were now added no less arduous official duties—but in Heidelberg his lectures on physiology and on the general results of science, as well as the direction of the work in the Laboratory, were no mere tasks to be reluctantly fulfilled. Nor did he regard the University lectures simply as an obligation laid upon him by the State, 'which provided him with sustenance, with scientific instruments, and with a good proportion of spare time,' and therewith had the right to claim from him that whatever he discovered by its aid should be freely communicated to his students and his fellow citizens; he always appreciated the fact that lecturing compelled him to test each isolated proposition strictly, to formulate each conclusion correctly, and, since he could only assume a limited amount of previous knowledge in his hearers, to state the evidence for the views he was maintaining in as simple a manner as possible. His audience took the place of his friends, whom he always imagined as present at his scientific lectures. ' I always pictured the most intelligent of my friends before me, as my conscience ; I asked myself if they would sanction what I was saying. They haunted me as the embodiment of the scientific spirit of an ideal humanity, and set my standard.'

' As a student in Heidelberg,' says Engelmann, ' I followed his lectures on physiology, and the public lectures on the general results of natural science, which he gave every winter at that time. In intellectual and social life there are two forms of energy, and it is the sum of these which determines the value of the whole. With Helmholtz only a small part of the enormous supply of energy stored up in him was actually in evidence at any given moment. The conversion of his potential energy into kinetic was slow, unlike what happens with those whom people are wont to describe as geniuses. As he never worked out the details of his lectures, but composed them as he went along, he spoke slowly, deliberately, and at times a little haltingly. His eyes looked away beyond his audience as though he were seeking the solution of a problem at an infinite distance. In the physiology classes he assumed no more knowledge and insight in his medical students than did any other teacher of the same department. He seldom gave the names of any experimenters, and least of all his own.'

He was a keen teacher in the laboratory, and every earnest student became one of his friends in science. As free from professional jealousy as Magnus, whom he had so often commended, he frequently supplied the fundamental ideas for the splendid work that issued from his laboratory, and provided a wealth of suggestions for the overcoming of new experimental problems, in which more or less ingenuity was required. ' Whoever had the luck,' says Bernstein, who for years was his assistant at the Physiological Institute, ' to watch Helmholtz experimenting, will never forget the impression which he gave of the purposeful activity of a master-mind when confronted with difficulties. He turned out models of ingenious contrivances with the simplest materials, corks, glass rods, bits of wood, cardboard boxes, and the like, before putting them into the hands of the mechanician. No accident ever disturbed the wonderful serenity and equanimity of Helmholtz's temperament; he was never upset by the clumsiness of others. Men who had worked for him for years never saw him excited under such circumstances.'

He was respected and admired by the Government of Baden, by his colleagues, by the students of every faculty, and it was but a slight token of this feeling that made him Pro-Rector of Heidelberg University as early as 1862.

The discourse which he delivered on this occasion (November 22, 1862), 'On the Relation of the Natural Sciences to Science in General,' was a model of style, and contained a wealth of ideas and points of view which he enlarged on and enriched on various subsequent occasions, and which were frequently utilized by others as the foundation of their efforts at organization. In contrast with the one-sided view of many scholars, knowledge does not seem to him the sole aim of mankind upon this earth. Even if the sciences evoke and educate the finer energies of man, it is in action alone that he finds a worthy destiny; his goal must be the practical application of his knowledge, or the enlargement of science itself, which again is an act that promotes the welfare of mankind. But it is not enough to have a knowledge of facts in order to collaborate in the progress of science: science consists in the unveiling of laws and the discovery of causes. If science aims at the predominance of mind over matter, it is none the less the duty of educated men to recognize the equality of both, and to distinguish them only by their content. If the physical sciences have been more perfected as regards their scientific form, the mental sciences which resolve the human mind itself into its different activities and impulses treat of richer material, more closely knit with the interests and emotions of man.

Such knowledge, however, is slow to make its way; before his death, Helmholtz was lamenting in his congratulatory address to the Academy at Berlin on the Jubilee for the fiftieth year of his friend du Bois-Reymond's doctorate, that a great gulf still divides the philosophical and historical interests in our nation (as in all civilized Europe) from those of natural science and mathematics; the two worlds hardly understand each other's aims in thought and work, and this is a serious hindrance to salutary co-operation, and to the concordant development of mankind. It is for this reason that Helmholtz advocates the increase of popular scientific lectures in the best sense, as a means of harmonizing the different scientific views, since it is not so much information about the results of these discoveries that is demanded by the more intelligent and cultured of the laity, but rather 'some idea of the mental activities of the scientific investigator, of the particular character of his scientific methods, his aims, and the new solutions which his work offers for the great mysteries of human existence'.

Helmholtz only alludes in passing to the question of instruction, which afterwards became of such burning importance; he gives the preference to classics over modern languages in the education of the young, on account of its fine aesthetic and logical training, and in discussing the question whether mathematics, as 'the representative of self-conscious logical activity', should not be made more important in school studies, he expresses himself in favour of this, since the individual will presently have to graduate in sterner schools of thought than that of the grammarian.

Helmholtz tried to define the characteristic difference between the physical and the mental sciences more particularly, by saying that the physical sciences for the most part reduce their inductions to definite and universal laws and theorems, while the mental sciences are chiefly concerned with inferences from the psychological sense of touch. In the preface to his translation of Tyndall's *Fragments of Science* he describes in clear and beautiful language the importance of the classics in the development of a moral and aesthetic sense, and in the evolution of an intuitive knowledge of human sensations, ideas, and conditions of civilization: but he denies that the exclusively literary method of education is the most important function in the methodical training of that faculty 'by which we subject the unorganized material, governed as it would seem more by chance than by reason, which we encounter in real life, to the systematizing concept, whereby it is rendered capable of being expressed in words'. He finds in the simpler relations of inorganic nature an instrument for the systematic development of a train of ideas, comparable with 'no other human invention in respect of its congruity, certainty, exactitude, and fecundity'.

In the Academic Discourse he insists on the incontrovertible fact that even if the antithesis between the moral and the physical sciences had been unduly emphasized by Hegel and Schelling, it had a real basis in the nature of things, and must be taken into consideration. In comparing the different physical sciences one with another, he points out the great advantage which the experimental sciences have over those which depend on observation in the investigation of the universal laws of nature, since they can arbitrarily modify the conditions under which the effect ensues, and may therefore limit themselves to quite a small number of characteristic observations, in establishing the validity of any law. He demands of experimental and mathematical science that it shall strive after the attainment of laws, to which there are no exceptions, 'since it is under this form alone that our knowledge prevails over space and time, and the forces of nature.' Thus he regards the Law of Gravitation as the greatest logical achievement of the human mind, but finds absolute certainty of inference in mathematics alone; there no authority is paramount other than pure reason, and the whole of science is constructed from the fewest axioms.

'In mathematics we see the conscious, logical activity of our mind in its purest and most complete form; we can here appreciate its travail as a whole—the precaution with which it must advance, the accuracy that is necessary in order to determine the exact import of the acquired general propositions, the difficulty of forming and of understanding abstract concepts—while at the same time we learn to put confidence in the certainty, the scope, and the profit of such intellectual labour.'

At this time Helmholtz was busying himself with difficult questions in physiological optics, and more particularly with the construction of the Horopter, while the issue of the *Lehre von den Tonempfindungen* (*Theory of the Sensations of Tone*) was completed by the end of 1862, and on December 14 Helmholtz writes to Thomson: 'I am much interested in the two papers you announce on the cooling of the earth, and the alterations of form in elastic spherical shells, which may conceivably have reference to the earth also, since I am now engaged on some lectures to the students of all faculties on the general results of natural science, in which I want to give a popular exposition of the law of the conservation of energy and its consequences, and to use it as a connecting thread to draw the different branches of the physical sciences together. I have so far given the history of the planetary system of the sun and earth, and convinced myself that many problems have been neglected by the astronomers and geologists, which might well be attacked now, under the present conditions of knowledge, though only by those who are trained physicists and mathematicians. Your undertaking to write a Textbook of Natural Philosophy is very praiseworthy, but will be exceedingly tedious. At the same time I hope it will suggest ideas to you for much valuable work. It is in writing a book like that, that one best appreciates the gaps still left in science.

'My book on acoustics is just out, with the title *Die Lehre von den Tonempfindungen, als physiologische Grundlage für die Theorie der Musik* (*On the Sensations of Tone, as a Physiological Basis for the Theory of Music*). The publisher has already informed me that the copy I intended for you has been sent to your address in Glasgow. The issue of this book and the pro-rectorial business that has devolved on me this year have taken up so much of my time that I have not been able to attend to anything else. Now I have gone back to the completion of my *Physiological Optics*, one section of which is still wanting.'

In his *Sensations of Tone* Helmholtz set himself the task of connecting the border-land of physical and physiological acoustics with that of the science of music and aesthetics, so that he leaves out of consideration pure physical acoustics, which is merely a part of the theory of elastic bodies. Following the principle he had adopted for the work on optics, he divides his physiological acoustics into three parts, the first of which is occupied with determining the mode in which sound is conducted to the sensory nerve within the ear, and contains the physical part of the corresponding physiological investigation of the sensations; the second, and more especially physiological part, treats of the excitation of the nerve itself, in correspondence with different sensations; and the third, and more essentially psychological, section endeavours to lay down the laws by which the ideas of definite external objects, or percepts, result from these sensations. The physical and mathematical basis of auditory sensation forms the subject of a later very interesting work, which is, however, intelligible only to mathematicians, while the physiological factors in audition, along with the psychological and aesthetic considerations, are submitted to a remarkable, and, for the most part, easily intelligible analysis in the work itself.

Part I, which treats of the composition of vibrations, the theory of over-tones, and that of timbre or quality of sound, presents, along with Part II, which deals with interference in harmony, combinational tones and beats, consonance and dissonance, an admirable and masterly treatise, popular in the best sense, with a penetrating analysis, and an exposition, illustrated by a wealth of new experiments, of the results already published by Helmholtz in his separate papers. He gives a precise account of the theory and construction of his harmonium with naturally just intonation, and shows how the siren of Cagniard-Latour, perfected by Dove, had now developed into his polyphonic siren. The first two parts of this unique work accordingly deal with such phenomena as are mechanically determined by the construction of the ear, and are therefore independent of volition, so that it is possible to determine the exact laws by which they are governed. Part III, which is eminently original, magnificently planned, and admirably carried out, deals with the relationship of musical tones, and with scales and tonality, and enters the region of aesthetics in order to establish the elementary rules of musical composition.

'The relations between the physiology of audition and the theory of music,' he said on a later occasion, 'are particularly clear and striking, because the elementary forms of musical composition depend far more essentially on the nature and individuality of our sensations than is the case with the other arts, in which the kind of material utilized and the objects to be represented have a much greater influence.'

Starting from the conviction acquired in the course of his

historical studies of the development of music, that the system
of scales and modes, and the harmonies built up from them,
do not rest merely on unalterable laws of nature, but are at
least in part the consequence of aesthetic principles, which
have been modified with the progressive development of
Humanity, he shows that music, like architecture, has evolved
along essentially distinct lines.   He distinguishes three principal
periods in the art of music—the homophonous (univocal) music
of Antiquity, with which we may connect the existing music
of Oriental and Asiatic peoples; the polyphonous music of the
Middle Ages, multivocal, but as yet having no regard to the
independent musical significance of harmony, which persisted
from the Tenth to the Seventeenth Century; and lastly modern
or harmonic music, characterized by the independent significance of harmony as such, which originated in the Sixteenth
Century.   The demonstration and deduction of this classification
for the history of music in all nations is not only one of
Helmholtz's greatest titles to fame, but is for all time an
admirable instance of the way in which it is possible to
connect historical with scientific investigation.

Even in his earlier works he had shown that the over-tones
play a great part in musical composition as regards harmony,
but that the law which determines the melody of harmonious
combinations of tones is unconscious, since, though the over-
tones are perceived by the nerves, they do not come under the
heading of conscious representations, although their consonance
or dissonance is none the less felt.   Harmony and discord
are but the means to the higher spiritual beauty of music,
while the melody expresses a movement of which the character
is plain and obvious to the direct perception of the hearer.
Since the degrees of the motion must be exactly measurable
to direct sense-perception by their velocity and magnitude,
melodious movement is for Helmholtz merely alteration of
pitch in time, and since the eye may follow a continuous
movement, while the ear fails to do so, inasmuch as it has
no capacity for retracing the path correctly and comprehending
it as a whole, melodic progression must advance by easily
estimated and definite stages.   In the music of all peoples the
alteration of pitch in melodies takes place by successive steps,
and not by a continuous progression: in both melodic and

harmonic music sounds with harmonic over-tones are preferred, and to produce a good musical effect there must be a certain moderate intensity of the five to six lowest partial tones along with a low intensity of the higher partials, which confirms the significance of the over-tones for melody also. He sums up his results by saying that in music the more or less harmonic effect of the intervals in melody and harmony is connected with the special sensible phenomena of the over-tones, which limit the harmonic intervals the more plainly and exactly in proportion as they are just and simple.

In treating of the difficult question of scales, for which he had previously developed the essential principles, he proposes the law of the relationship of musical sounds. He defines sounds as related in the first degree when they have two common partial tones, and in the second degree when they are both related in the first degree to the same third tone, so that the strength of the relation depends upon the strength of the common over-tones, and on this ground of the natural relationship of tones to one another he develops the scales, although he admits that they were not exclusively derived from the law of relations of tone in all epochs, so that it was to some extent an arbitrary principle of style.

Helmholtz's theory of scales, and of harmony and melody, threw light on some of the darkest and most difficult points of general aesthetics, and showed that these considerations were closely allied to the doctrine of sense-perception, i. e. to physiology, while the aesthetic analysis of complete musical works of art, and the comprehension of the reasons of their beauty, seemed to him still to be stopped by apparently insuperable obstacles. He subsequently affirmed on various occasions, as in his Goethe Lecture at Weimar, that it was a mistake to suppose that any aesthetic investigations could lead to the discovery of rules for the guidance of artists.

'The real difficulty lies in the complexity of the psychical motives that here come into play. It is indeed at this point that we reach the most interesting part of musical aesthetics . . . since in the last resort we are seeking to explain the marvel of the great works of art, the expressions and impulses of the different psychical temperaments. Attractive, however, as the goal may be, I would sooner leave these inquiries, in which

I feel myself too much of a dilettante, to others, and remain on the firm ground of natural science to which I am accustomed.'

This splendid work, which was intended for the instruction of an extensive public in the literary world, was widely read, but could be understood as a whole only by a chosen few, since not a little training in physics and even mathematics was indispensable for its real appreciation. On February 27, 1864, Helmholtz writes to Ludwig, in answer to his expressions of amazement at the stupendous production :—

'I am delighted that you are satisfied with my *Sensations of Tone*, because you are one of the few musical men of science who I can hope will succeed in understanding the whole. The book appears to me so far to have had rather a *succès d'estime*, than any real effect in convincing people. Not that I had ever cherished any illusions to the contrary. At all events I see that it has made an impression, and venture to hope that it will gradually win its footing.'

While his *Sensations of Tone* was passing through the press, Helmholtz had occupied himself almost exclusively with problems in physiological optics, and was now engaged, in connexion with his work on the horopter, upon a series of ingenious experiments, and a profound mathematical analysis of the very difficult subject of the movements of the eye, and their relation to binocular vision, in which he referred all the theorems previously discovered by himself and others to one single law, that of the simplest orientation in space. He published these researches at length in Graefe's *Archiv f. Ophthalmologie*, with the title, 'On the Normal Movements of the Human Eye.' After it had been proved by Donders' experiments that the purpose of single binocular vision is not promoted by the movements of the eye, Helmholtz endeavoured to find an optical law for eye-movements, starting from the conviction that an organ so well adapted to its functions as the eye, must fulfil some optical aim in these movements also. He arrived at this law by a further development of that of simplest orientation. He connected the proposition that every given position of the line of vision corresponds with a given degree of rotation of the eyeball, with the question how the latter is retained during its movements, or how it has become possible for the eye to remain accurate in its orientation when the fixation point in the visual field is moving. To obtain a definite answer to this, the further question (of great importance to optics and the theory of knowledge) must be considered: how it comes about that in the movement of the eye, owing to which the light impression varies constantly at each point of the retina, our inference should be that in spite of this variation of all the luminous impressions there is no displacement nor alteration of the object, but only a motion of the eye; it is obviously sufficient if this inference obtains for infinitely small displacements of the eye. But in order to convince ourselves that every alteration of the image upon all points of the retina collectively depends on the altered position of the eye alone, and not on any change of the object in the field of vision, we must fulfil the condition in virtue of which the transition of any point of the image from the retinal fovea to a definite point on the retina at infinitesimal distance, can only occur by rotation round a given axis, which is unalterable relatively to the eye.

It follows from the law of simplest orientation and from the well-known theorem of mechanics, according to which the axial directions of infinitely small revolutions are compounded by the law of the parallelogram of forces, that the movement of the point of fixation to any second point of the visual field at infinitely small distance, must be caused by its revolution round an axis lying in a given plane, which is unalterable in relation to the eye. Now since the axes of rotation for all the movements which occur lie in one plane, no infinitely small rotation of the eye can produce a rotation of the same round the line perpendicular to this axial plane, which Helmholtz terms the atropic line of the eye. But since rotations of finite magnitude can obviously not be compounded by this mechanical law, the necessary condition for the maintenance of orientation in the visual field is not altogether fulfilled in the movements of the eye. Hence we must look for a law of eye-movements which makes the sum of all the deviations from this principle a minimum.

Helmholtz now arrived quite unexpectedly at the law which Listing had already expressed without giving any reason for it.

If we call that position of the eye, from which all infinitely small movements of the eye occur without rotation round the visual line, the primary position, and all others secondary positions, then the position of the eye may be found at any given secondary position if it is moved from the primary to the secondary position by rotation round an axis, which is perpendicular to the primary and secondary directions of the line of vision. The great importance of this axiom only became apparent through the interpretation given by Helmholtz of Listing's law as the solution for a minimum of the given form.

In the closing words of this fundamental paper he says, ' I therefore believe that the law of the movements of the eye, as explained above, is acquired by the use of the eyes, in which we are continually proving the need of the most exact orientation possible, and that the deduction I have made from this need is in the last resort the origin of the law. We should expect that the development of the muscle would eventually enable these movements of the eye, as required by the need of orientation, to be effected with the least possible exertion. The movements of the eye are controlled by the habit arising from the need of orientation, and I do not see the necessity of seeking for anatomical contrivances to account for the law of these movements.'

The fatigues of his year of office, his lectures, the laboratory, and above all his unbroken scientific work had so affected Helmholtz, that his physician Friedreich urged him at the beginning of the summer holidays to travel, in order to recuperate himself as soon as possible. On August 29, 1863, he writes from Heiden (Appenzell) to Donders: 'As last year's cure at Kissingen was not much good, Friedreich ordered me this summer to drink whey, which I have been doing here at Heiden, and am now going off to the mountains with my colleague Bunsen. I am to meet him on September 3 at Amsteg, and we intend to go round about the Gotthard to Disentis, Airolo, the Tosa Falls, and the Eggischhorn. It is a sad moment when a man is first compelled to become a hypochondriac, and to pay so much attention to his health.'

The scientific work of the ensuing winter was again devoted entirely to the *Physiological Optics*, Part III of which was once more to include a number of highly complicated problems; at the same time he was occupied with numerous public lectures.

'This winter,' he writes on February 27, 1864, to Ludwig,

'I have had to serve the Public and Mammon, and to treat the Conservation of Energy as the milch cow. I have given eight lectures on it in Karlsruhe, and am preparing to do the same in London at Easter in English. I always look on a journey to England as a kind of intellectual "cure", which shakes one out of the comfortable indolence of dear old Germany into more active life, and lectures such as I gave there once before are a good means of establishing closer working relations with the English men of science.'

In 1863 the families of Helmholtz and Kirchhoff moved into the new 'Friedrichsbau', which for those days was a fine and roomy group of buildings, containing laboratories, lecture-rooms, and dwellings for the staff. Helmholtz's house was always the centre of a delightful society, where plain living and high thinking were the order of the day. He had formed close friendships with his colleagues, Kirchhoff, Bunsen, and Zeller, while the Helmholtz family was in intimate social relations with those of von Vangerow, Haeusser, Gervinus, Friedreich, Kopp, Wattenbach, and others. Under these improved conditions he was able to attend more to his children, and personally superintended the education of his son Richard, who had entered the Heidelberg Gymnasium in 1862.

The latter writes: 'With regard to the intercourse between my father and his children, it was chiefly at meals and out walking that we saw him. In bad weather we went by the Rohrbacher Landstrasse, otherwise generally to the Wolf's Höhle, Gaisberg, Sprung, Philosophenweg, &c. It gave him keen pleasure to show us any natural phenomenon; I shall never forget one autumn morning of thick fog, when he saw there would be sunshine up above, and took us by the Sprungweg, to show us the rolling, sharply defined sea of mist, with only a few spires rising out of it. In the winter of 1862 my father taught me to draw with mathematical instruments, and in 1863 essayed to teach us the elements of thorough-bass, which succeeded very well with my sister at any rate.'

In the Easter holidays Helmholtz spent some weeks in England, staying on the way in Utrecht with his friend Donders, whom he found 'as blooming, affectionate, and poetical as ever', and in whose house he passed several very pleasant days.

On March 14 he writes to his wife: 'We went to a smoking-concert, i. e. to the rehearsal for the great orchestral concerts, where they give certain *soli* that are left out in the concert proper, and which the gentlemen of Utrecht listen to over their wine and cigars. I heard the *Symphonic Preludes* of Lizst, which are effective and extraordinary enough, but hardly beautiful; the *Oberon* Overture was very good, and as a piano solo in between we had the *Variations Sérieuses* of Mendelssohn, in the style of church music, which were very fine, and which I recommend you to study. Donders had been giving public lectures here on Acoustics, so that my book on the *Sensations of Tone* is known to every one, even to the musicians. O. Jahn could not understand it, but hoped to study it with G., and told me he had had an enthusiastic letter about it from Claus Groth.'

He went on through Brussels to London, and received a warm welcome from his friend Bence Jones. He sent a full report of his doings to his wife, some of which are interesting enough to transcribe.

'I have cast myself into the whirlpool of the great Babylon, and so far am swimming merrily. After writing to you at the Royal Institution, where I waited in vain for Tyndall, I went up to see Faraday, who lives there. He was as charming as ever, but has given up his lectures, as his memory is failing him; and the general impression that he makes on one is less acute than it was formerly. . . . Then I went on to the meeting of the Royal Society, where Tyndall was giving an address on some new and very ingenious experiments he had made, the interpretation of which, however, gave rise to much discussion. After arranging with Prof. Stokes to be in Cambridge the Friday after Easter I went at eleven o'clock to a party at Mr. Gladstone's, the Minister. . . .

'Yesterday I did more work; in the morning I wrote part of my Croonian Lecture; at twelve o'clock I met Prof. Tyndall at the Royal Institution, to get things together for my first two lectures; for the second of these I have made an original drawing in water colours, which represents a sunbeam seen from the side, and vies with Turner in its clouds and the boldness of the colour. . . . On Wednesday I worked in the morning, and then went to the College of Surgeons, to see Mr. Huxley,

Professor of Zoology, who is just now the chief partisan of Rationalism against the Biblical view of Science, a most intelligent young man, whom I had met before. . . .

'Yesterday morning I went to Oxford, and am staying with Max Müller. He is a clever young man of the world, whose like I have never yet seen in a professor of philology, and grasps everything, even the scientific matters with which he is less familiar, with extraordinary rapidity. His wife is an English lady, who is also most attractive, well-informed, and pretty, so that I spent two very pleasant days there. Oxford is probably unique of its kind in the world; its many old, and characteristic-ally beautiful, and well-preserved buildings, with trim grass lawns and handsome trees, are all stately to a degree, and very magnificent. It is quite impossible to picture it at home until one has seen it, and I now understand the devotion of an Englishman to his University. The system works admirably for the education of "gentlemen" but it cannot lead to much in science, and it needs an extraordinary interest in science to prevent a Fellow from sinking into indolence. My journey to Glasgow went off very well. The Thomsons have lately moved to live in the University Buildings; formerly they spent more time in the country. He takes no holiday at Easter, but his brother James, Professor of Engineering at Belfast, and a nephew who is a student there, were with him. The former is a level-headed fellow, full of good ideas, but cares for nothing except engineer-ing, and talks about it ceaselessly all day and all night, so that nothing else can be got in when he is present. It is really comic to see how both brothers talk at one another, and neither listens, and each holds forth about quite different matters. But the engineer is the most stubborn, and generally gets through with his subject. In the intervals I have seen a quantity of new and most ingenious apparatus, and experi-ments, of W. Thomson, which made the two days very interest-ing. He thinks so rapidly, however, that one has to get at the necessary information about the make of the instruments, &c., by a long string of questions, which he shies at. How his students understand him, without keeping him as strictly to the subject as I ventured to do, is a puzzle to me; still, there were numbers of students in the laboratory, hard at work, and apparently quite understanding what they were about.

'Thomson's experiments, however, did for my new hat.   He had thrown a heavy metal disk into very rapid rotation ; and it was revolving on a point.   In order to show me how rigid it became in its rotation, he hit it with an iron hammer, but the disk resented this, and it flew off in one direction, and the iron foot on which it was revolving in another, carrying my hat away with it and ripping it up.

'I got to Manchester on April 4 ; the Roscoes live outside in a charming cottage at the edge of a great park.   Roscoe had two friends to dinner Mr. Joule, a brewer and the chief discoverer of the conservation of energy, and his colleague, Clifton, a physicist, who were both very pleasant, lively individuals, so we spent a most interesting evening.   On Sunday morning we were alone after breakfast, and boldly planned out new ventures in physical chemistry : we discussed the English Universities, and were both of the same mind.

'Yesterday, in London, I went to see Mr. Graham, the Master of the Mint, one of the first English chemists, who took me round himself and explained everything to me.   I was the most interested in Graham's own laboratory, where he showed me a quantity of marvellous new experiments, and presented me with coins, instruments, and chemicals.   Then I went with an old Berlin friend to Kensington, to see Prof. Clerk Maxwell, the physicist at King's College, a keen mathematician, who showed me some fine apparatus for the Theory of Colours which I used to work at ; he had invited a colour-blind colleague, on whom we experimented.'

These many-sided interests, and the absorbing work of preparing his Croonian and other lectures, were darkened by the first shadow of the fatal illness of his son Robert.   But his wife worded her letters so as to keep Helmholtz from any immediate return to Heidelberg, and he hoped that his own advice and that of the friendly physicians attending the boy might avert the danger.

On April 14, 1864, Helmholtz gave his Croonian Lecture to the Royal Society, 'On the Normal Motions of the Human Eye in relation to Binocular Vision,' in which he sketched out his conclusions in regard to the horopter, and the movements of the eye.

'It was ten before I had finished the first part of my lecture.

I broke off and left the tribune. But it was decided, at the motion of General Sabine as President, that I should go on speaking, and so I held forth on the movements of the human eye, and their relation to visual perception, till half-past ten, when I had pretty well done. It comforted me, however, to see that several gentlemen rose after me, and made some confirmatory observations. Sabine proposed a vote of thanks, in which he praised my facility in English. I fear it flowed rather like a mountain torrent from my lips, but I could hardly speak at all at the end.'

During his four-weeks' stay in England he also delivered six popular lectures in London, 'On the Conservation of Energy'; the full report of which was sent to du Bois-Reymond from Heidelberg on May 15, with the news that a daughter had been born on April 24, who received the names of Ellen Ida Elizabeth :—

'I stayed six weeks in England, most of the time in London ; during Easter Week I went also to Oxford, Glasgow, and Manchester. I saw a great deal that was interesting, and find an occasional visit to London both pleasant and inspiring. As to the popular lectures at the Royal Institution, I quite agree with you that one would have to think a good while before undertaking them again. I had no reason to be dissatisfied with the apparent results in my own case, for I had a steady audience of three hundred, and among them a number of scientific men. But the competition of popular lectures in London is so great that they are on the verge of degenerating into a mere shop-window display. Tyndall, as a matter of fact, has a vast talent for popular discourses, and is much appreciated by his public. A spirit-rapping medium recently spelt out his celestial name, which was "Poet of Science". . . . As I found the general opinion to be that your experiments were too subtle to come off as a certainty, I took the opportunity of showing a few of your fundamental demonstrations at my last lecture.'

The year 1865 brought Helmholtz a number of honours from various sides : but what gratified him more than any of these was the fact that a second edition of the *Sensations of Tone* was called for, scarcely two years after its first publication. His friend Ludwig was again the first to whom, in February 1865, he sent the second edition of his book. While he expressed renewed admiration of the author's marvellous genius, Ludwig felt that he must protest against the following passage: 'Among our great composers, Mozart and Beethoven are only at the beginning of the period in which equal temperament predominated. Mozart still had opportunities of making extensive studies in the composition of songs. He is a master of the sweetest melody, wherever he desires it, but in this he is almost the last. Beethoven's bold genius took possession of the domain which the development of instrumental music brought him; in his hands it was the pliant and appropriate tool which he was able to manipulate as none else had ever done. But he always treated the human voice as a handmaid, and consequently it never lavished the highest magic of its melody upon him.'

Ludwig took umbrage at this view, and on March 30, 1865, Helmholtz replies: 'In your last letter from Leipzig you attack my remarks on Beethoven. Perhaps I had better not have expressed myself merely critically about him, if I did not wish to be misunderstood, for I too find him the mightiest and most moving of all composers, and I myself play hardly anything but Beethoven, when I do play. Had I been speaking about the vehicle of musical emotion, I should certainly have placed him above all others. I was, however, talking exclusively of melody, and the fine artistic beauty of the flow of harmony, and there I do hold Mozart to be the first, even if he does not affect us so powerfully. Speaking generally, as one grows older, and bears more scars within one's breast, one ceases to feel that emotion is really the greatest thing in art.'

The objections urged by Helmholtz's gifted friend Fechner, in a letter of June 6, 1869, were more serious and of greater import:

'You explain the melodic no less than the harmonic relations of tones by the presence of over-tones, and if I grasp your meaning rightly, though I am not quite sure about this, in the absence of over-tones the difference between the pitch of two notes would be like the difference between their intensity, so that we should lose all the characteristic and gradual degrees of relationship and disparity between the tones which are known to us as melodic. An octave appears so like the fundamental, because the latter contains all the partial tones of the octave in its over-tones; the fifth is less similar, because the coincidence in this respect is less perfect, and so on. This idea is so simple,

and fits in with the facts of tone-relations in ordinary instruments so well, that the problem seems to be solved by it.   But
I am not prepared to admit that this relation of the octave to the
fundamental is the cause of the melodic relation of the tones, which
appear in all cases, just as plainly in the tones of rods, plates,
and bells, as in those of stringed instruments and the human
voice, notwithstanding that in instruments of this kind, according to your observations, the over-tones may be musically
speaking neglected, or, if they were taken into consideration,
would necessarily produce quite different melodic relations. . . .'

Helmholtz replied on June 3:—

'(1) A weak accompaniment of harmonic over-tones is inevit-
ably present, at least in all *strong* simple tones.   They arise from
the same law as combination tones, partly accidentally outside
the ear, partly in regular series within the ear, as often as the
vibrations become so great that the elastic forces are no longer
exactly proportional to the displacements.   I proved by my
work on the mechanism of the auditory apparatus (*Pfl. Arch. f.
Phys.* Vol. I), that the conditions for this are especially favourable inside the ear, so that there may even be a clashing of
tones between the malleus and incus.

'I did not bring this out strongly enough in the first edition of
Sensations of Tone, and have made it plainer in the second
edition, the MS. of which has just gone to Vieweg, and will
shortly be in the printers' hands.   This unmistakably gives the
series of harmonic over-tones a new subjective meaning.   At
the outset I only characterized them as the series which
emerges in all *exactly periodic* vibrations that excite *persistent
and equal* sensations.

'(2) I believe, however, that a melody can be recognized, when
it is given out in *weak* simple tones, without evoking over-tones
of perceptible strength.   But on the other hand, I do not believe
that music would ever have been discovered if the relation of
tones and over-tones had always been lacking, as it is in colour.
Pitch of tone and intervals can be remembered and recognized,
even where the distinguishing marks, i.e. the over-tones, which
give the specific distinction from the adjacent tones, and on
which the immediate sensory recognition of their proper value
rests, are wanting.   Compare this with the case in which we
see an object that is usually red as white . . . in the latter case we

have an entirely new sensation that is otherwise wanting. But if the over-tones are absent in a melodic interval, we have no new perception; the only result is that a part of the sensation to which we are accustomed in greater or less intensity, which makes us more certain about the magnitude of the interval than our memory of it, is now wanting. But nothing new or unfamiliar appears in its stead. I might rather compare it with the binocular vision of an object, and that of a picture. The former, like a melody with over-tones, gives sensational data, which enable us to judge very definitely of the dimensions of depth; the picture, which does not give these, is like the melody without over-tones; but if we know the object well, we can form a lively conception of it, and under many conditions it is really hard to determine without direct experiment whether binocular vision actually assists our perception of depth or no. The essential point seems to me to be, that melody is the image of a movement, and that it is possible to measure the intervals by direct sense-perception. If we are able from memory to recognize any given interval, then in particular cases we can forgo the standards of measurement, without being altogether astray, even if the impression of the melody takes on somewhat of the weakness of the memory-image. On the other hand, I must say from my own experience, that tones with unharmonious partials (unless these be very weak, or very remote from the over-tone), give quite false melodies, which, however, can be recognized in memory as copies of the true melody. The principle you require in order to obviate the undifferentiated fusion of the over-tones, and also to give the relation of tones in melody, is, I think, provided by the fact (or hypothesis) that tones of different pitch affect different nerve-fibres.'

Helmholtz's researches in physiological optics were only interrupted for a very short time by his work on the formation of ice and glaciers. On February 24, 1865, he gave a lecture to the Nat. Hist. Med. Verein at Heidelberg, 'On some Properties of Ice,' in which he discussed the origin of the phenomenon known as the regelation of ice, while in the same month in a popular lecture 'Ice and Glaciers', which opened with a brilliant description of the glacier world, he went more closely into the question then so much discussed, of the movement of glaciers.

After the lecture du Bois writes to him on June 8, 1866:—

'You see that I am somewhat rabid—as usual, when I cannot hammer out my own work, and see others shaking one fine thing after another out of their lap. Our good Tyndall will be not a little astonished to find you a master of glacier problems also.'

In the lecture above referred to, which was published in the *Philosophical Magazine* for the following year, with the title 'On the Regelation of Ice', Helmholtz confirmed James Thomson's explanation of the phenomenon of the regelation of ice at zero, when two pieces of ice if pressed together freeze again and form one mass. He proves that the freezing-point is lowered with increased pressure, and points out, as against Faraday, that time is an essential factor in this phenomenon; he shows by a number of experiments that with strong pressure two pieces of ice can be united into one block by the freezing water at their surface of contact, while under weaker pressure it is necessary to wait longer, and the parts are correspondingly easier to separate again. He finds the plasticity of ice most marked in that which has been welded together by great pressure from snow, while the regular, crystalline ice can indeed be united by regelation, but only forms a mass of irregular pieces.

By applying these observations to glaciers, Helmholtz was able to explain the well-known and never properly interpreted phenomenon of the flow of ice in glaciers as a viscous mass. The ice mass of a glacier is everywhere permeated with runnels of water, so that its internal temperature is always at freezing-point, seeing that the water would freeze if the temperature were lower, and the ice would melt if it were higher. But a mixture of ice and water grows colder and colder in proportion to the pressure exerted upon it; as no heat is withdrawn, the free heat must become latent, and the ice in the mixture melts. The pressure exerted by the glacier mass, which forces the water out of the cracks, will, in Helmholtz's opinion, cause the compressed ice (since its melting-point is lowered by pressure, while the freezing-point of the non-compressed water is not lowered) to give ice which is colder than 0°, in contact with water at 0°. There will accordingly be constant congelation of the compressed ice-water round it, with the formation of new ice, while a portion of what is compressed melts simultaneously, and the ice itself moves as a viscous fluid mass.

The explanation which Helmholtz gave in his popular lecture, 'Ice and Glaciers,' of that mysterious and misinterpreted phenomenon the *Föhn* is very interesting, and the foundation of the whole theory of rainfall. When the warm air of the Mediterranean is driven northwards by the south wind, a portion of it is compelled to ascend the great mountain wall of the Alps. In consequence of the diminished pressure of the air it expands by about half its volume, is considerably cooled in temperature, and at the same time deposits the best part of its moisture as snow or rain. When the same air afterwards descends to the valleys and plains on the north side of the mountains as the *Föhn* wind, it is again condensed and grows warmer: thus the same current of air that is warm in the plains on either side of the mountains can be bitingly cold upon the heights, and deposit snow there, while it is insufferably hot in the plains.

The year 1865 brought a change in Helmholtz's domestic relations; his mother-in-law, Frau von Velten, took up her permanent abode at Dahlem, and during the long period that elapsed before her death in 1881, only once returned to Heidelberg, when, in 1874, she came to stay with her married granddaughter Käthe.

In the autumn vacation Helmholtz went as usual to Switzerland, where long and arduous excursions refreshed him in mind and body: but he was soon recalled to Heidelberg by disquieting accounts of the state of his son Robert. His wife again endeavoured to keep him away from home as long as possible:—

'Enjoy your journey thoroughly, and get your poor head well, dear Hermann, so that we may both be fresh and vigorous, if we are threatened with new illness. We must keep our courage up, if we are to pull through. Don't imagine that I am giving way; I am trying to keep well and cheerful, and scold myself for my faint-heartedness, when I think of you and your hatred of all exaggeration. . . .'

But after the diagnosis of the physicians Helmholtz could cherish no further illusions as to the nature of his child's illness, and returned direct from Geneva, stopping only a few hours in Freiburg, to listen once more to the strains of the organ which he had admired so much in bygone years:—

'The organ is truly wonderful, from the point of view of acoustics even more than from that of music. I confess that till now I had no suspicion of the effects that could be produced by such an instrument, in regard to mass and power, as well as to variety of timbre.'

Part III of *Physiological Optics* was to appear in the next year, 1866, and Helmholtz was constrained to hasten the publication of this last portion, in order not again to omit a mass of new results by other workers, in connexion with his own researches, as had occurred with the first two separately published sections. Great inconvenience had arisen from the fact of the work being published as a part of Karsten's *Allgemeine Encyclopädie der Physik.*

Du Bois writes: ' I never open your *Optics* without getting angry at your having let yourself in for fathering the still-born projects of Karsten, which in the first place damaged the circulation of the book, and in the second, compelled you to use a form that by no means makes it more lucid, or easier to understand. The colossal pages of the closest print, crammed with the most abstruse matter, give one no resting-place, and anything you have written hardly needs to appear in small print.'

It was not until the work had appeared independently as the *Handbook of Physiological Optics* that du Bois was able to write to him on April 25, 1867 :—

'The book will only produce the greatest part of its effect now, when it comes into the market freely, as a whole. In my own laboratory, for example, the young people like Rosenthal and Hermann hardly know it at all, since it is by no means the sort of book one can work through in the time for which one can decently borrow it.'

Helmholtz found it a severe task to incorporate the new matter, and to utilize it for Part III, and for his full Bibliography.

' How delightful the state of a learned theologian, jurist, or historian must be, who spends his whole life in bringing out new editions of the same book with minute alterations, while we poor men of science cannot get one work ready before the beginning of it is already out of date,' he complains to Donders: but he does not falter ; and most of the facts and theories that had become known were submitted to a searching criticism.

The whole of the year 1865 was thus devoted to the preparation of Part III of *Physiological Optics,* a gigantic task that tried his health severely. His persistent attacks of migraine obliged him to go to Engelberg for three weeks in the autumn, to drink whey. After a sharp walking tour through the Mont Blanc district the attacks became less frequent and less severe, but when he resumed his work, and more especially during the epistemological portions of it, his health once more suffered severely ; 'the attacks still make all occupation impossible, each onset robs me of twenty-four hours' work.'

His condition obliged him to take a fortnight's rest again during the Easter holidays, and he went to Paris, where he found a hospitable and affectionate welcome from his wife's uncle Julius von Mohl, the famous Orientalist. A short break in the journey was devoted to Strassburg, where he ascended the gallery of the Cathedral Tower, and gloried in the bold stonework. ' I looked into old Ulrich's riddle about the square and the octagon ; the solution is very simple.' He spent the first evening in Mohl's house, 'peacefully, and I hope with mutual satisfaction.' He sent full and interesting accounts of his daily doings by letter to his wife, who was familiar with Paris and all its striking personalities from her long stay with her aunt.

'. . . At eleven o'clock I had to be back for a breakfast with M. Hermite and the mathematician Prof. Smith from Oxford. It was said in course of conversation that there had been some notion of inviting me to go to Oxford as Professor of Physics. However, they could not offer more than £700 salary, which of course is more than we get in Heidelberg, but hardly enough to live comfortably in England. . . . So I think Prof. Max Müller was right to say he could tell them decidedly that I should not accept it. . . . M. Hermite was very complimentary to me, and introduced me to a M. Grandeau, who came to welcome me, and escort me to the École Normale, where the chemist, St. Claire Deville, a rising man of the first rank, received me very warmly. He took me into the Physical Department, where we had to pass through a class-room in which a lesson was being given in physics. I was presented to the scholars, and received with rounds of applause, since they are all, at least so I was told, well acquainted with my acoustical theories. . . .

' Grandeau and Laugel took me to the first of organ-builders, Cavallié-Col, who showed us his workshop, and then accompanied us to the Church of St. Sulpice, to inspect the largest organ in Europe, built by him, but on account of the service we were unable to do this properly; we are going to see it more thoroughly this afternoon. What I saw interested me greatly. M. Cavallié, who has raised himself from a working man to be a master-hand, is a most intelligent and original person. . . . At the concert at the Conservatoire we had a Symphony by Haydn, a piece from Beethoven's Ballet of *Prometheus*, and the whole of the music from the *Midsummer Night's Dream*, as well as a chorus of Bach, and Handel's *Hallelujah Chorus*. One hears better choral singing in Germany, but the perfection of the orchestra is unique of its kind. The oboes in Haydn's Symphony sounded like a gentle zephyr; everything was in perfect tune, including the high opening chords of the Mendelssohn Overture, that are repeated at the end, and generally sound out of tune. The *Prometheus* was the most enchanting melody, with the horns predominating. This concert, after the Venus of Milo, was the second thing of purest beauty that life can give. . . . I went with MM. Cavallié and Bussy to the house of a harmonium-maker, Mustel, who wanted to show me his latest invention, a *tuning-fork piano*, with sustained tones. This confirmed my theoretical assumptions, and produced no special effect, which fact, however, is of some importance for my theory. The advance in the construction of the harmonium was very striking; it was like a very perfect and easily responding piano, with every kind of contrivance in the mechanism, for bringing out the treble parts. I used this opportunity to preach the unequal temperament for the organ, and M. Cavallié seemed inclined to make the experiment. . . .

'On Wednesday I went first to M. Regnault's lecture at the Collège de France. I was in hopes of seeing him experiment, since he is one of our most famous experimenters, but he did not; he showed me his instruments, a collection renowned in the history of physics.

'I went to the École Normale, where MM. Grandeau and Deville had invited me, to visit the latter, and to see Herr König's instruments. To my surprise M. Duruy, the Minister of Instruction, also turned up with a member of his council, and they begged me to give him a lecture on the analysis of the vowel tones, which I did. . . .'

Returned from Paris, Helmholtz at once went back to the completion of his *Physiological Optics*, but was sorely disturbed in his task, which required much concentration, by the troubles in South Germany, consequent on the war between Prussia and Austria. A Prussian by birth, and devoted with his whole soul to his own father-land, he was greatly distressed by the position which Baden occupied, in consequence of the peculiar development of affairs. Helmholtz never courted extremes in religious and political matters; just as by education and conviction he was religious in the noblest sense, but never ecclesiastical in the orthodox signification, so while he had never taken an active part in politics, he had been from his youth up, owing to the traditions of his parents' house, and to his own clear and deliberate judgement, a Liberal in the best sense of the word, keeping clear of reactionary passions and radical agitations. The letters give us no indication of the political views which he professed in his youth during the heroic and stormy period of 1848 to 1849; the vicinity of his father enabled him to discuss the political situation by word of mouth with that old soldier of the Freiheitskampf, and his post as military surgeon naturally imposed upon him the greatest reserve in letters to his friends. But his youthful mind, inspired for all that was good and noble, was deeply shaken by the struggle of the nations for political unity and freedom.

'I know as an absolute truth,' writes his sister-in-law, 'that he sympathized in the conflict almost too passionately for the balance of his nature. On the day following March 18 he was in a passion of excitement, of which a little trait gave striking illustration. He came straight to us from Berlin on one of those days, and when I showed him my two-weeks' old infant for the first time, he beamed, and drew a red, black, and gold cockade out of his waistcoat pocket, fixed it on to the child's little cap, and congratulated the "citizen mother, on her first-born in freedom".' The quip was a sign of his passionate sympathy with the growing spirit of nationality. At a later period he followed the debates in the Paulskirche, the sad decline of the movement, and its final decay and extinction, with the completest and most heart-felt sympathy.

So in the tumult of the year 1866, he was in his enthusiasm for the unity and freedom of Germany entirely on the side of Prussia, in which he recognized the centre of power to which all must gravitate, if external equilibrium were to be maintained, and in this he was not deceived. His wife too, although she was of South German extraction, embraced the cause of Prussia with enthusiasm : on July 12 she writes to her mother, ' Every right-minded person is Prussian, since Austria has made this French alliance.'

Helmholtz's dearest wishes were fulfilled sooner than could have been anticipated, and he returned with fresh zest and courage to his great work on visual perception, which formed part of the *Physiological Optics*.

His earliest observations in optics and acoustics had taught him that besides the sensations of the nervous apparatus there enters into our sense-perceptions the further factor of a specific psychical activity, which co-operates in the representation of the external object that has excited our sensation. In his lecture on Kant he had already, in agreement with Lotze, treated the impressions made upon our sensory nerves as being merely the signs of certain external objects ; holding that correct inferences from the sensations to the corresponding objects had arisen through experience. His observations on the blind spot in the eye, on over-tones, &c., now brought in a new point—the recognition of a law that is valid for all our sense-perceptions, viz. that we attend to our sensations only in so far as they enable us to recognize external objects, while we do not analyse such sensations as have no direct relation with external objects, until we begin to investigate our impressions scientifically. Helmholtz now went on to the difficult problem of the nature of the correspondence between the percept and its object,—in other words, what kind of truth are we to ascribe to our ideas and perceptions ?

Just as the sensations of the eye, ear, and tactile sensibility are intrinsically so different that no comparison in regard to quality and intensity can be made between those of different senses (this is called a difference in the mode of the sensation, while the disparity between homogeneous sensations is described as one of quality): so the same is the case if a comparison between the percepts of psychical states (which Kant refers to a special sense, the innate or intuitive) and those of the eye or ear be attempted. Yet in spite of many differences they have one thing in common, that the percepts of the internal as of the external senses are arranged in time-sequence

by a persistent activity of memory, which makes it possible
to observe and recognize the regular repetitions of such
sequences of homogeneous percepts. Hence, even if the
qualities of sensation are merely intuitional forms, the sensations
themselves being only signs, the specific nature of which
depends entirely upon our organization, they still are signs
of something that exists or is happening, and thereby supply us with the law of this happening. Conformity in the
phenomenal may thus be accepted as unequivocal and actual.
If we give the name of substance to that which remains
identical, independent of all other things, through all changes
of time, and if on the other hand the persistent ratio between
alterable magnitudes is the law that binds them together, then
this law is all that we can perceive directly, while the concept
of substance must for ever remain problematical. 'It is only
the relations of time, space, equality, and those derived from
them, namely those of number, magnitude, and conformity,
in brief mathematical relations, which are common to both the
outer and the inner world, and in these we can actually strive
for complete correspondence of the percepts with the things
perceived.'

From this philosophical basis Helmholtz proceeds to develop
his Theory of Space-Perception, constructed from his conclusions in physiological optics. To the nativistic theory of
space-perception as enunciated by Johannes Müller, Helmholtz
opposes his empirical theory of vision. According to Müller
the retina itself is sensible in its spatial extension, this intuition
of space is innate, and the impressions excited from without
are referred directly to the corresponding points on the spatial
image of the organ : on Helmholtz's view our sensations are no
more than signs for external things and processes, which we
must learn to interpret by experience and practice. According
to the empiricist theory we have to learn the significance of
the local signs of sensation (such as are excited by the same
colour on different points of the retina), in reference to the
external world ; while on the nativistic theory, these local signs
are the direct intuition of spatial differences both in kind and
in degree. The theory of the stereoscope, simple vision with
both eyes, and a long series of other optical phenomena, give
' a remarkable confirmation of the assumption of the empiricist

theory, that spatial separation is, generally speaking, to be predicated only of such sensations as can be separated by actual movement from each other '. We learn to interpret the signs, by comparing them with the results of our movements and with the changes we can produce by means of the latter in the external world. According to Heimholtz the only difference between the inferences of the logicians and those of induction (the results of which become evident in the percepts of the external world as derived from experience) is, that the former can be expressed in words, while in the latter words are replaced by memory images of sensations. This region of the conceptional faculty combines only those sensory impressions which are not capable of expression in words ; 'in Germany we term this Cognition (*das Kennen*).'

The 1868 lectures on ' Recent Progress in the Theory of Vision ' were an amplification of certain points in *Physiological Optics*, in which Helmholtz with his accustomed brilliancy and perspicacity gathered up some details of general interest, which would have been overlooked in the larger work.

In describing the defects of the optical apparatus of the eye, he insists (in conformity with his empiricist attitude) 'that it is not the mechanical perfection of the sensory instrument that creates these marvellously true and exact impressions', and after discussing visual sensation, and the theory of colour, after-images, and contrast, he says: 'Whatever inexactness and incompleteness we may have found in the optical apparatus and retinal image, is as nothing compared with the incongruences which we encounter in the region of sensation. We are tempted to believe that Nature had advisedly perpetrated the wildest contradictions, and was determined to destroy all dreams of a pre-established harmony between the outer and inner world.'

In his Commemorative Lecture on Helmholtz, du Bois-Reymond remarks that 'just as the principle of the conservation of energy has been a safe clue to Helmholtz's train of thought in the preceding period, so in the later part we have a similar guide. The fundamental principle of these researches is the empiricist attitude, which Helmholtz favours in preference to the nativistic, which he rejected. This is the same contrast that obtained in the sixteenth century between Leibniz's pre-established harmony and Locke's sensualism, and to which Kant gave a decided turn in favour of the former doctrine'.

Even at this time, and far more forcibly later, Helmholtz declares himself in opposition to Kant, who affirmed that the law of causation, as well as the intuition of time, and of tri-dimensional space with its geometrical axioms, were of transcendental origin, *a priori* ideas, innate in us. At the same time Helmholtz was fully aware that his empiricist theory was, and would remain, no more than a hypothesis. He believed, however, that hypotheses are essential to action, and that every man must choose for himself according to his own ethical or aesthetic sense; experiment alone, in which 'the chain of causes runs through our self-consciousness', can be regarded critically, while observation, a process that ensues without our connivance, may be modified by physical and psychical causes. He was well aware that his hypothesis would meet with much contradiction, and was not surprised when du Bois wrote to him on April 28, 1868 :—

'The great objection to the strict empiricist attitude always seems to me to be that it ought to be possible to carry it through consistently, which, as you yourself admit, is not the case ; for if it is innate in the calf to go after the smell of the udder, why should not all its faculties be innate? It appears to me that so much nativism which one cannot get rid of is still left, that a handful more or less does not much matter. In regard to motion, for example, there are countless complicated cases in which we cannot get rid of it. You will say that one can at least try to limit it as far as possible, and that I do not deny. I must confess that on these points my craving for causality is capable of greater resignation than yours.'

Helmholtz subsequently answered all these objections in his lecture 'On the Facts of Perception', as follows :—

'To a great number of physiologists, whose views we might term nativistic, in contrast to the empiricist which I have myself endeavoured to defend, the conception of an acquired knowledge of the field of vision appears untenable, because they do not clearly realize what is so plain in the case of speech, namely, how much the accumulated impressions of memory can do. A number of different experiments have accordingly been made with the intention of referring at least some proportion of the visual perceptions to an innate mechanism, in the sense that definite sensations are supposed to set free definite, already formed, spatial conceptions. But the nativistic hypotheses in the first place do not explain anything; they only assume that the fact to be explained exists; in the second place, the assumption made by all nativistic theories, to wit, that already formed representations of objects are brought out by the organic mechanism, is far more dubious than the assumption of the empiricist theory that it is the raw material of sensations alone which depends on external conditions, while all ideas have to be formed from that in accordance with the laws of thought. In the third place the nativistic assumptions are unnecessary.'

Notwithstanding these arguments Helmholtz met with little sympathy even from the best and most sympathetic of the physiologists, who were not only, like du Bois, biased by a certain nativistic tendency, which made them averse to the consistent development of the empiricist hypothesis, but further objected to it on the ground that it did not seem to them compatible with the existence of sensory illusions. Donders objected to Helmholtz's hypothesis from the same point of view, and received the following answer, dated May 26, 1868:—

'I regard the publication of careful observations on the mode of vision of people who squint as very desirable and important (provided it is borne in mind that, from the nature of the thing, this may possibly not be constant). The statements we have hitherto had about it seem to me to be influenced throughout by preconceived ideas. And although for the time being you are still in the clutches of the nativistic theory, I have sufficient confidence in you (witness your experiments on stereoscopy with electric illumination) to believe that you set facts above theory. For the rest I am well aware that my empiricist theory is at present merely one of the possible aspects of the matter, and that facts may shortly be discovered that will render it impossible: when that happens it will have had its uses, and may disappear. Not indeed that I think this very probable as regards ideas and percepts. As to motor impulses, the case is rather different. Some such are truly and indisputably present in the new-born as much as in the grown person, and the possibility that certain combinations of movements are *a priori* easier than others is conceivable; this may be the case with the eye-movements also. But to speak of compulsion in these instances is beside the mark. All that I desire is *proof* that there is a natural disposition in favour of these movements.

'With all this confounded trafficking in hypotheses about invisible nervous associations, with all manner of inconceivable properties, which have checked the progress of the physiology of the central nervous system for so many years, I do believe it to be most important to open people's eyes to the number of superfluous hypotheses which they are making, and would rather exaggerate the opposite view, if need be, than proceed along these false lines. Reflex motion may at present be defined as everything in physiology which we can't explain. These are the disadvantages of an exaggerated materialistic metaphysic, from which people must be brought back to facts.'

Precisely because Helmholtz wanted to weaken the objections raised to his hypothesis on account of the existence of sensory illusions, he laid down as a rule in all illusions, that we always think we see such objects before us as would have to be present in order to bring about the same retinal images under normal conditions of observation; and he chose the name of unconscious inference for these processes, in which words are replaced by sensations and memory images, although these involve the same intellectual activity as the ordinary inferences. Even the supporters of the nativistic theory must, he insists, admit that the peculiar completeness and refinement of sensory intuition depend upon experience.

When Helmholtz was pursuing his acoustic researches upon the aesthetic side of sensations of tone, he proved that the forms of musical configuration depend more strictly than in the case of any other art upon the nature and idiosyncracies of our sensations. And in the lectures which he gave at Berlin, Düsseldorf, and Cologne, 1871–1873, on *The Relation of Optics to Painting*, he succeeded in establishing for painting (in which the nature of the material to be employed and of the objects to be represented have far more influence, though here too the specific sensibility of the visual organ is not without significance) that it is not only profitable for physiological optics that attentive consideration should be given to the works of the great masters, but, further, that the investigation of the laws of sensation and perception are useful to the theory of art, and to its right application.

Helmholtz came by the circuitous route of the physiology of the senses to his artistic studies, and compares himself 'with a traveller who has made his way into the lovely land of art, across a sterile, stony mountain barrier, but in so doing reached many points which gave him good views of the country below him'. He does not conceive it to be his task to furnish instructions by which the artist is to work, but would endeavour to understand the problems which he must solve, and the ways in which he attempts to arrive at his goal; 'the artist cannot transcribe Nature, he must translate her.'

But this translation is effected not by any conscious logical activity of the mind, but with the help of the most refined and accurate observation of sensory impressions, and of a specially exact memory for retaining these impressions, which (since what he can fix by hasty sketches at the moment is but scanty) must be more exact in regard to the details of the phenomenon than it is for the majority of people. In his *Sensations of Tone* Helmholtz had pointed out the extraordinary development of memory in musicians, who, without any notes before them, can execute countless compositions on their instruments; and it is in the relative importance assigned to memory that he places the main divergence in the paths of investigator and artist, as he says in his splendid Goethe Lecture at Weimar:—

' That which we can express in words can be fixed in writing ; it is only the first creative idea that must always be formed and emerge in the same way in both modes of activity, and this in the first instance can only happen after a fashion analogous to artistic intuition as the apprehension of a new law of nature.'

The first and greatest difficulty for the painter is to enable his spectator to estimate the depth of the objects represented in his painting, since the binocular vision of solid objects is here wanting. To this end he has to make a careful selection in arranging the perspective objects, their position and aspect, their light and shade ; above all, aerial perspective, or the artistic representation of the opacity of the air, will be his great help in indicating exactly the relative distances by the greater or less predominance of the colour of the air over the colour of the objects represented. In addition to the form of the objects, degrees of brightness have to be considered. Since it is impossible for the painter to depict the light and shade in a picture as they are presented in nature, he can only strive by his colours to produce the same impression upon the eye of the spectator. He does this unconsciously in virtue of Fechner's psycho-physical law, that within very wide limits of brightness differences of light-intensity, if they form an equal fraction of the total quantity of light compared, are equally distinct and therefore appear equal in sensation. The ratio of brightness is our only sensory sign of the lighter or darker coloration of bodies, and the painter therefore need but select in his colours the same ratio of brightness as is exhibited by the bodies themselves. But when the mean limits of Fechner's law are transgressed, then with lessened illumination the darker objects become more like the darkest, and with greater illumination the brighter objects become more like the brightest, and so in representing glowing sunshine the painter is obliged to make all objects almost equally bright, while in moonlight only the very brightest objects can be bright, and the others must be unrecognizably dark.

But the question of degrees of brightness is complicated by colour differences, since the scale of intensity of sensation is different for different colours. The phenomena of dazzle are weaker with increased brightness for red than for blue, and Helmholtz observed that even with a small proportional increase of intensity this was especially striking in the red and violet colours of the spectrum, so that with mixed colours very bright white appeared yellowish, dull white bluish in colour. The painter accordingly, to reproduce the impression of sunlit white with faint colours, must by an admixture of yellow in his white make this colour preponderate just as it would in actually brighter white.

Lastly, the phenomena of contrast also come under consideration. These cannot be represented in paintings as they are in the real objects, since the colours of pictures are not as bright and intensely luminous as they are in reality. The painter accordingly must represent an evenly illuminated surface as brighter where it is contiguous with a darker part, and darker where it impinges on what is bright. The artist again has to make an objective imitation of the subjective phenomena of the eye, such as the irradiation caused by its transparent but not perfectly clear media; while most of all, it is the harmony of colours that comes into question, since the reciprocal relations of the colours of a picture have much to do with the aesthetic enjoyment of it, and even strong colours can convey expression (in the artistic sense) of the most delicate alteration or illumination.

'What is the effect to be produced by a work of art, using this word in its highest sense? It should excite and arrest our attention, awaken a rich train of sleeping associations and correlated feelings into activity, and direct them to a common end, in order to unite all the features of an ideal type—which are lying scattered in our memory in isolated fragments, overgrown by a confused and fortuitous mass of ideas—into a vivid conception. We can only explain the frequent preponderance of art over reality in the human mind, by saying that impressions of the latter are always mingled with something that disturbs, distracts, and injures us, while in art the elements which are to produce the desired impression are gathered together and allowed to act without restraint. The force of the impression will, however, undoubtedly be stronger in proportion to the depth, refinement, and truth to nature of the sensory impression which is to arouse the series of images and the emotions associated therewith. Its effect must be prompt, certain, unequivocal, and exact, if it is to call up a vivid and powerful impression.'

After the publication of his *Theory of Sensations of Tone* and *Physiological Optics*, Helmholtz gave himself up more and more to problems in mathematical physics, and pure mathematics; the few physiological papers that he published were in connexion with his earliest work on the physiology of nerve, which had been pushed into the background of late years owing to the extraordinary output of his new work. He was so exhausted by his labours in physiological optics that he found himself reluctantly obliged to forgo the pressing invitation of Roscoe to attend the Meeting of the British Association, and set off in the autumn holidays of 1866 with his wife for Switzerland, where he met the Kirchhoffs and Bunsen. After a short journey through North Italy he returned a few weeks later to Heidelberg, to resume his nerve work, and if possible bring it to a conclusion, as his mind was busying itself over problems of quite another kind.   On February 6, 1867, he wrote to Wittich:—

'In regard to rate of transmission in nerve, I have been making some experiments myself this winter with one of my Russian laboratory assistants, which are not yet fully worked out, and which give about 34 m.; these, however, refer to the motor nerves of man, as I have recorded upon the myograph the muscular contractions of the ball of the thumb excited from the wrist and axilla respectively.   We spent a long time on the improvement of our method, but eventually obtained very good and concordant results, which are infinitely superior in regularity of effect to my old method.   I think one might apply it to many other questions, e. g. the supposed difference of velocity in different parts of the nerve.'

These experiments were complicated by the difficulty that an instantaneous excitation of the motor nerves of man is not transmitted in an absolutely unaltered form through any considerable length of nerve.   It is accordingly necessary to take precautions that the electric shock shall be so far weakened for the upper portions of the nerve that the contraction which it excites shall be of the same height and strength as the maximum of contraction excited from the lower point: the two instantaneous excitations of the nerve will then produce equal external mechanical effects, the delayed response on exciting the upper portion being referred solely to conductivity within the nerve. The curves recorded by the myograph indicate that weaker stimuli are propagated in nerve more slowly than stronger shocks, and three long series of experiments gave rates of transmission of about 31, 33, and 37 meters per second.

Owing to external circumstances the experiments were interrupted, and Helmholtz only took them up again three years later.   He showed in a paper published in 1870, from experiments undertaken with Fick's pendulum myograph, that the rate of transmission of the nervous impulse was more than twice as great in nerves at higher temperatures, e. g. in the arm, as at lower temperatures.

'This is a most extraordinary thing,' writes du Bois on April 4, 1870.   'Such a dependence on temperature is unheard of; one would suppose then that the velocities would be enormously increased in fever. It is excellent for you, and I rejoice that it explains your first statement of the 60-meter velocity.'

The continuation of these experiments, presented to the Academy on June 8, 1871, under the title 'On the Time necessary to bring a Visual Impression to Consciousness. Results of work done by Herr N. Baxt in the Heidelberg Laboratory', gave a further series of results that were very interesting, and of the greatest importance in optics. Since positive after-images last as long as 12 seconds under favourable conditions, and during this time the forms of the larger objects are still recognizable in them, there will always, even with the shortest duration of light-stimulus, be a certain time during which the observer is able by means of the after-image to perceive a series of details in the object viewed, for the observation of which the direct light-stimulus could have given no time. In order to ascertain the time that is necessary for recognizing a more or less composite visual image, the positive after-image must be so submerged in a new and powerful light impression, that it loses its value for perception.

Helmholtz had previously constructed the Tachistoscope, in which the observer looks at the object through the slit of a rotating disk for a very brief period, while the slit is immediately replaced first by a black and then by a brightly illuminated white sector, the illumination of which is designed to extinguish the after-image. With the help of this apparatus he found, as expressed in a definite numerical ratio, that large spatial differences in the field of vision, as well as large differences in brightness, were perceived more quickly than small ones; the influence of different figures used as objects was also strikingly evident, according as they were more or less well known, simpler or more complex. In conclusion Helmholtz appended another observation, which he had made much earlier. If he employed a persistently bright spot in the dark field before him as the fixation point he was able, without leaving this point of fixation, to direct his attention upon this or that portion of the dark field, even before its illumination by a spark, and then to see what appeared there.

'This fact seems to me of great importance, since it shows that what we term the voluntary direction of attention is a change in our nervous system, independent of the motions of the external movable parts of the body, whereby the excited state of certain fibres is preferentially transmitted to consciousness.'

These investigations speedily became the starting-point for the most important discoveries of modern psycho-physics. With them Helmholtz closed the series of his purely physiological investigations, and turned in the first place to the mechanics of physiology, and then almost exclusively to physics and mathematics, in which he once more did epoch-making work.

The results communicated by Helmholtz under the title of 'The Mechanics of the Auditory Ossicles' on July 26 and August 9, 1867, at Heidelberg, and at greater length in the year 1869, in *Pflüger's Archiv*, as 'The Mechanics of the Auditory Ossicles and of the Tympanum' (which dealt with the very complicated minute anatomy of the inner ear, and in which Helmholtz discussed the mechanism of the oscillations of the tympanum and small bones of the ear), were of supreme importance for the mechanics of physiological acoustics. Riemann, 'that unusually penetrating intellect,' had indicated in a note published after his death in the *Zeitschrift f. rationelle Medicin,* that the capital task of aural mechanics was to explain how the apparatus of the tympanic cavity was able to transmit such excessively fine gradations of aerial waves to the fluid of the labyrinth. He had constructed a theory to this end, based on the assumption that the tympanic apparatus conveyed the alterations of air pressure from moment to moment with exact fidelity, in a constant ratio of magnification, to the fluid of the labyrinth. Helmholtz, on the contrary (who had taken up this subject directly he had concluded his *Physiological Optics*, without knowing of Riemann's note), finds in his theoretical considerations that it is only necessary for exact perception that each tone of constant pitch should excite a sensation of the same kind and intensity as often as it recurs.

'Riemann's acoustic problem,' writes Helmholtz to Schering 'occupied me also for some time; the empirical solution as effected for the human ear is, as a matter of fact, different from what he supposed.' Starting from the assumption that had been merely suggested by Ed. Weber, that the auditory ossicles and the petrosal bone must be regarded as fixed incompressible bodies, and the endolymph as an incompressible fluid, in relation to the conduction of auditory oscillations, Helmholtz discusses the vibrations of the petrosal bone and endolymph, on the basis of Kirchhoff's theory of the conditions of equilibrium in an infinitely slender elastic rod, investigates the consideration of the anatomy of the tympanum, and proceeds farther to the form of a membrane stretched by air-pressure alone, with inextensible radial fibres.

The completion of this work, which is a model of the most delicate dissection, of the most ingenious physical methods, and of the profoundest mathematical analysis, took up the whole of the winter after Helmholtz had communicated its elementary details at Heidelberg in the summer of 1867. In August, 1867, he went to the Ophthalmological Congress held in Paris during the Great Exhibition, and gave a lecture '*Sur la Production de la Sensation du Relief dans l'Acte de la Vision Binoculaire*', in which he outlined some of the new work published in his *Physiological Optics*.

'Yesterday and the day before,' he writes to his wife on August 14, 1867, 'I spent the mornings at the Ophthalmological Congress, where they made a great deal of me. Graefe is here, but unfortunately neither Donders nor Bowman. I was solemnly received with acclamations by the Society, and then had to promise a lecture, which I delivered early yesterday morning in French, of course *ex tempore* as there was no time for preparation. . . . I was invited to the Society's Banquet at Véfour's; the first toast was proposed by Graefe in my honour, to which I had to reply, and later they toasted me again in a poem made by Bowman's friend Critchett, and seconded by a young Spaniard, in this style: " *L'ophthalmologie était dans les ténèbres, Dieu parla, que Helmholtz naquit—Et la lumière est faite!* " You will see I had to forget how to blush!'

All the letters written from Paris to his wife, who was on the Tegern See with the children, betray his regrets that she could not be with him, since her long residence there in former days would have led her to enjoy the stir of the Exhibition, and intercourse with all the distinguished persons staying there at the time, even more than he did himself.

' Still,' replies the wife, ' since God has cut our poor Robert off for ever from a normal existence, he must and will be our first charge. It was perhaps my greatest sorrow to forgo this journey with you, but that is a trifle in comparison with the long sad doom of half-existence. And every day convinces me that the future will never improve either for him or for us, although it is not much use talking about it.'

Helmholtz was obliged to go off to the mountains to recruit after the fatigues of Paris; 'the fêtes, &c. in the sultry heat were so exhausting that I began again to have the fainting fits, from which I had been free for some years.' On returning refreshed to Heidelberg a few weeks later, he plunged once more into his researches in mechanical acoustics, mathematical philosophy, hydrodynamics, and electricity. On November 19, 1867, he writes to Donders: 'For the moment I am waiting for new acoustic instruments, and am worrying over certain psychological questions, the principles of space-perception, and the psychical processes of sense-perception without words. I fancy one could make a better analysis of this last chapter than the philosophers have accomplished so far. . . . The French seem to be nibbling now at my *Sensations of Tone*, and to more effect at any rate than the German musicians.'

During this winter Helmholtz and G. Wiedemann conceived the notion of letting their wives undertake the translation of Tyndall's lectures on *Heat as a Mode of Motion*. The scientific portion of the book was to be carefully edited, and there was to be a preface written and signed by both. Some scruples of Wiedemann were set aside by Helmholtz in the words: 'My wife thinks there would be no harm in letting our friends know who did the translation; she thinks it would be more objectionable if the world supposed that you and I had wasted our time over such work.'

This translation appeared in 1871—that of Tyndall's commemorative paper on 'Faraday as a Discoverer' having been published the year before with an interesting preface by Helmholtz, in which he expressed his great veneration for Faraday in magnificent language. We have already seen how cordially Faraday welcomed Helmholtz on his repeated visits to England: 'the absolute simplicity, modesty, and untroubled purity of his disposition had a charm such as I have never encountered in any other man.' But in Helmholtz's determination to translate Tyndall's lecture the personal element was completely subordinated. He was not even swayed by his delight in describing how Faraday had with a mysterious instinct made the most pregnant discoveries in natural science, although he was unable subsequently to give any clear account of the train of ideas that led to them : Faraday's development rather appeared to him of the greatest general human interest for many theoretical questions in psychology, and for a number of practical problems in education, and he regarded it as a most interesting phenomenon that the man who had remained true to the pious faith of the small sect of his forebears, should have developed a philosophic vein, 'in virtue of which he ranks among the foremost in the general scientific thought of the age.' In characteristic language, Helmholtz (without direct allusion) sums up the total of the great researches which he himself had so ably shared in and initiated during the past thirty years of his life.

'After our era had destroyed the old metaphysical idols in its legitimate effort to render human knowledge above all the true image of reality, it was arrested by the traditional forms of the physical concepts of matter—force, atoms, imponderabilities—and these names became to some extent the new metaphysical catch-words of the very people who had seemed the most enlightened. It was these concepts that Faraday sought again and again, in his maturer work, to purify from whatever they still contained that was theoretical, and not the immediate and just expression of the facts.'

In the same year he also published the first volume of the German translation which he and Wertheim had made of Thomson and Tait's *Textbook of Theoretical Physics*, with a short preface by Helmholtz, in which he expresses the gratitude of the scientific world to William Thomson (Lord Kelvin), one of the most inventive and penetrating of thinkers, for admitting us to the laboratory of his thoughts, and unravelling for us the clues which had aided him in controlling and ordering the confused and refractory material with which he had to deal. He points out that in this work physical consistency was preferred to elegance of mathematical method. 'Perhaps when science is perfected, physical and mathematical order may coincide.'

The second part of Vol. I of Thomson's *Theoretical Physics* only appeared in 1874 (when Helmholtz and Wiedemann also published their translation of Tyndall's *Lectures on Sound*), with an introduction written at the end of 1875, entitled 'Critical'.

This contains an answer to the attacks made by Zöllner upon
Thomson and Helmholtz, which were a source of great annoyance and disturbance to the latter.

'One of the most painful moments in his rich and vigorous
life,' writes Blaserna, 'was the violent attack made by Zöllner
on him and other scientific workers. I could not understand
this till I heard that Zöllner had been converted to spiritualism
by that enterprising swindler, Slade. His hatred was thus
directed in the first place against Tyndall, who had embarked
on a vigorous campaign in England against spiritualism, and
then against Helmholtz, who had translated Tyndall's works
into German, and put his name to the translation. He often
talked about it; and we soon discovered that the solution of
the so-called spiritualist problems lay in legerdemain. Every
conjurer who came to Pontresina could reckon on patronage
from myself and Helmholtz. We sat in front, and there was
keen competition to see which of us would be the first to
explain one or other of the tricks. Often we succeeded, often
not. "It is a very pleasant mental gymnastic," Helmholtz used
to say, "and one never knows how it may come in useful some
day."'

Helmholtz expressed himself to the same effect in a little
pamphlet called *Suggestion and Imagination*, which he published
at a much later time. 'Dear Sir! I have never made any
scientific study of the question you propound to me. What
I know of it was learned accidentally. But I am familiar from long
experience with the thirst for miracles of the Nineteenth Century,
and the obstinacy with which such faith will overcome the most
obvious proof of gross deception; for my youth reaches back
into the days when animal magnetism flourished. Since then
there have been many different phases of the same trend of
thought. Each has only a short life; when the disillusionment
becomes too apparent, they merely change the method.

'If you ask why I have not gone into it more closely, I can but
reply that my time has always been taken up with work that
I believed to be of greater utility than the curing of marvel-
mongers who do not want to be cured. And on the other side
I must say that even if I had exposed the trick to myself, I could
hardly hope to make much impression upon the faithful. If
I had not succeeded I should have put a pretty argument into

their hands against myself. And as I cannot succeed in deciphering the greater part of the tricks exhibited before me by a skilful conjurer, I certainly could not undertake to interpret all the magnetic or spiritualistic or hypnotic wonders that any one may show me; the less so as the social position or sex of the confederates generally prohibits a really searching investigation; often enough too they will urge the ingenious excuse that the presence of an obstinate unbeliever has broken the spell.

'As far as I am personally concerned, it has always been the psychological phenomenon of credulity that has interested me in these matters, and I have therefore successfully adopted the rôle of impostor from time to time in table-turning or thought-reading, of course explaining afterwards that I had been the sinner.

'If after these explanations you are still interested in my private opinion, I can only say that I entirely agree with my friend and colleague Herr E. du Bois-Reymond. For the rest I do not deny that there is a core of truth in the phenomena of hypnotism. But what there is of truth in it will hardly appear so very wonderful.

'As to the employment of such mystical influences in poetry, I can only speak as spectator and reader. As such, I find that I can only comprehend and sympathize with accountable beings. Charms are not repugnant to me, so long as they only constitute an abbreviation of some natural psychical process, which would actually require more time and more intermediate stages. Where that is not the case, my sympathy with the processes immediately vanishes, the theoretical explanation of this being quite obvious.'

Helmholtz's scientific interests and discoveries were steadily turning away from physiology to an almost exclusive devotion to physics and mathematics, and, as was only natural, he began to wish that he could also concentrate his teaching more entirely in this direction.

In the summer of 1868, while his wife was on the Baltic coast for the sake of their son Robert's health, and Helmholtz, already fully occupied with lectures, laboratory and other scientific work, was also teaching plane trigonometry to his son Richard in his leisure hours, to prepare him for the Polytechnic at Stuttgart, he received proposals from Bonn to undertake the Professorship of Physics there, which caused him a good deal of agitation and unpleasantness.

The Prussian and Baden Governments had already had one tussle for the possession of Helmholtz, but the Baden authorities did not see any need for complying with the wish of Prussia, and releasing Helmholtz from his obligations. They knew too well what a powerful intellect they had secured for Heidelberg.

Helmholtz had now spent ten years of activity in Heidelberg, and had as the greatest scientific man of the day, along with Bunsen and Kirchhoff, supported the glory of the University; he was happy in his family relations; he had all the advantages of intercourse with his many distinguished colleagues; and it would have required very strong inducement to make him contemplate the idea of leaving Heidelberg.

The Chair of Physics and of Mathematics in Bonn had been left vacant by the death of Plücker, and on May 28, 1868, the Curator of the University, Beseler, approached Helmholtz with the inquiry whether it would be possible to induce him to take the Professorship of Physics. Helmholtz made an interesting and characteristic reply:—

'Physics was really from the outset the science which principally attracted my interests: I was mainly led to medicine and thereby to physiology by the force of external circumstances. What I have accomplished in physiology rests mainly upon a physical foundation. The young people whose studies I now have to direct are, for the most part, medical students, and most of them are not sufficiently grounded in mathematics and physics to take up what I should consider the best of the subjects that I could teach. On the other hand, I see that the younger generation in Germany is not making any substantial progress in scientific, and especially in mathematical physics. The few great names in this branch, which is the true basis of all proper natural science, are old, or begin to recede into the older generation, while there is no new generation rising up to take their place; and on this account I must say to myself that if I could get an influence over my pupils in this department, I might perhaps do more important work there than in physiology, where a vigorous school is now in full and growing activity. That would be an aim that might repay me for the labour of taking the new work of a new post upon me, instead of working on upon my old lines. To this end, however, I should have, in addition to experimental physics, which is the popular subject for lectures, to undertake at least the teaching of mathematical physics and the direction of the practical work. Lectures in pure mathematics I could not well undertake; in those on mathematical physics I should treat mathematics as the means and not as the end. Wherever possible I should include the physiology of the eye and ear, but would undertake no obligations in this particular.'

Beseler urged the nomination of Helmholtz in pressing terms upon the Minister von Mühler.

But notwithstanding these negotiations the correspondence did not lead to the desired result, because the Prussian Government could not proceed with the liberality of the Baden Ministry. On Jan. 2, 1869, Jolly addressed a very courteous communication to Helmholtz:—

'I now hope for a certainty that we shall succeed in re-taining you for beautiful Heidelberg. Willingly as we would otherwise follow the Prussian lead, it is in this case our bounden duty to declare war to the knife on the Berlin Cabinet, and I must add that it would be personally a matter of great pain to me, whose intellectual life is rooted in Heidelberg, if while I am at the head of affairs I had to see it robbed of its chief ornament.'

The satisfaction of all his very modest demands by the Baden Government, and the wishes and inclination of his family, decided Helmholtz on staying in Heidelberg. In the midst of the negotiations his son Friedrich Julius was born, on October 15, 1868.

'From his birth,' writes Frau v. Schmidt-Zabiérow, 'he was a weakly child, who was only kept alive by unremitting care and attention, and whose mental as well as bodily development was a source of incessant anxiety to his parents. It required exceptional courage on the part of my sister not to give way to the double grief of the illness of her two sons, and to avert any gloomy consequences to her husband's life.'

At this period the enormous output of Helmholtz's work assumed a distinct tendency towards the most arduous problems of physics, mathematics, and philosophy.

His researches in acoustics had led him directly back to his earlier work in hydrodynamics, and his new results were laid before the Berlin Academy (April 23, 1868), in the paper 'On Discontinuous Motions of Fluids'.

In the same year Helmholtz astonished the scientific and mathematical world by the far more comprehensive and fundamental researches which he published in the essay sent to the Göttingen Scientific Society, 'On the Facts that underlie Geometry.' At a later time he endeavoured to present its most important results in a form intelligible to non-mathematicians, in the lecture given to the Docentenverein at Heidelberg in 1870, 'On the Origin and Significance of Geometrical Axioms.' These investigations, along with the famous work, 'On the Hypotheses that underlie Geometry,' which Riemann had published as his *Habilitationsschrift*, in 1854, were epoch-making for the development of the mathematico-philosophical conceptions of the second half of the last century.

Helmholtz, indeed, had occupied himself with the philosophical analysis of the fundamental conceptions of mathematics and physics at a very early period, as is proved by an interesting sketch published some years before his essay on the Conservation of Energy, which not only shows how he strove in his youth for clearness of fundamental concepts, but already indicates the direction in which he was to do such pioneer work thirty years later.

On April 21, 1868, he writes to Schering at Göttingen: 'In thanking you for sending me the two little notes about Riemann, there is one question I should like to ask. In your notice of his life I find it stated that he gave a *Habilitations-vorlesung* on the Hypotheses of Geometry. I have myself been occupied with this subject for the last two years in connexion with my work in physiological optics, but have not yet completed or published the work, because I hoped to make certain points more general. For instance, I cannot yet make everything as universal for three dimensions as I can for two. Now I see by the few indications you give of the results of the work, that Riemann came to exactly the same conclusion as myself. My starting-point is the question: What must be the nature of a magnitude of several dimensions in order that solid bodies (i.e. bodies with unaltered relative measurements) shall everywhere be able to move in it as continuously, monodromously, and freely, as do bodies in actual space? Answer, expressed according to our analytical geometry: " Let x, y, z, t be the rectangular co-ordinates of a space of four dimensions, then for every point of our tri-dimensional space it follows that $x^2 + y^2 + z^2 + t^2 = R^2$, where R is an undetermined constant, which is infinite in Euclidean space." I venture to ask you to let me know if Riemann's essay is already in print, or if there is any prospect of its being published shortly, as seems to me most desirable; in the event of Riemann having taken the same point of departure, my own work would become useless, and I need not go on expending as much time and headache as it has already cost me.'

Schering replied that ' the most important point in Riemann's treatment of the proposition stated that the magnitude defined by Gauss as the measure of curvature is a differential invariant for homogeneous differential expressions of the second degree and first order, in two variables', and Helmholtz resumes on May 18:—

' I am much obliged for the copy of Riemann's *Habilitationsschrift*. Herewith I send you a short account of the part of my own studies of this subject which is not covered by Riemann's work, begging you to lay it before the Royal Society to be published in the *Göttinger Anzeigen* (Proceedings of the Society). I believe a detailed discussion of the whole, consecutively, to be very desirable, and for choice I would have it published in the Proceedings of your Society, along with Riemann's. I therefore beg to ask if communications are accepted from corresponding members, of which I am one, and when you are bringing out the next volume? . . . Forgive me for Riemann's sake, for troubling you with these matters.' The paper was published in 1868.

Helmholtz in the first place endeavoured to distinguish the development of concepts in geometry from the facts of experience, which appear to be necessities of thought, while it was only in the lecture delivered ten years later on the Facts of Perception that he gathered up the results of his researches towards a unified system of philosophy that differed essentially from that of Kant. If this divergence from Kant had been partly apparent in his earlier physiological optics, he only proclaimed it definitely in the 1868 paper on the axioms of geometry. Twenty years later, in criticizing a book that excited general interest, he observes :—

'The strictest Kantians emphasise the particulars in which Kant in my opinion suffered from the imperfect development of the special sciences in his day, and fell into error. The nucleus of these errors lies in the axioms of geometry, which he regards as *a priori* forms of intuition, but which are really propositions tested by observation, and which if proved incorrect might eventually be rejected.

'This last is the point I have tried to establish. Therewith, however, we reject the possibility of laying down metaphysical foundations for natural science, in which Kant as a matter of fact believed. Now for my point of view it is exceedingly interesting to see in the papers he left behind him, how this contingency disturbed the philosopher as he grew older, how he turned it over and over, again and again seeking new formulae, and finding none that satisfied him. Among these we find in details instances of the most amazing insight, such indeed as we might expect from a man of his intellect, e.g. as to the nature of heat. . . . In my opinion it is only possible to retain the great work done by Kant, if one recognizes his error in regard to the pure transcendental significance of the geometrical and mechanical axioms. But along with this we renounce the possibility of making his system the foundation of metaphysics, and this appears to me the reason why all of his disciples who cherish metaphysical hopes and tendencies adhere so tenaciously to these disputed points.'

In his inquiry into the sense-perceptions Helmholtz had proposed to himself the question, What in the simplest forms of our spatial perception had been derived from experience, and what could not have originated therein, and how much must necessarily have been inferred from experience, in order to give support to the other ? Arguments and counter-arguments had already been brought forward, stating either that the axioms of geometry were *a priori* forms of our mode of intuition, anterior to all experience, and fundamental to our mental organization, or, on the other hand, that they were empirical theorems of the most universal character. In his attempt to transfer this inquiry from philosophical physiology to mathematics, Helmholtz endeavoured for the more precise definition of the question to

determine what other properties of space besides that of a
magnitude of several dimensions were logically conceivable,
or, since the question is one of relative magnitudes, algebraically
possible, if we set aside the axioms of geometry as hitherto
accepted.

It had been of essential importance in Helmholtz's investigations that he had, in his work on physiological optics, met with
two other cases of magnitudes with several variables, which in
their system of measurement exhibited certain fundamental
differences as compared with spatial measurements. Whereas
in space there is a relation of magnitude between any two
points, comparable with that existing between any two others—
i. e. the numerical ratio of the distances $ab : bc$, of the three
points a, b, c—in the region of colour, when the differences of
brightness are taken into consideration, the simplest relation is
that between four colours, a, b, c, d, when these can each be
made by mixing two of them, when they lie in a straight
line in the colour table—i. e. the ratio of the two proportions
in which a and c must be mixed, in order to produce on the one
hand b, and on the other d. He had further found, on investigating the formation of our visual measurements in the two-
dimensional field of vision, that the measurements very probably
depended on the fact that the retina was carried by the movements of the eye as a fixed circle past the retinal image; with
this difference, however, from measurements in external space
that we practically cannot utilize this circle in our measurements of the comparison of the lines in different directions.
This drew his attention to the influence exerted by the means
of measurement upon the system of measurement as a whole,
and the form of the results, and these considerations led him
to investigations not only of space but of all other poly-dimen-
sional regions, in which a magnitude (distance) given by only
two points can be compared by measurement with another
corresponding to it, relating to any other given pair of points.
Helmholtz showed that it is entirely a question of the formulation of special postulates, under which the square of the distance
of two infinitely near points is brought under the more general
form of the Pythagorean proposition, i. e. it is given by a homogeneous function of the second degree of the differentials of any
three magnitudes used for determining the position of the points.

'I believe that the considerations here adduced are not without weight for the question of the original discovery of the geometrical propositions. For when men were seeking for a mathematical formula which should coincide with their more or less exact observations and measurements, they could find none that they could consistently carry through, save that expressed in the Pythagorean proposition, since as a matter of fact there was no other. And in this, as I believe, lies the foundation of the peculiar sort of conviction that we cherish in regard to the axioms that are unprovable either in theory or in practice. We have indeed no choice but to accept them, unless we mean to forgo all possibility of spatial measurement.'

Helmholtz dissents altogether from Kant's doctrine of the *a priori* forms of intuition and of the axioms of geometry, and inquires into the facts that underlie geometry, or the question what geometrical laws express actual facts, and what on the contrary are merely definitions, or conclusions from definitions, and from the special modes of expression selected. The answer to this question, however, presents enormous difficulties, because geometry always has to do with ideal figures, to which the material figures of the actual world can only approximate. The decision whether, e. g., the surfaces of a body are plane, its sides straight, &c., can only be solved by the laws of geometry, the positive accuracy of which has first to be proven. We see without difficulty, that in addition to the Euclidean axioms as usually proposed for geometry, a whole series of other facts are tacitly admitted. It is essential to note in particular that we can only conceive intuitions of such relations of space as can be represented in actual space, and that we must not let ourselves be misled by this power of conception into assuming as a matter of course, what is in reality a particular and by no means self-evident characteristic of the external world that is before us.

But since analytical geometry only treats of spatial figures as magnitudes, which are determined by other magnitudes, since all the spatial relations known to us are measurable, i. e. can be referred to determinations of magnitude, length of line, angles, surfaces, &c., it has no need of intuition for its proof, and Helmholtz was led by this consideration to the further question what analytical properties of space and spatial magnitudes must be assumed in analytical geometry, in order to establish its propositions completely from the outset. He was then able to consider the possibility of the logical formulation of a different system of axioms, since the necessary calculation of analytical geometry is a purely logical operation, incapable of yielding any relation between the magnitudes involved in it, other than those already contained in the equations proposed for the calculation.

It has been shown by Gauss that while the square of the length of a linear element in a plane is expressed by the sum of the squares of the increments of the two rectangular co-ordinates, the square of a linear element upon any given surface appears as a homogeneous function of the second degree of the increments of two general co-ordinates, which determine the situation of a point upon a surface. If figures of finite magnitude are to be movable towards all parts of such a surface without alteration in their measurements as made upon the surface itself, and capable of rotation round any given point, then further the surfaces must have a constant measure of curvature at every point, the measure of curvature of the surface at any point being defined by Gauss as the reciprocal ratio of an infinitely small part of the surface surrounding this point to that part of the surface which is drawn through spherical radii parallel to the normals, upon the unit-sphere. But even upon surfaces with a constant measure of curvature, where free mobility of the figures is possible, geometry would assume a form wholly different from our geometry.

Helmholtz starts with the assumption that as inhabitants of tri-dimensional space it is possible for us to conceive the various ways in which beings living in a surface would form their conceptions of space, and to picture to ourselves their sensory impressions; spaces of more than three dimensions are, however, inconceivable to us, since all our means of sensory perception extend only to tri-dimensional space; and then he goes on to consider geometry as it would appear to intelligent beings of only two dimensions.

He propounds the question what would become of the axioms of our geometry, as, that there is only one shortest distance between any two points in space, the straight line; that, further, through any three points that do not lie in a straight line, a plane surface can be drawn, which must entirely contain the straight lines joining any two of these points; and, lastly, that through any point lying outside a straight line only one straight line can be drawn, parallel to it, and never cutting it. The two-dimensional being would indeed be able, as a rule, to draw shortest lines between two points, which he terms 'straightest' lines, but even in the simplest case of the sphere, an infinite number of straightest lines could be drawn between any two poles; parallel straightest lines that did not intersect could not be drawn at all, and the sum of the angles of a triangle would always be greater than two right angles, and the more so, the larger the surface of the triangle. The space of these beings would no doubt be unlimited, but it would be found to have finite extension, or at any rate be postulated as having it. Only when the constant measure of curvature is of zero value, i. e. when, according to Gauss, the surface can be spread out on a plane by flexion without extension or disruption, would our geometry hold good.

Both for Riemann and Helmholtz, however, the question of primary importance was not under what conditions our geometrical axioms might be valid, but under what hitherto not clearly explained conditions we arrived at the knowledge of them. Riemann shows how by a generalization from tri-dimensional space the universal properties of space, its continuity, and the multiplicity of its dimensions, could be expressed, by saying that each particular in the complex which it presents, i. e. each point, could be determined by measuring n continuously and independently variable magnitudes, which are its co-ordinates, so that space becomes an n-times extended complex, and we ascribe to it n dimensions. Riemann adds as a further necessity that the length of a line must be independent of place and direction, so that every line must be measurable by every other, and since in our actual space the measure of each linear element is the square root of a homogeneous function of the second degree of the increments of three measurements of whatever kind, he starts in his general investigation from this form of linear element as if it were hypothetical. He finally generalizes the definition of the measure of curvature for n-dimensional space, and shows that, if he adds the final condition that spatial figures shall everywhere be movable without change of form, and able to rotate in every direction, then the measure of curvature must be constant. He thereby proves that the fundamental assumptions do not require the infinite extensibilty of tri-dimensional space; space can have the same relation to a quadruply extended complex, as a surface with a constant measure of curvature has to tri-dimensional space.

Helmholtz's investigation was to a large extent implicit in that of Riemann, but was distinctly original in one particular, so that it was of great importance for all later work, and for the question of the axioms of geometry. He tries to establish the conditions under which the Pythagorean Law as hypothetically assumed and generalized by Riemann would be valid, and makes the condition, which Riemann only introduced at the close of his paper, the basis of his whole treatment of the subject, i.e. that spatial figures should have, without alteration of form, the degree of mobility which is postulated in geometry.

'For the rest I must observe, that even if the publication of Riemann's work has cancelled the priority of a whole series of my own results, it is of no little importance to me, in regard to such a recondite and hitherto discredited subject, to find that so distinguished a mathematician should have thought these questions worthy of his attention, and it has been to me a certain guarantee of the validity of the way, when I found him upon it as my companion.'

For Helmholtz the starting-point of the investigation was the fact that all primitive measurement of space rests on the observation of congruence. But since there can be no verification of congruence unless fixed bodies or systems of points can be moved relatively to each other with unaltered form, and unless the congruence of two spatial magnitudes be a fact independent of all motion, he set himself the task of seeking the most universal analytical form of a complex of manifold extension in which the desired mode of motion shall be possible. He inquires in the next place how much the conditions which he postulates for the investigation, viz. (1) continuity and dimensions, (2) the existence of mobile solid bodies, (3) free mobility, (4) independence of form of solid bodies on their rotation, restrict the possibility of different systems of geometry. These assumptions led him to a measure of the linear elements, as independent of direction, in the form laid down by Riemann, and he shortly sums up the conditions required by the latter, in saying that a point of an n-fold complex is determined by n co-ordinates, that there is further an equation between the 2 n co-ordinates of any pair of points infinitely close together, independent of their motion, which is identical for all congruent pairs of points, and that, lastly, with otherwise perfectly free mobility of the solid body, the property of monodromy of space must be fulfilled, whereby when a solid body of n dimensions rotates round $n-1$ fixed points the rotation shall bring it back without reversal to its original position. And in applying these conditions to the case of three independent variables, he is able to show on purely analytical grounds that a homogeneous function of the second degree exists between the increments of the same, which persists unaltered during rotation, and which accordingly gives a measure of the linear elements, independent of direction.

In his development of these considerations an error crept in owing to Helmholtz's statement that if infinite extension of space be required, no geometry other than the Euclidean is possible, whereas Beltrami showed that the geometry of Lobatschewsky is also admissible, by which in a space extended infinitely in all directions, figures congruent with a given figure can be constructed in all parts of the same, while, further, only one shortest line is possible between any two points; but the axiom of parallel lines no longer holds. It is only when the measure of spatial curvature is everywhere at zero value that such a space corresponds with Euclid's axioms, and this space is then termed by Helmholtz a plane space. If the measure of curvature is constant and positive, we arrive at spherical space, in which the straightest lines return upon themselves, and there are no parallels; such a space is like the surface of a sphere, unlimited but not of infinite magnitude. If, lastly, the measure of curvature is constant and negative, then in such pseudo-spherical surfaces the straightest lines proceed to infinity, and in each planest surface a bundle of the straightest lines can be drawn through every point, which do not intersect any other given straightest line of the same surface. In a space of which the measure of curvature is other than zero, triangles of large superficies will have a different angular sum from those of small superficies; but the results of geometrical and astronomical measurements which give the sum of the angles of a triangle only approximately, and never exactly, as two right angles, only justify us in concluding that the measure of our spatial curvature is exceedingly small; that it actually vanishes is not to be proven, it is an axiom.

In an interesting passage in the lecture Helmholtz describes how we can picture to ourselves the appearance of a pseudo-spherical world extending in all directions, and hence the axioms of our geometry can in no wise be founded on the given form of our capacity of intuition. Beltrami had constructed a pseudo-spherical space within a sphere of Euclidean space so that every straightest line and planest surface of the former was represented by a straight line and plane surface in the latter: Helmholtz makes it probable by similar considerations that if our eyes were provided with suitable convex glasses, pseudo-spherical space would no longer appear very singular to us, and it would only be at the outset that we should be deceived in our estimation of the size and distance of remote objects.

In April, 1869, Beltrami contributed an interesting letter to the discussion, pointing out Helmholtz's error as above, and Helmholtz lost no time in correcting his statement in a communication to the Scientific Society at Heidelberg.

Helmholtz, like all philosophers and scientific men at the beginning of the Nineteenth Century, was profoundly exercised by epistemological questions: 'What is true in our ideas and conceptions? How far do our notions correspond with reality?' These and kindred problems relating to the theory of knowledge were the logical outcome of such work as the preceding, although not explicitly developed till a later period.

A note found among Helmholtz's papers gives us in this connexion a slight but highly interesting 'Analysis of Knowledge as we actually have it':

' *The content.* (1) Sensations are the only direct and pure perceptions. (2) Our conceptual images of external individual objects are the aggregate of a large number of different conceptions. (3) The concept of an object *present* expressly includes the assurance that with suitable conditions of observation the same sense-impressions of that object will always obtain. (4) Existing objects alter, but we seek and find *laws* for such alterations, i. e. *concepts* for them, which remain themselves unaltered, but only become active, i. e. as *phenomena*, so often as the same conditions of their activity recur. It is by this that they are differentiated from the existence of substances whose phenomenal appearance can only be contemplated as dependent on the observer, that of the laws of nature depending upon the changes in the existing order. (5) The postulation of a law of nature entails the assurance that in all future corresponding cases the phenomena will conform to this law. A perfect law, which states the conditions and extent of the result completely and exactly, is for our knowledge an adequate reason for a certain conclusion as to the result. So likewise it may be regarded objectively as *force*, as the objectively sufficient ground for the event. (6) The hypotheses of natural science are attempts to discover laws of a more extended import than can be immediately deduced from observation.

'*The empirically demonstrable significance of knowledge....* Ideas are signs, which can be translated back to reality by movements. Temporal relations alone are really equal.—

'*The psychical processes that underlie the origin of knowledge.* ... The source of all knowledge is the transference of what has already occurred in experience to what is about to be experienced. *Deduction* of the fundamental concepts that follow from the nature of comprehension, and from the presupposed possibility of the complete solution of this task.'

From this starting-point Helmholtz seeks for a connexion with Kant, who had already perceived that the qualities of our sensations must be determined by the idiosyncrasies of our mode of conception (which was first established as unquestionable by modern physiology), but apprehended space and time in the same way, since we can perceive nothing in the external world without its happening at a given time and occurring at a given place. Here too, Helmholtz is still with Kant unconditionally, when he defines time as the given and necessary transcendental form of internal, space as the corresponding form of external intuition; he further agrees with him that spatial intuition is a subjective form of intuition, like the other qualities of sensation, since space appears to us sensibly with the qualities of our sensations of motion, as that through which we are able to move and see. Space to him is, further, the necessary form of external intuition, since it is that which we perceive spatially which is for us the external world, all else being the world of internal intuition or of self-consciousness, and for him as for Kant space is a given form of intuition, prior to all experience, since the perception of it is bound up with the possibility of motor volitional impulses, the mental and bodily capacity for which must be given by our organization before we can have intuitions of space. Kant, however, went farther, in that he assumed not only that the universal form of space-intuition was given, but that it also implied *a priori*, and anterior to all possible experience, certain more exact determinations, viz. the familiar axioms of geometry—so that these are also of transcendental origin.

It is here that Kant and Helmholtz part company, since to the latter the question whether the axioms of geometry are transcendental or laws of experience, is entirely separate from that of whether space in general is a transcendental form of intuition or no.

'Kant's doctrine of the *a priori* forms of intuition is a very happy and lucid expression of the facts, but these forms must be sufficiently free and void of content to include every sort of content that may turn up anywhere in the forms of perception under consideration. The axioms of geometry, however, limit the intuitional forms of space to such an extent, that all conceivable contents are no longer admissible, if, that is to say, geometry is to be applied to the real world at all.'

If the axioms really were an innate form of spatial intuition, we should not be justified in applying them to the phenomenal world till it had been proved by observation and experiment that the fractions of space taken as equivalent by the presupposed transcendental intuitions were physically equivalent also. Helmholtz shows Kant's assumption of the *a priori* character of the geometrical axioms to be superfluous and unjustifiable.

On the strength of his previous investigations he is able to show that it is possible to construct a geometry on the basis of the single definition of physical equality, according to which, under the same circumstances, in the same time, the same physical processes or circumstances will take their course, the equality being demonstrable by means of measurements with compasses. We should then obtain a geometry, the propositions of which would indeed be covered by our axioms, but which would be founded solely on empirical data, so that we should not require *a priori* axioms at all. Kant's assumption that spatial relations that contradict the Euclidean axioms are unrepresentable is, however, invalidated by the preceding discussion, since Helmholtz interprets the whole of Kant's conception as a simple process that cannot be further analysed, and is influenced by the whole developmental state of the physiology of the senses.

'When it is possible to state completely and unequivocally the whole series of sensory impressions, which must, in accordance with known laws, ensue from an object that has never been seen, then in my opinion the object must be held to be conceivable; since *ex hypothesi* the object has never been seen, no earlier experience can help us, or direct our imagination in the discovery of the necessary series of impressions; this can only arise from the *concept* of the object or relation to be represented. The concept of spatial figures that do not correspond to our ordinary intuitions can only be developed with certainty by the calculations of analytical geometry.'

Helmholtz was greatly fatigued by the mathematico-philosophical studies necessitated by his work on the axioms of geometry. On March 28, 1869, he writes to Ludwig:—

'I have for the moment returned to electrical work on the time-relations and dispersion of discharges, to which I was incited by physiological experiments and problems. For the time being I have laid physiological optics and psychology aside. I found that so much philosophizing eventually led to a certain demoralization, and made one's thoughts lax and vague; I must discipline myself awhile by experiment and mathematics, and then come back later to the Theory of Perception. It is well to hear in between what others have to say about it, what they have to object, what they misunderstand, and so on, and whether they take any interest at all in these questions. My following in these matters has been small enough so far, but I have some good people with me'.

As a matter of fact his philosophical views spread but slowly even after his Academic Discourse in 1878, on 'The Facts of Perception.' On March 2, 1881, he writes to Lipschitz :—

'I have been interested in seeing that you have hit on the same train of ideas as myself in the Theory of Knowledge. I am pleased, and it renews my courage, although I have quite given up hope of living long enough to see any reformation in philosophy. In my thoughts I rail against the faculty philosophers, like Schopenhauer, but I will not put this on paper. Each can only read himself, and is incapable of understanding the thoughts of others. Yet when I see the mathematicians and physicists gradually coming round to my ways, it at least gives me hope for the future. I expected opposition as a matter of course from the faculty people, who had preached the opposite ideas all their lives, but I did not anticipate that after all the trouble I have taken to set forth my meaning in different aspects, they would only deduce the wildest misunderstandings. On the other hand, I do not know how to meet (and this enrages me, often as I have sworn not to get annoyed about it) the calmness with which people, who are incapable of grasping the simplest geometrical statement, pronounce upon the most complex problems of the Theory of Space in the sure conviction of superior wisdom. In conclusion, it would be very profitable for the subject if you were to work up and publish your views. It will have more weight when it gradually appears that the people who have made a profound study of mathematical questions are obliged as a class to judge in this way. The individual, even if he be a Riemann, will always be regarded as a crank who is discussing unfamiliar matters as an amateur. You won't get much pleasure from it, but one must bestir oneself to see that the community of right-thinking persons increases gradually. At bottom it is the false rationalism and theorizing speculation that is the most crying evil of our German education in all directions.'

Helmholtz felt the necessity more and more of freeing his mind from philosophical speculations, and in order not to return at once to the physico-mathematical problems that had occupied him for so long a time, he took up and completed certain earlier physiological and electrical questions, which compelled him to devote himself in the first instance to purely experimental work.

In his experiments on the transmission of excitations in nerve, Helmholtz had remarked (as already noted by others) that electrical induction shocks had little effect upon the deeper-lying nerves of the human body, while it is an easy matter to produce contractions, even in the deeper nerves, by the constant currents of a battery of ten to twenty platinum-zinc cells. In a lecture given to the Nat. Hist. Med. Ver. at Heidelberg on February 12, 1869, 'On the Physiological Action of Brief Electrical Shocks within Extended Conductors,' he described the experiments made to establish these facts on the thigh of the frog, which proves the accuracy of his observations. But the explanation of these phenomena, which he referred back to the investigation of the distribution of electrical discharges in extended conductors, involved a certain knowledge of the oscillation-frequency of the currents in an induction coil, whose terminals are connected with the coatings of a Leyden jar. In another lecture delivered on April 30, 1869, to the same Society, 'On Electrical Oscillations,' Helmholtz presented the results of his experiments in this direction, in which a frog's nerve was used as current-indicator and reagent for the detection of the electrical movements, and in which the electrical oscillations took place between the coatings of a Leyden jar, in a complete and uninterrupted circuit which had no spark gap. It was then found that in using a Grove's cell for the primary current, the total duration of the perceptible electrical oscillations in a coil joined up with a Leyden jar was about $\frac{1}{50}$ of a second. The determination of the oscillation-frequency is required to make it possible to set up exact experiments in proof of the above facts.

Helmholtz gave an address at the Opening of the Natural Science Congress at Innsbruck in September, 1869 (which he attended with his wife), entitled ' The Aim and Progress of the Natural Sciences.' It was designed to give an account of 'the progress of natural science as a whole, the aims for which it strove, and the magnitude of the steps by which it advanced towards its goal'.

Amid the wide circle of his undertakings we find a solitary note on Hay-fever, taken from a letter addressed to Binz, and published in 1869, in *Virchow's Archiv f. path. Anatomie.* In an attack of hay-fever (from which Helmholtz was a chronic sufferer), he discovered pathogenic vegetable germs in the mucous membrane of the nose, and successfully combated them with quinine, at a time when, as du Bois observes, there was as yet hardly any question of antisepsis.

By the beginning of 1869 it was obvious that a third edition of *Sensations of Tone* was wanted. It appeared in the following year with considerable alterations. Helmholtz not only remodelled the sections on the history of music, and connected them together more closely, but, on the strength of recent discoveries, essentially modified his account of the function of the rods of Corti, while he included his own later work, which propounded the articulation between malleus and incus as the reason why soft harmonic over-tones arise in the ear itself from the stronger primary tones. The publication of the new edition again led to a few important final observations, which formed his last physiological communication to the Heidelberg Society (June 25, 1869), 'On the Auditory Oscillations in the Cochlea.' This gave fresh support to a hypothesis advanced by Hensen as to the function of the *membrana basilaris*.

Helmholtz now turned to his vast undertakings in electrodynamics. Even if his main work in this direction was to be done a little later, it was in Heidelberg that he began the investigations of which, on Jan. 21, 1870, he presented a part to the Nat. Hist. Med. Ver. with the title 'On the Laws of Inconstant Electrical Currents in Materially Extended Conductors', which was published at greater length in the same year in the *Journal f. reine u. angewandte Math.*, as 'The Theory of Electro-Dynamics. Part I. On the Equations of Motion of Electricity for Stationary Conductors.' This was a preliminary study to orient himself in the department of hydrodynamics.

The majority of physicists in Germany deduced the laws of electrodynamics from the hypotheses of W. Weber, which endeavoured to refer the phenomena of electricity and magnetism to a modification of the assumption made by Newton for the force of gravitation, and by Coulomb for statical electricity, of forces acting in a straight line at a distance, their extension through infinite space being regarded as instantaneous, with infinite velocity. Coulomb's view that the intensity of the forces was inversely proportional to the square of the distance of the electrical quantities that exerted reciprocal action, and directly proportional to the product of the two quantities, with repulsion between like, attraction between unlike charges, was supplemented by Weber by the hypothesis that the velocity with which the two electric charges approached, or receded from each other, as well as their accelerations, must have some influence on the magnitude of the force between them. This assumption of forces which are dependent, not only on the position, but also upon the motions, of the acting points, seemed to contradict Helmholtz's observations, since he was led by his inquiry into the conservation of energy to the view that forces depending on distance and velocity are contrary to the universal law of the conservation of energy, which had been thoroughly confirmed for the phenomena of electrodynamics also. It is true that Helmholtz had not at that time taken into consideration the more complicated case of Weber's law, in which the forces further depend on acceleration, and it was in fact shown that Weber's law admits of no cyclical process by which work can be evolved out of nothing.

Along with Weber's hypothesis were a whole series of others, all having this in common, that they regarded the magnitude of Coulomb's force as modified by the influence of some component of the velocity of the moving electrical charges. Such were the hypotheses of F. E. Neumann, of his son C. Neumann, and other physicists, but the observed facts, and conclusions from theories that were not well founded, all ran confusedly together. Helmholtz undertook to clear up the region of electrodynamics, and to search for crucial results of the several theories, so as, wherever possible, to decide between them by means of suitable experiments. He found in the first place that all the phenomena incident on the passage of fully closed currents in their circulation through closed metallic circuits, in which during the passage of the current there was no perceptible change in the electric charges accumulated in any part of the conductor, were equally well accounted for on any of the above hypotheses. The results agreed as well with Ampère's law of electromagnetic action as with the theorems discovered by Faraday, and amplified by F. E. Neumann. With incompletely closed circuits, however, these hypotheses led to essentially different results, since electrical charges accumulate at the open ends of unclosed conductors, owing to the interpolation of insulating masses, at each electrical disturbance along the conductor, these electric charges being due to the electricity accumulated near the ends of the conductor, and unable to traverse the insulator.

Since the hypothesis resorted to by W. Weber (i. e. that electricity has a certain degree of inertia like that of heavy bodies) proved untenable, because the apparent inertia is due to induction, Helmholtz next endeavoured to convert all these laws into one single theorem, which should contain a still undetermined constant, whence he could theoretically deduce all the conclusions, and then test them empirically.

The potential of the current elements of two linear conductors due to one another proposed by Neumann, and derived from Ampère's attractive force between two current elements, was directly proportional to the product of the length of the elements, the cosine of the angle between them, and the product of current intensity in both, and indirectly proportional to the distance between them, with a factor of proportionality which is the negative square of the reciprocal of the velocity of light; the validity of this expression of potential was tested and confirmed on closed currents. Helmholtz then looked for the most general form of expression for the potential of a single current element, which in all cases where one of the currents is closed gave the same value as Neumann's formula, and he finds this form expressed in the product of the two infinitely small elements, and the second partial differential quotients, taken with respect to the elements of a function of the distance of these elements and of the current intensities. He further submits this function to the condition that it shall be proportional to current intensity, and inversely proportional to distance, and obtains for the potential an expression which differs from Neumann's in that, instead of the cosine of the angle of the two elements, an expression is introduced which is linear in respect of this cosine and of the product of the cosine of the angle which the elements form with their distance from one another, and which contains a new constant k. This expression also includes the two different potential expressions of the theories of W. Weber and Maxwell for each pair of current elements. From the expression of the potential the two elements due to one another it is now possible (by a method of Kirchhoff) to develop the values of electrodynamic potential for currents that are continuously distributed in space, and it was shown with the help of Green's law that the value of the electrodynamic potential produced by all the currents present in relation to the three components of current in a volume element, are constant everywhere, with the exception of points at which the electrical currents are infinite.

With the help of this expression of potential we obtain the equations of motion for electricity, which lead to an analogy between the motions of electricity in a conductor and those of a gas, and Helmholtz next investigates the nature of these differential equations, and the course of the electrical disturbances as determined by them, in regard to the value of the constant introduced by him as above into the law of potential, which has the value 1 in F. E. Neumann's law, o in Clerk Maxwell's (under a given assumption), − 1 in Weber's and C. Neumann's. He finds that if k is zero or positive, the differential equations with given potentials give the same initial value for the motion of electricity, and that the work equivalent of the electrical motion is positive; for a negative value of k it may be negative, i. e. less than in a state of rest, so that the equilibrium of the electricity at rest in conducting bodies for negative values of k must be unstable. Helmholtz proved that if this quantity of work once becomes negative, the motion, left to itself, will increase continuously, and lead to infinite velocities and densities of electricity. These motions and infinite progressive disturbances of electrical equilibrium, however, on the unstable side can actually be produced with the methods at our command for causing electrical motions if k has a negative value (as indeed happens, generally speaking, whenever electric disturbances are produced in a homogeneous conducting sphere, by bringing an electrically charged body near it, and taking it away again), and he thence concluded that the assumption of a negative value for the constant k, as made in Weber's law of induction, is inadmissible.

Helmholtz next investigated the influence of the constant k with practicable experiments, and finds that if $k=1$ or is not disproportionately greater than 1, the motions of the electricity in experiments with earth conductors will not differ perceptibly from the case in which $k=0$. The analytic treatment of the problems of the motions of electricity can also be simplified if k is not a very large number, by making $k=0$, or assuming the propagation of the longitudinal waves to be infinitely great, as long as the dimensions of the conductor used are vanishingly small in comparison with the wave-lengths of the oscillations that come under observation. Thus with such electric motions as are produced within a conductor by external forces after a previous state of electric equilibrium, there can only be free electricity (on the assumption that $k=0$) at the surface of the conductor, or at the limiting surfaces of different conductors. The investigation of a very long wire as conductor, compared with whose diameter the wave-length is very great, also shows the influence of the constant k only in the small terms of the higher order. Helmholtz concludes from this that in electrical experiments in the laboratory the velocity of the electric longitudinal waves depending on the constant k need not be taken into consideration, unless we have the means of detecting extraordinarily minute time-differences.

After carrying out these experiments rigidly, without allowing himself to decide on any particular hypothesis, and taking the electrostatic and electrodynamic effects as action at a distance, which did not affect the surrounding insulating media and was not affected by them, he accepted the Faraday-Maxwell theory, which replaces action at a distance by the polarization of a medium, and assumes that the electric disturbances propagate themselves across an insulating dielectric in transverse waves, the velocity of which in air is equal to the velocity of light.

Faraday, like Newton, wholly rejected the hypothesis of the existence of forces acting at a distance, according to which there is direct and immediate action between two bodies separated from each other in space, without any alteration of the intervening media. He found that magnetism or diamagnetism exists in almost all the bodies previously held to be non-magnetic, and that in the same way good insulators suffered a change under the action of electrical bodies, which he termed the electric polarization of the insulator; and in virtue of this he sought to explain magnetic and electric action at a distance as due to the agency of the intervening polarized media. 'His ideas were clothed in an abstract language difficult to follow, and made but little way, until they found their interpreter in Clerk Maxwell.' On this hypothesis there were no open currents, since the accumulation of the electric charges at the ends of the conductors, and consequent dielectric polarization of the intervening insulators, represented an equivalent electrical motion in the insulators, and it was in this that Helmholtz recognized the cogency of Faraday's views.

Helmholtz then, 'in view of the immense significance which this result may have in the further development of physics, and because the question of the rate of transmission of electrical action has recently been raised in many directions,' set himself the task of investigating the results of the law of induction as generalized by himself, in the presence of magnetizable and dielectrically polarizable media. The discussion of the equations of motion of electricity, transformed in view of dielectric polarization, led him, without adopting the particular form of Clerk Maxwell's hypothesis, and while retaining the idea of electrical action at a distance, to the same results as Maxwell, i. e. that for a very large capacity of polarization the velocity of the transverse waves is equal to the velocity of light, while for a very small capacity it is infinitely great. The velocity of the longitudinal waves in air is found, however, to be directly proportional to that of the transverse, and indirectly proportional to the square root of the constant k, so that for $k=0$ the assumption made in Clerk Maxwell's theory is confirmed, that the rate of transmission of the longitudinal electrical waves is infinite, i. e. that there are no longitudinal waves. Further conclusions as to the velocities of the transverse and electrical longitudinal waves in other insulators harmonized equally well with the theory advanced by Clerk Maxwell.

In this first treatise on electrodynamics Helmholtz completely fulfilled his primary object, of sifting and clearing up the opinions and methods already obtaining.

At the beginning of the year 1870 Helmholtz, with Kirchhoff, received the great distinction of being elected an external member of the Academy at Berlin; at the same time an event occurred in the Berlin University, which was to have the most important consequences to his career.

On April 4, 1870, du Bois-Reymond informed him of the death of Magnus, adding:—'I could tear my hair now for not having gone to the Minister when there was the question of Bonn, and begging him to let me conduct the negotiations with Prussia for you. If you were only in the Chair of Physics at Bonn, it would be a much easier matter to get you appointed to succeed Magnus at Berlin.' ...

Helmholtz replied on April 7: 'I do not reckon too much on a call to Berlin, because I think Kirchhoff's appointment is much more on the cards, and would be easier to arrange. He is well in health now, is bright and energetic, and hardly wants his crutches even where the ground is not level. What you want in Berlin above all is a mathematical physicist, and I must say that Kirchhoff is a trained and practised force in that field, which I am not, however good the opinion I may have of my own deserts in other respects. I should be content to be his successor here.'

Helmholtz indeed contemplated the eventuality of his call to Berlin with great calmness. While his wife's clear judgement and intellectual vigour soon recognized that the stirring life of art and science in Berlin would afford a very different scope for her husband's work and her own talents to that of Heidelberg, for Helmholtz it was only a question of being able to devote his entire activities in teaching and research to physics. He replies on May 7 to Borchardt's congratulations on his own and Kirchhoff's election to the external membership of the Academy. '... If fate should so dispose that one of us should not long be an *external* member I should greatly rejoice, because it would give me the opportunity of devoting myself to physics. But between physics in Berlin and physics in Heidelberg the balance is so nicely weighted, that I don't yet know where it will come to rest when its oscillations are over, and can calmly await the decision of the gods and of Herr von Mühler; and I believe Kirchhoff is much in the same mind.' Meantime the possibility of Helmholtz's call to Berlin was rumoured in the papers, and on May 1 the Minister Jolly came to assure him that he should leave nothing in his power undone to make his attachment to Heidelberg permanent, and to comply in every way with his wishes.

The Philosophical Faculty of the University at Berlin proposed Helmholtz and Kirchhoff in a letter to the Minister, and gave the following reasons for their opinion :—

'If Helmholtz is the more gifted and universal in research, Kirchhoff is the more practised physicist and successful teacher. While Helmholtz is the more productive, and is always occupied with new problems, Kirchhoff has more inclination to teaching; his lectures are a pattern of lucidity and finish; also from what we hear he is better able to superintend the work of elementary students than Helmholtz.... If it happens therefore to be easier to win over Kirchhoff than Helmholtz, the Faculty feels itself justified in most respectfully begging to submit to Your Excellency the name of Professor Kirchhoff as successor to G. Magnus.'

The then Rector of the Berlin University, du Bois-Reymond, was empowered by the Prussian Minister to treat with Kirchhoff, in the first place, by word of mouth, and started for Heidelberg at the beginning of June with this object, with directions from Olsweisen that if Kirchhoff refused he was to sound Helmholtz, and with letters from the mathematicians Weierstrass and Kronecker to the latter.

Kirchhoff remained true to his friends in Heidelberg. It was in the course of a little dinner given by du Bois on July 12 at the Hotel zum Europäischen Hof in honour of Kirchhoff and Helmholtz, at which Bunsen and Königsberger (who had been called to Heidelberg as Hesse's successor at Easter, 1869) were the only other guests, that the Minister's reply to du Bois' telegraphed inquiry arrived, authorizing him to open negotiations with Helmholtz. The author, who is the only survivor, will never forget the splendid words in which du Bois proclaimed with enthusiasm 'that Heidelberg had been the centre of scientific research for long enough, and that while he could understand that Kirchhoff preferred not to leave his friends, Helmholtz by the nature of his work was being gradually driven exclusively into physical research, and that it was fitting for him to transport himself to the capital of the rapidly unifying Germany, whence indeed he had set out'. Not one of us suspected that the great struggle for the real unity of Germany was to break out a few weeks later.

Du Bois returned to Berlin next day with his report, and

received a letter dated June 12 from Helmholtz, which formulated the conditions he had verbally expressed:—

'Dear Friend! In reply to the question which you put to me on behalf of the Minister of Education, Herr von Mühler, as to the conditions under which I would transfer myself to Berlin to take up the Chair of Physics vacated there by the lamented death of Magnus, I reply that I am willing to undertake it on the following stipulations:—(1) Personal salary of 4,000 thalers (£600). (2) The promise, in so far as it can be made in the present state of affairs, that a Physical Institute shall be built, with the necessary equipment for instruction, for the private work of the Director, and for the practical work of the students. (3) The promise that I shall have sole charge of this Institute and of the collection of instruments, and that it be left to my judgement how far and under what conditions I can permit the use of it to be shared by other teachers (in regard to Professor Dove I should naturally exercise the utmost consideration). The Auditorium in the Physical Institute must equally be retained for my sole use, so that it may be possible to set up complicated arrangements of instruments within it. (4) An official lodging for myself in the Institute, and a corresponding allowance for rent until it shall be ready. (5) Provisional use of rooms hired in the vicinity of the University for my own work in physics, and for some of my students, with the necessary service. (6) A proper allowance for expense of moving. As soon as I hear from you that His Excellency is ready to comply with these conditions I will come to Berlin myself to survey the situation, and determine the accessories so far as they can be arranged beforehand. If it is desired that I take up the post in the autumn, the matter must be so far in train by July 1 that I can hand in my demission here.'

The Minister of Education lost no time in applying for the necessary funds to the Minister of Finance, writing to him on June 14:—

'In view of Helmholtz's universal and unrivalled fame in the scientific world, it would politically be of the greatest importance to get him here.'

On June 28, the Minister of Education addressed a letter to Helmholtz in which he acceded to all his demands, stating that as there were only 2,000 thalers in the University chest the other 2,000 thalers should be forthcoming for the next year from the funds of the Academy of Sciences, as an academic stipend to be paid, like the University salaries, in annual instalments during his life, by obtaining the necessary grant from the General Revenue.

Helmholtz now entered on a period of great agitation : to the tension with which he awaited the conclusion of his appointment was added the increasingly threatening political news. 'I was on the point of sending Käthe instructions for the event of war,' he writes on July 3 to his wife, who, with the children, was staying with her parents, 'when the telegram came saying that Prince Leopold has been good enough to abdicate. I wish King William had not intervened ; it will only produce a brief respite, and looks like a concession from weakness.'

In the days that followed he was much excited. Bunsen, Kirchhoff, and Königsberger took long walks · almost every day with him, and generally met him in the evening at the Darmstädter Hof. On July 11 he wrote to his wife :—

'I am beginning to fear that we really are in for a war, since the attitude of the French Government can only be explained by supposing that they have been waiting for an opportunity, and now think they have got a good one ; otherwise it is all sheer madness. Nor do I think that the Prussians will shirk the war, for once it is certain that it is bound to come sooner or later, they will accept it at once. This may alter all our plans and prospects very considerably.'

Helmholtz's thoughts and time and energy were now wholly taken up by the important events that were happening. 'I myself,' he writes early in October to du Bois, 'have worked here for two months preparing the Field Hospital, and specially undertook to manage the reception and expedition of the wounded, and of the officials at the station. I went one day with a party of the younger doctors to Wörth, and learned the horror of a battle-field after the battle. At one time this intense activity was a godsend to work off our agitation ; but afterwards, when things took a more peaceful course, and there was less for me to do, I was warned by sharp and recurrent attacks of headache that I needed rest. I first went to my wife's relations at Starnberg, where our little family had passed the time of the war. But it had become too wintry there, so I went for three weeks to Meran, and yesterday returned home by the Engadine and Chur.'

Owing to the happy and unexpectedly rapid course of the war, du Bois was able by October 13 to assure Helmholtz that the Diet was to meet in November, when his appointment would be definitely concluded, but that in view of current events the building of the new Institute would have to be postponed for a time, to which Helmholtz agreed on October 17, provided a promise were given him that the matter should be proceeded with so soon as the State had recovered its normal financial balance, and, further, that such temporary provision was made for himself and a few students, as would enable him both to do some experimental work himself, and to direct his pupils. This was agreed to by the Prussian Ministry on December 16, 1870.

Before the end of the year Helmholtz went to Berlin with his wife, where they found a fine, detached dwelling in the Königin-Augusta-Strasse, and soon brought the provisional arrangements for the Physical Institute to a satisfactory conclusion. The Ministry at once began to negotiate for the purchase of a site for the new Institute, giving him temporary quarters in the University for his instruments, and a Laboratory in the Herbarium, which was accommodated elsewhere, while they acceded to all minor demands with alacrity. Helmholtz and his wife returned to Heidelberg, well satisfied with their reception from the du Bois-Reymonds and other distinguished people in Berlin.

On January 2 Helmholtz applied for his demission from the service of the Baden Government, and in a few weeks' time received the document, signed by the Emperor William at Versailles on February 13, 1871.

A few days after his return from Berlin he received a letter from Sir William Thomson, asking if he were disposed to accept the Professorship of Experimental Physics at Cambridge, which, despite the munificent conditions, he was of course obliged to refuse.

'And thus,' writes du Bois, 'occurred the unparalleled event that a doctor and professor of physiology was appointed to the most important physical post in Germany, and Helmholtz, who called himself a born physicist, at length obtained a position suited to his specific talents and inclinations, since he had, as he wrote to me, become indifferent to physiology, and was only really interested in mathematical physics.'

His son Richard, who knew that his father would be gratified if he presented himself at the theatre of war ('an ardent patriotism was ever one of my father's salient characteristics '), had though barely seventeen enlisted as a volunteer in the mounted division of the Baden Field Artillery in August 1870, and was sent to the front in November, where, besides several small skirmishes, he took part in the three days' fight on the Lisaine, and was wounded by a mishap with his gun, though not severely.

In the last weeks of his stay at Heidelberg, Helmholtz took leave of the cultured audience who had so often listened with delight and admiration to his brilliant Popular Lectures, in a discourse ' On the Origin of the Planetary System '.   The rostrum of the over-flowing hall was decked with laurels, a wreath lay upon it, and the whole audience rose as he entered.   With astonishing lucidity, and in his consummate style, he discussed the Kant-Laplace hypothesis from the mechanical and physical sides, and the subtle considerations by which W. Thomson had proved that the density of the ether may conceivably be far less than that of air in the vacuum of a good air-pump, but that its mass is not absolutely *nil*, and that a volume of luminiferous ether equal to the volume of the earth cannot weigh less than 2,775 pounds.

' The basis of this calculation would no doubt be removed if Clerk Maxwell's hypothesis should be confirmed, according to which light depends on electric or magnetic oscillations.'

On March 5, 1871, the Faculties and many of the educated inhabitants of Heidelberg combined to give a banquet at the Harmonie in honour of Helmholtz.   The words spoken by him and others can never be forgotten by those who were present, but all were possessed by the feeling that the greatest thinker and man of science in Germany belonged of rights to the place where the Founder of the German Empire was supported by the grandest Statesman and the most gifted General.

CHAPTER X

HELMHOLTZ AS PROFESSOR OF PHYSICS IN BERLIN : 1871-1888

HELMHOLTZ had hardly removed to Berlin when the engagement in the same year, and subsequent marriage, of his daughter brought considerable changes into his household.

'Helmholtz's two children,' writes his sister-in-law Betty Johannes, 'had been, since his second marriage, with their grandmother, who made them her special charge, and lived in the same house with them, while they came to visit me every year in the country. Käthe was a serious creature, almost morbid in her striving after the highest aims, never satisfying herself, never able quite to bring the world and its phenomena into harmony with her ideas. She was greatly beloved and admired. As she grew up and developed a marked talent for painting, she was, thanks to her second mother, encouraged in every way that could further the development of her gifts, and give her a wider outlook and new impressions. She went to Munich, Vienna, the Tyrol, the Bavarian Highlands ; she painted in the *ateliers* of Berlin and Paris ; she spent a year in France and England in the house of the famous Orientalist, J. Mohl, whose wife had great influence over her. At the age of 19, she translated Tyndall with the help of her step-mother and Frau Wiedemann, and she followed her father's work with untiring eagerness. Her love and admiration of her father amounted to worship. It was in my house at Dahlem that Käthe met her husband Dr. Branco ; they were engaged in 1871, married in 1872, and immediately afterwards spent a long time in Italy, the country of Käthe's warmest aspirations. On their return, Branco bought an estate at Genthin for the sake of his wife's health, and there in 1873, a daughter, Edith, was born to them ; but after this her health grew steadily worse. They again spent a long time in Switzerland and at Baden-Baden : they moved to Heidelberg and then for a second time to Italy: but all was in vain. She returned from Italy in 1877, and died at her home in Dahlem on April 25. Her coffin stood before the altar in the village church, where her parents had been married.'

Helmholtz, as an Ordinary Member of the Academy, to which he had been elected on April 1, contributed a Paper 'On the Rate of Transmission of Electrodynamic Action', on May 25, 1871. He connected this with the researches of Blaserna, and in it discussed a question, then of great moment in the development of Electrodynamics, to which he had already alluded in the great electrodynamic memoir cited above. According to C. Neumann, and on the hypothesis of Faraday and Clerk Maxwell, which assumes that electrodynamic action at a distance is caused by changes in the medium with which space is filled, this action must be produced by forces which are propagated through space with finite velocity, and this velocity must approximate to that of light. Helmholtz had, however, shown in his earlier criticism of the electrodynamical theories that, on the assumptions made as to the susceptibility of the air to magnetic or dielectric polarization, other values of the velocity of propagation are compatible with the facts. After Blaserna had convinced himself by experiments that the propagation at least of the inductive action of electrical currents proceeded at a very moderate velocity in air, Helmholtz, who had long been occupied with experiments on the course of very brief electrical currents, felt compelled to test the accuracy of these experiments as regards the propagation of the action in air. He arrived at the result that 'the separation of the two coils to the considerable distance of 136 cm. does not alter the position of the zero-point of the induced current by one division of the micrometer, i. e. not by $\frac{1}{231170}$ second. So that if the inducing currents are really propagated at any calculable speed, this must be greater than 314,400 m. or about 42·4 (German) geographical miles er second'.

In the same summer (July 6, 1871) Helmholtz, at the Leibniz Session of the Academy of Sciences, delivered a beautiful and reverent address 'In Commemoration of Gustav Magnus', whose successor he was, and whose personality and conduct he felt himself the more bound to do justice to, since from Magnus's somewhat chilling reception of his 'Conservation of Energy' it had seemed (or, at any rate, his opponents said it had seemed) as if there had been a radical contrast between their scientific labours, and a certain depreciation of each other's work. Even in the early letters to du Bois-Reymond it had been apparent how highly Helmholtz appreciated the ready help which Magnus gave to young men of science, free as it was from all professional jealousy, as well as (the point now more particularly emphasized) the faithful, patient, modest industry with which he invariably worked on till no further improvement was possible, and which, when he noted the same trait in any of his pupils, made him hail them as his personal friends.

The germs of the Physical Society of Berlin had been sown in the Conferences which Magnus had held on stated evenings in the form of discussions and reports on physical problems at his own house; and it was there, in the winter of 1847, that Helmholtz, while repeating his experiments on the function of yeast in alcoholic fermentation in Magnus's Laboratory, had made the acquaintance of Wiedemann.

'At that time there were no lectures on Mathematical Physics,' he wrote twenty years later in the congratulatory address dedicated to Gustav Wiedemann, and contributed to the Jubilee volume of the *Annalen*: 'G. Wiedemann and myself, being ambitious to learn something of mathematical physics, to which we were incited by Gauss's magnetic investigations, agreed to study some of Poisson's works together in private, e. g. his theory of elasticity, which we did with great regularity and profit.'

The works of Magnus obtained undying fame from the classic perfection of his method, and the accuracy and reliability of his results.

Helmholtz esteems him happy in that he was permitted to strive in pure inspiration towards ideal principles. 'Of such men it can be said that they are not hampered by an envious destiny, since, working for pure aims, and with a single heart, they find satisfaction even without external results.'

The main interest in this lecture, however, attaches to Helmholtz's general observations upon different methods of physical research, which convey some notion of the revolution that had taken place in the past thirty years. Magnus was not one of those investigators who embraced the extremes of modern empiricism, a school which confines itself to the discovery of facts, and declines to seek for any law or connexion in the facts discovered.   On the other hand, he was far from posing as the theorist, who holds it unnecessary to obtain experimental confirmation of the conclusions derived from the hypotheses which he accepts as axioms.   Above all he was the enemy of metaphysical hypothesis, and his fear of any resurrection of Hegel's 'Naturphilosophie' may sometimes have made him a sterner critic of the works of others than would otherwise have been the case.

As Helmholtz said on another occasion, 'It is unworthy of a would-be scientific thinker to forget the hypothetical origin of his propositions.   The arrogance and vehemence with which such masked hypotheses are defended are, as a rule, the usual consequence of a sense of dissatisfaction which their champion feels in the depths of his consciousness as to the validity of his contention.'

Helmholtz trusted that the conviction might gain ground that the only successful experimenter in physical science is the man who has a thorough theoretical knowledge, and knows how to propose the right questions in accordance with this, while, on the other hand, those only could profitably theorize who had a wide practical knowledge of experimental work,— as had been so brilliantly demonstrated in the discovery of Spectrum Analysis.   In his eyes mathematical physics is also an empirical science, and he endeavours in his Address to break down the barrier between experimental and theoretical physics.   In our experience we only meet with extended and composite bodies, whose actions are compounded of those of the separate parts.   If we would learn the simplest and most general laws of interaction between the masses and substances that exist in nature, as abstracted from the form, size, and position of the effective bodies, we must go back to the laws of action that govern continuous and homogeneous volume-elements, and not to the disparate and heterogeneous atoms, so that mathematical physics thus becomes as subject to the control of experience as experimental physics.

He attacks the same question of the reciprocal relations between experimental and mathematical physics in his essay 'On the Attempt to Popularize Science', published in 1874 as a preface to his translation of Tyndall's *Fragments of Science*, where he first distinguishes, and then reunites, the two ways of investigating the coherent sequence of nature—by abstract notions, and by copious empirical observations. The first way, which leads by mathematical analysis to the quantitative know-ledge of phenomena, seems to him to be indicated only when the second method has already to some extent opened up the field, and provided an inductive knowledge of the laws for at least some groups of the phenomena which it covers.

We are then concerned only with the transition to the ultimate and most universal laws, and with deductions from the same in this field. The purely experimental method, on the contrary, leads to the recognition of Uniformity in the same way as it is grasped by the artist, which Helmholtz had already indicated in his Goethe Lecture as the sensible lively perception of the type of its activity, developing later into the form of pure concept. The two ways must necessarily be concomitant, if we are to escape the danger, on the one hand, of erecting a structure on insecure foundations, on the other of losing sight of the aims of science.

'The first discovery of hitherto unknown laws of nature, i. e. of new uniformities in the course of apparently disconnected phenomena, is an affair of wit—taking this word in its widest sense—and comes about in nearly every case only by comparison of numerous sensory concepts. The completion and emenda-tion of what has been discovered subsequently devolves on the deductive labour of conceptual, and preferably of mathematical analysis, since it all turns finally on equality of quantity.'

In the autumn holidays of 1871 Helmholtz attended the Meeting of the British Association at Edinburgh, first visiting Mr. Tait at St. Andrews.

'St. Andrews,' he writes on August 20 to his wife, 'has a beautiful Bay, with fine sands sloping sharply up to the green links. The town itself is built on rocky cliffs. There is a lively society of bathers, elegant ladies and children, and gentlemen (*sic*) in sporting costumes, playing golf. . . . Mr. Tait thinks of nothing here beyond golfing. I had to go out too; my first strokes came off—after that I hit either the ground or the air. Tait is a peculiar sort of savage, living here, as he says, only for his muscles, and it was not till to-day, on the

Sabbath, when he might not golf, and did not go to kirk either, that he could be induced to talk of reasonable matters. . . . At dinner we had a chemist Andrews from Belfast, and Professor Huxley, the famous evolutionary zoologist from London, both most agreeable and interesting men. . . Andrews showed us some remarkable experiments, on the passage of gases and liquids into one another at high pressure. . . .

'We dined with Prof. Brown, with whom a great mathematician Sylvester was staying, who has been very badly treated by Mr. Gladstone, which has caused much excitement.'

From there he went to Glasgow, and stayed a night with Prof. Brown, in college, where a nephew of Sir W. Thomson did the honours.

'The house was not yet finished internally, no carpets, nor paint, full of old furniture not yet in place, and it looked unspeakably desolate as if no one cared for it, in contrast to the old house which Lady Thomson had managed. In a corner of the dining-room was an exceedingly fine and expressive portrait of her, with the sofa on which she always lay, and her coverlet. I felt very sad, and could hardly restrain my tears, while the young people were merry enough over the tea. It is sad when men lose their wives, and their life is left desolate.'

From there he went on to the yacht-races at Inverary, taking part in them on Thomson's yacht, a two-master, and one of the finer and more commodious of the forty yachts, all fairly large, well-appointed and elegant, that were competing; he admired the dexterity with which Thomson and his men manœuvred their boat. After visiting Lady Thomson's parents at Largs, where her death had taken place, they went on for some longer expeditions on the *Lalla Rookh*, of which he writes, 'The yacht is like a movable watering-place, and makes a pleasant home in fair weather.' Helmholtz and Thomson studied the theory of waves, 'which he loved to treat as a kind of race between us.' They put in at a number of the finest parts of the west coast of Scotland, till they reached the northern extremity of their wanderings, the Island of Skye, after many stoppages due to heavy storms. On the way back they visited the family of the mathematician Blackburn, near Glasgow, and Helmholtz was delighted with Mrs. Blackburn's extraordinary talent for animal painting, having already admired her pictures in the Exhibition in London.

'It was all very friendly and unconstrained. Thomson presumed so much on his intimacy with them that he always carried his mathematical notebook about with him, and would begin to calculate in the midst of the company if anything occurred to him, which was treated with a certain awe by the party. How would it be if I accustomed the Berliners to the same proceeding? But the greatest *naïveté* of all was when on the Friday he had invited the party to the yacht, and then as soon as we were under way, and every one was settled as securely as might be in view of the rolling, he disappeared into the cabin to make calculations, while the company were left to entertain each other so long as they were in the vein; but you may imagine that they were not very lively. I amused myself by strolling up and down the deck, "in schwankender Anmuth."'

The return voyage was very pleasant and comfortable, and on calm days he and Thomson experimented on the rate at which the smallest ripples that appeared at the surface of the water were propagated, a subject on which Thomson had recently been working.

'Still,' he writes to his wife on September 4, 'I find that a husband who is no longer in his first youth feels uncomfortable when he wanders about in the world, all by himself, without higher guidance, and I think if the world were peopled with men only it would not be particularly beautiful, but would be very practical, and not at all refreshing.'

In his work Helmholtz now turned almost exclusively to Electricity. In his first treatise on the theory of electro-dynamics, which deals with electrical motions in ponderable conductors at rest, and is of fundamental importance for the principles of mechanics, he had succeeded in giving F. E. Neumann's potential-expression a form in which it included the two different potential-expressions laid down by W. Weber and Clerk Maxwell for each pair of current-elements. Investigation of the law for the different values of his constant k had shown that Weber's law led to inconvenient results; on the other hand, Maxwell's hypothesis, in the case when motions of electricity or magnetism in dielectric or magnetic media have electro-dynamic effects, required a knowledge not only of the indeterminable constant k, but also of the dielectric constant of the air, or the velocity of transverse electric waves in air, which likewise could not be determined from previous experiments. It was thus of primary importance to determine this latter constant by experiments, which were accordingly undertaken by Boltzmann in his laboratory, with the view of testing Clerk Maxwell's now famous electromagnetic theory of light. This distinguished physicist, whom Helmholtz vainly endeavoured to secure for Berlin at a later time as successor to Kirchhoff, wrote to Königsberger in April, 1902, that in consequence of Helmholtz's supposition that Maxwell held the refractive indices to be equal to the dielectrical constants, the requisite agreement was not obtained ; he therefore left Berlin in the firm conviction that Maxwell was entirely wrong, and was on the point of printing his criticism of the theory. As early as November 1, 1872, however, he wrote to Helmholtz : 'I cannot forbear to tell you of another thing. I was always under the impression (and I believe you expressed the same idea when I was in Berlin) that on Maxwell's theory of the identity of light and electricity, the dielectric constants which I had determined must always be equal to the refractive indices. On now putting the values of all the dielectric constants together in a table, I was much worried at their deviating so far from the refractive indices, but noticed at the same time that they were always nearly equal to the squares of the latter. The thought flashed through my mind that Maxwell's theory might require this, since the velocities of transmission are always proportional to the square root of the forces. I looked up Maxwell's treatise, and there sure enough was plain to read that the dielectric constants must be proportional to the squares of the refractive indices (the magnetic induction constant is about equal to unity for all these substances) ; so that I must look on my experiments as a confirmation of Clerk Maxwell's Theory.'

Neither from theory nor experiment was it possible as yet to decide for one or other of the hypotheses mentioned by Helmholtz in his first paper, and both in the note laid before the Academy on April 18, 1872, 'On the Theory of Electrodynamics,' and in the article that appeared in the *Jl. für reine u. angewdt. Math.*, in 1873, 'On the Theory of Electrodynamics, Part II : Critical,' Helmholtz partially devoted himself to refuting the objections that had been made to his former work. He points out, in reply to Bertrand, that the expressions for the potential of each pair of current-elements are not expressions of ultimate elementary forces, but refer in each current-element, taking this as a solid body, to one force and to a pair of forces ; the quantity, and to some extent the direction, of these forces depend not merely upon the position of the elements, but also upon the velocity of the electrical currents, so that it should be as legitimate to speak of the potential of two current-elements as of the potential of two magnets. But he endeavoured, above all, to refute the objections of W. Weber to his argument, since even in the highly special case of the motion of two particles of electricity along the line joining them, in accordance with Weber's law, the acceleration may become infinitely great, and at a less distance the co-efficient of the acceleration, corresponding with the mass, becomes negative. He further shows that on the assumption of Weber's law for an electrified particle, which is movable within a hollow sphere covered evenly with electricity, the case may occur in which the co-efficient of acceleration becomes negative, thus producing perpetual motion ; and he again points out that the differential equations proposed by Kirchhoff for the motions of electricity on the assumption of Weber's law would lead to an unstable equilibrium of electricity in conductors.

He then advanced a step farther in his comparison of the different theories and their consequences, and set himself the task of deriving Ampère's forces from the Potential Law of F. E. Neumann. This was suggested to him by Riecke's objection that when the potential of a closed current referred to a current-element is deduced by means of Helmholtz's potential expression, it follows that the action of a closed current on the movable part of another current is not, as it must be according to Ampère, perpendicular to the latter. Helmholtz laid his conclusions before the Academy in a short note entitled 'Comparison of the Laws of Ampère and Neumann for Electrodynamic Forces', on Feb. 6, 1873, while the full account appeared the next year in the *Jl. f. Math.*, 'On the Theory of Electrodynamics, Part III: Electrodynamic Forces in Moving Conductors.' His further 'Criticism of Electrodynamics,' published in 1874 in *Poggendorff's Annalen*, is directed solely against the objections raised to his mathematical theory of electrodynamics.

The Potential Law of F. E. Neumann (which Helmholtz in a letter to Schering calls one of the most brilliant achievements of mathematical physics) was designed and well fitted to comprise the whole department of electrodynamic motive forces included under Ampère's Law, as well as the electrodynamic induction produced by the movement of conductors, and alteration of current intensity, under a single and very simple law. This, however, according to Neumann's proof, could only, in the case of closed currents, coincide with Ampère's law (which was actually correct in this instance), on the assumption that the two conductors in question were moved without alteration of form or magnitude. In order to express the law of the electrodynamic motive forces for conductors of three dimensions, Helmholtz analyses the latter into conducting threads, which everywhere follow the direction of the lines of current present, so that no electricity can escape from one of the threads to its neighbours. Now since Ampère's law only recognizes forces which act from current-element to current-element, Helmholtz was able to show that when in applying the law of potential other forces are taken into account which act between the ends of the current and the current-elements, and between the current-ends of the two conductors themselves, then, from the potential set up by the current-elements, motive forces may be derived for two open parts of the current, which, for these portions of the current, can be brought into the form which Ampère has given them. If, as in the motion of the so-called rotation apparatus, points of slip make their appearance, Helmholtz regards them as current-ends, and in his opinion the solution in these cases is found without difficulty, if we suppose that the discontinuous displacement which is theoretically assumed as the limiting case at the point of slip is in reality only the limit of what is physically speaking a perpetual continuous displacement.

In Part III of the Theory of Electrodynamics, as above, Helmholtz not only gives a full account of these results, but goes a step farther in the development of the general theory. Till now he had only dealt with the action of electrical currents upon one another and upon conductors on the assumption that all conductors were at rest, so that it was only the alterations of current strength that had to be taken into consideration, the potential (as extended by him) of two superposed current-elements due to one another being definable as the work-value of the electrical currents present in them. He now went on to derive the equations of motion of electricity in moving ponderable conductors from the same principles, and endeavours to show that his generalization of Neumann's law of potential contradicts none of the known results which referred almost exclusively to closed circuits, while at the same time it agrees with the law of the conservation of energy. On the other hand he did not extend the inquiry to the case in which, besides the moving conductors, the dielectric polarizable media are also in motion, so that the electric motions occurring in these are also electrodynamically active.

In his three published papers on Electrodynamics Helmholtz had thus in the first place expressed F. E. Neumann's law of potential (which derived the strength of the induced currents not from the action of one point on another, but from that of one longitudinal element of the conductor on another), and was able in this way to represent, all the phenomena of closed circuits in quantitative agreement with the facts, more simply than by Ampère's original law. For the usually much weaker electrodynamic action of open currents, in which electricity tends to accumulate at single points of the conductor, he was able to show that the application of the potential law never contradicted the universal 'axioms of mechanics, wherein lay the great superiority of Neumann's law to all other hypotheses of electrical action at a distance. It differed, however, in one important particular from Faraday's assumption, since electrodynamic action was only ascribed to the passage of currents in the conductors, while the dielectric charges generated in the insulators lying between the conductors were not thought to be electrodynamically active. It thus remained for Helmholtz to plan experiments which should enable him to decide for one or other of the two hypotheses.

In the memoir laid before the Berlin Academy in June, 1875,

'Experiments on the Electromotive Forces induced in Open Circuits by Motion,' he describes the experiments made with this object on the electricity that accumulates at the surface of a conductor rotating in the magnetic field. By the ordinary laws of induction, electromotive force must be induced in any conductor that is thrown into rotation round the axis of a magnet, which does not follow from the law of potential alone; and Helmholtz set himself to test the discrepancy between the two theories experimentally. On the assumption that the universalized law of potential of Neumann (considering only the motions of electricity occurring relatively to the conductor in the conductors proper) gave a complete statement of the law of electrodynamic action, the experimental results did not agree with Neumann's law of induction. This discrepancy only disappears when the potential law is combined with Faraday's view, that the dielectric polarization which occurs in the insulators between two conductors in process of being charged is an electric motion, equivalent in intensity and in electrodynamic effect to the current with which either portion of the conductor is charged. All other theories, in which forces at a distance (with intensities depending upon the distances, velocities, and accelerations) have to be assumed, correspond fully with the phenomena of closed currents, but they are contradictory to the universal axioms of dynamics, when they are applied to open currents. Weber's hypothesis results in unstable electrical equilibrium in every conductor of moderate tri-dimensional extension, so that no practicable laws can be derived from it for the motion of electricity in materially extended conductors. The same applies to Riemann's law, which, moreover, contradicts the axiom of equality of action and reaction, while Clausius's hypothesis, which is free from these errors, has to resort to a space-filling medium, between which and the electricities the forces he postulates come into play.

Thus Helmholtz was led to recognize Faraday's hypothesis as the only one that agreed with the observed facts, and was in no way contradictory to the universal laws of dynamics. While Clerk Maxwell had actually worked out the theory for the case of closed circuits only, Helmholtz found that it also agreed with the few facts that were then known for open conductors, as had appeared from his own experiments on the electric charges of the surface of rotating conductors in the magnetic field. According to Faraday, dielectric polarization must occur in all insulators lying between the conductors, when the limiting conductors are charged electrically, and must be of such intensity that the motion of the electricities associated with the setting up of this condition may be regarded as the equivalent continuation of the electric current with which the conductor is charged. Every current accordingly must be a closed current, for which all the divergent theories lead to the same result. It follows also that any direct action of forces at a distance, which was still admitted, must vanish in favour of alterations of dielectric and magnetic strains in the ether-pervading space.

'Every radical alteration of the fundamental principles and postulates of a science,' said Helmholtz at a later time, 'necessarily involves the formation of new abstract concepts, and unfamiliar associations of ideas, which the contemporary student can only assimilate slowly, if he be inclined to take the trouble of doing so at all. The import of a new abstraction can only be understood clearly when its application to the chief groups of individual cases which it comprises has been thought out, and found valid. It is very hard to define new abstractions in universal propositions, so as to avoid misunderstandings of all kinds. It is, as a rule, much harder for the creator of such a new idea to make out why others fail to understand him, than it had been to discover the new truth. I will not disparage Faraday's contemporaries, because his words appeared to them uncertain and dark sayings. I remember too well how often I have sat gazing hopelessly at one of his descriptions of lines of force, of their number and tensions, or have sought to puzzle out the meaning of some law in which the galvanic current is treated as an axis of force, and so on. A Clerk Maxwell was required, a second man of the same depth and independence of insight, to build up in the normal forms of our systematic thinking the great structure whose plan was present to Faraday's mind, which he saw clear before him, and endeavoured to render apparent to his contemporaries.'

Whatever Helmholtz's inclination to support the views of

Faraday, on the ground of the experiments which he had under-taken with the object of deciding for or against the theory of action at a distance, he first endeavoured as a cautious critic to include a series of other and apparently remote pheno-mena in the circle of his considerations.

The communications which he made to the Naturforscher-Versammlung at Leipzig, August, 1872, 'On the Galvanic Polarization of Platinum,' and to the Berlin Academy in the following year, 'On Galvanic Polarization in Gas-free Liquids,' which are of a purely experimental character, originated in theoretical considerations, arising from the law of the conserva-tion of energy. It was known that when a Daniell cell of zinc and copper is connected to an electrolytic cell with platinum electrodes, a polarizing current is set up which declines rapidly, but does not entirely cease even after a long time. It was further known that if, after removing the Daniell cell, the platinum plates were connected with the galvanometer, the depolarizing current in ordinary liquids, saturated with gas, is initially strong, and then soon diminishes so as to be im-perceptible. Helmholtz now asked upon what this apparently unlimited duration of the polarizing current depended, and found that the persistent current was in close relation with the gases present in the liquid, or at the electrodes, before the passage of the current. A portion of the electrolytic oxygen is neutralized by the presence of hydrogen, which again sets free some of the hydrogen at the other electrode, which then dissolves in the liquid or penetrates the platinum, so that the decomposition of a corresponding amount of water again occurs. This process of conduction of electricity by the motion of its material carriers is termed by Helmholtz electrical convection. The motion of a gas enclosed in the electrodes ensues very slowly when the liquid itself is free from gas, so that the depolarization current in gas-free liquids may persist for a very long time. By assuming that in galvanic polarization it was not merely gas on the surface, but also that which had penetrated deeper into the platinum that came into play, and that the same laws held for the motions of the gases occluded in the metals as for the conduction of heat, Helmholtz removed the contradic-tion to the law of the conservation of energy. The products of electrolysis need not make their appearance at all, nor need the chemical affinity be overcome by the electromotive force; the process may be persistently maintained by the diffusion of the hydrogen, so that the initial presence of a limited quantity of gas suffices for a long-sustained current. In order actually to demonstrate the penetration of the gases into the platinum in galvanic polarization, Helmholtz set up experiments in his laboratory to see whether the hydrogen produced on one side of a thin platinum plate by electrolysis could be detected after a certain time at the opposite side, by the fact of its causing galvanic polarization there. The paper laid before the Academy on March 16, 1876, 'Report on the Experiments of Dr. E. Root of Boston, on the Permeation of Platinum by Electrolytic Gases,' established as a fact that hydrogen does make the opposite side of the platinum more positive.

The further question whether electric convection is electro-dynamically equivalent to the passage of electricity in a conductor, was answered in the 'Report on the Experiments on the Electrodynamic Action of Electric Convection, as carried out by Mr. Henry A. Rowland,' laid before the Academy on the same day. The convection currents thus obtained could actually be substituted for the motions of electricity in open conductors, thus affording possibilities of deciding important theoretical questions. The result of the experiments harmonized both with the theory of W. Weber, and with Maxwell's potential theory, which considered the dielectric polarization of insulators.

When an ebonite disk, gilded on both sides, was thrown into rapid rotation round a vertical axis, between two resting disks of gilded glass, while they were charged by means of a point with positive or negative electricity from the coatings of a Leyden jar, it was found that the action of this electricity conducted by convection was not merely the same in quality as that of the galvanic current, but that it agreed quantitatively also with that required by Weber's theory.

The proof hereby afforded that electricity transported convectively with its carriers also has electromagnetic action, was for Helmholtz (in conjunction with his previous work) conclusive evidence that Neumann's extended law of potential must be combined with Faraday's hypothesis, and that the appearance of electric or magnetic lines of force in space is invariably associated with the production of dielectric or magnetic polarization in the ether, and in the ponderable medium. Since on this assumption all electric currents are to be regarded as closed, the disparity between the different theories of electro-dynamics (which give identical results for closed currents) disappears, inasmuch as the experiments can be shown to tally with the facts.

At the beginning of 1873, Helmholtz was tempted by an invitation from Knapp to give a series of public lectures in America; but after deliberate reflection he replied on January 5, 1873:—

'I get very weary of the Berlin rush, so that at the end of the term the one and only thing I wish is to see no living soul, and to collect my thoughts in some quiet spot. America would be exactly the opposite to all this. And as regards lectures, I am convinced that although I can put scientific matters before people who understand them, in a dry technical fashion, I have not sufficient command of language to do so in a way that will rivet the attention of a large audience who are not professionally trained. Then the preparation in a foreign language costs me double the time, and even if I had the assistance of an Englishman it would only be patchwork. There are still many things that I want to do for science, and I must not lose too much time. Indeed I begin to think that I shall never see America in this life.'

He had in fact at this time, in addition to his great electrical researches, begun some investigations in Aero-dynamics, the first results of which, under the title 'On a Theorem referring to the Geometrically Similar Motions of Fluid Bodies, with applications to the Problem of guiding Air-balloons', was presented to the Academy on June 26, 1873.

The amount of resistance opposed by air or water to a body of complicated form that is moving through it, comes essentially into consideration when it is a question of constructing a ship or balloon, which is to be propelled by any kind of motor apparatus. Since the resistance of the water or air to the oars, paddles, or screws gives the propelling force, while the same resistance against the body of the ship or balloon gives the force of resistance to be overcome, the velocity of progress which can be attained must depend on the ratio of these two forces. Yet it was seldom enough that mathematical analysis had been able to discover the integrals proper to the conditions of the given special cases from the differential equations proposed for the motion of liquids and gases, taking into account the pressure and friction, from which these resistances could be calculated. On the other hand, we have plenty of experience in regard to ships of the most varied construction, since we know the amount of force required in order to give the desired velocity to any ship or boat, and we have succeeded in discovering the most advantageous forms for the body of the ship, and for the size and shape of the motor apparatus ; in the air, on the contrary, apart from the few experiments with balloons, birds are the only instances we have of flying machines. This consideration led Helmholtz (by means of the general hydrodynamic equations that hold good for liquids and gases) to transfer the results of experiments made with ships, to the corresponding problems in aerostatics. He shows, by rigid mathematical reasoning, that it is possible to transfer the empirical results obtained from a fluid and from apparatus of given size and velocity, to a geometrically similar mass of another fluid, and to apparatus of other sizes and other speeds, and establishes the ratio in which the velocities, the pressure, and the corresponding energy must be magnified, if the ratio of the physical constants of the fluids is given.

In the application of this principle there is, indeed, the objection that the density of the air alters perceptibly under pressure. But since air can escape freely on all sides, and the most successful results appear to be produced with the lower velocities of wings or screws, only those differences of pressure come under consideration which are caused by the accelerations of the displaced particles of air, and these, with the altered volume of air depending on them, may be disregarded (as Helmholtz shows), so long as the resulting velocities are negligible in comparison with that of sound. It follows, amongst other things, that the size of birds must find its limit unless the muscles could be further developed in the direction of performing more work with the same mass than they do at present. In the structure of the Great Condor, Nature has apparently reached the limits of size at which any creature can soar upward by its wings, and remain a long time in the air. Man, in his opinion, has no prospect of raising his weight into the air, and maintaining it there, by even the most ingenious winged mechanism, if it is to be worked by his own muscular power. If air-balloons and ships are compared on Helmholtz's principle, we obtain the interesting result that if the balloon weigh once and a half as much as the operator whom it carries, the ratio between working force and weight would be the same as in a war-ship.

At the close of the summer session (1873) Frau von Helmholtz took the children to their home in Baden, while Helmholtz, overwhelmed with work, spent the month of July in comparative solitude at Berlin.

'Last night I was alone in the house, and was led by Heyse's novel to look up Schopenhauer's Essay on Woman, but only got to the chapter on Love, which I read on the balcony by lamplight. He is a clever fellow, but has a passion for vulgarity, and turns away from every higher suggestion, even where it is obvious.'

On August 3 he writes to his wife :—

'I stayed at home, prepared the concluding lectures of my mathematical course, and have at last finished reading Zeller's *Kirche und Staat*. I must say that the book interested me, although it deals with things that have been overmuch talked about. I had previously seen nothing so reasonable and well grounded on this subject.'

At the beginning of the holidays he went as usual to Pontresina, and when the never-failing cure of the Engadine had relieved his cardiac trouble, he went on with his wife to see the Exhibition at Vienna, and thence alone for a first visit to Florence, sending his wife enthusiastic descriptions of all that he saw both in Art and Nature.

'I am enchanted and bewildered by all this completeness and beauty,—what we have in Germany are only poor fragments ; here one has the principal works of the Masters in inexhaustible fullness.—Fra Angelico is distractingly lovely, in whatever he really executed . . . then in the Accademia there are things of Perugino, which in colour and expression come very near the best Raphaels,—marvellous things by one Mariotto Albertinelli, of the same period as Raphael, of whom I never heard, nor saw anything before,—profound, full of expression, of the most tender poetry of colour.'

His brief stay in Florence only permitted him further to visit the Galleries of the Uffizi, which he left, after a five hours' visit, almost fainting with hunger and fatigue, to take the magnificent walk round the city, at sunset, by the southern heights. After meeting Beltrami on the return journey at Bologna, as had been arranged, for the discussion of a number of geometrical speculations, and problems in mathematical physics, he joined his wife in Vienna (where she was staying with her sister, the wife of the Sectionschef von Schmidt-Zabiérow, who was afterwards Governor of Carinthia), and returned to Berlin *via* Munich.

At the end of the summer session, and during the autumn holidays, Helmholtz had been occupied, in addition to his electrodynamic researches, with some very abstruse problems in physical optics, which he communicated to the Academy on October 20, 1873, in a brief note 'On the Limits of the Efficiency of the Microscope', afterwards published at length in the jubilee volume of *Poggendorff's Annalen* for 1874, as 'The Theoretical Limits to the Efficiency of the Microscope'. His researches and results were on the same lines as those of the great master in that branch of optics, Herr Abbe of Jena. Helmholtz attacked the question which is so important for all branches of science, how much it was possible to increase the efficiency of the microscope, and points out that its development had already reached a point at which each minute improvement could be attained only by a disproportionate outlay of mental and mechanical labour. The reason for this was generally held to lie in the fact that the spherical aberration of small lenses with high curvatures is difficult to overcome; while Helmholtz considered diffraction and brightness as the essential factors. The ratio of brightness and magnification he finds to be wholly independent of the special construction of the instrument, so that increased magnification only becomes possible with the application of much stronger light; the dimness of the microscopic image thus increases with increasing magnification.

Helmholtz, moreover, finds that with compound microscopes diffraction produces far more pronounced deviations of the rays from their focal point than do chromatic and spherical aberration, and he therefore subjects it to exact investigation. If the size of the smallest perceptible object is judged by the distance of each pair of bright lines that can just be recognized as distinct from each other, then this magnitude must be equal to that which in the magnified image of the object is equal in breadth to the outer diffraction fringe of each bright point. A given length in the object is accordingly no longer perceptible as a particular length, if it appear equal to the breadth of the fringe in the magnified image. Since the magnitude depends only on the angle of divergence of the impinging rays, and not upon the construction of the instrument, and the indistinctness of the image produced by diffraction increases with the narrowing cone of light, the limit for the differences of magnitude that we are able to distinguish plainly is in general found equal to half the wave-length of the particular light employed. A further increase in optical power beyond that of the best modern instruments does not therefore seem possible.

Another important work in physical optics was communicated to the Academy by Helmholtz on October 29, 1874, with the title 'On the Theory of Anomalous Dispersion', which had occupied him for a month on his return from a long tour in Switzerland. On the whole he agrees with the hypothesis put forward in explanation of anomalous dispersion by Sellmeier, which assumes the presence of ponderable molecules embedded in the ether, and capable of sympathetic vibration. This was not, however, adequate for the case in which the specific oscillation-period of the sympathetically vibrating molecules was equal to the period of the luminous oscillations. Since the dispersion is essentially due to absorption, Helmholtz takes the cause of the absorption to be, on the one hand, the sympathetic vibrations of the ponderable masses, produced by an elastic force acting between the ether and the ponderable atoms; on the other, a frictional resistance, which the vibrating ponderable particles encounter from the ponderable masses which do not vibrate in sympathy with them. This frictional force is proportional to the velocity, as in the slow vibrations of a pendulum and of resonating bodies. If only one kind of ponderable atom be present, and if the ether and the ponderable molecules are regarded as two continuous and interpenetrating media (as is permissible when the distance between the ponderable parts is vanishingly small in comparison with the wave-length), there result from the differential equation of the motion of the ether, and of the sympathetically vibrating atoms, those equations for the velocity of transmission, and absorption constants, which Ketteler had already deduced from his observations. In the case of weak light absorption, as in solutions of dyes with anomalous dispersion, these agree well enough with the observed facts. With a stronger degree of absorption the theory corresponds with the phenomena in the vicinity of the maximum of absorption ; as is found by observation, the curve of refraction reaches its maximum before the maximum of absorption, its minimum after the absorption-maximum, and falls continuously from the former to the latter. With colours that are far from the absorption-maximum, we must, however, have recourse to new theories as to the structure of the ether in the body. Lastly, Helmholtz shows that the extension of the theory to media with a larger number of absorption-bands presents no insuperable difficulties, provided different kinds of sympathetically vibrating ponderable masses are presupposed.

It was about this time that Helmholtz took up the preliminary studies for his meteorological work, coming forward with a popular lecture on 'Whirlwinds and Thunderstorms', which he delivered in the year 1875 in Hamburg. After describing the mechanical conditions from which it follows that the constant alternation of the state of our weather depends (as Dove had long ago shown in detail) upon the displacement of cool, dry polar winds by warm, moist equatorial winds, and vice versa, he goes on to investigate the motions of the air by which the regularity of tropical weather is interrupted, such as the hurricane or cyclone.

We learn from one of Helmholtz's letters that it was the accident of his observing the formation of cloud and storm from the top of the Rigi that drew his attention to these natural phenomena, and led him to the wonderful experiments in which a vertical tube filled with air is formed in the centre of a circulating mass of water, in the exact shape in which a waterspout is usually represented. The storms too develop in vortex form, and at the centre of such a vortex there is generally a space where there is little motion of the air. While the storm travels in the direction of the earth's rotation, the side which it presents to the equator invariably blows a west wind; if dry and moist air come together, great masses of air may accumulate, as Reye has shown, which were originally in stable equilibrium, but with alterations of temperature pass gradually into unstable equilibrium. For instance, cloudy and dry air lying upon or by the side of each other may be of such temperatures that they are of exactly equal weight at a moderate height in the atmosphere; in this case, in the lower half of the atmosphere, where the pressure is greater, the foggy air will become denser, and sink to the ground, while in the upper half of the atmosphere the same foggy air becomes more attenuated with lower pressure than the dry, grows lighter, and rises. The originally stable equilibrium will then (since with prolonged action of the sun the lower layer becomes warmer and moister, while the upper loses heat by its radiation into space) gradually pass into unstable equilibrium. If the equilibrium is interrupted at any point, so that pressure becomes less owing to the lighter ascending foggy air, the lower air will rise, and be drawn into the ascending current, while round it, where the equilibrium was still stable, it will become even more so from the evacuation of the moist air and sinkage of its upper surface; the rise would continue until the whole of the lower layer had mounted up. In discussing thunderstorms, Helmholtz indicates the store of negative electricity with which the earth is permanently charged, as the source of the electric discharges. In conclusion, he lays stress on the difficulty of predicting the weather, and the circulation of air in the atmosphere.

In general it is to be remarked that we can only calculate beforehand, and understand in all observable details, those natural processes in which small errors in the formulation of the premises involve only small errors in the final results. As soon as unstable equilibrium comes into play, this condition is no longer fulfilled. Thus chance still exists on our mental horizon ; but in reality it is only an expression for the complexity of our knowledge and the clumsiness of our methods of combination. A mind endowed with exact knowledge of the facts, whose thinking operations were accomplished so rapidly and precisely as to precede events, would discover in the wildest caprices of the storm, no less than in the motions of the stars, the harmonious ruling of eternal laws, that we can only guess at and assume.

On November 4, 1875, a heavy blow fell on Helmholtz and his family. Robert von Mohl, who had come a few days

previously to Berlin to attend the Reichstag, was there seized
with apoplexy. His daughter went to the funeral at Karlsruhe,
and Helmholtz spent the time in quiet retirement with his
children, finding an echo of his deep emotion in music.

After one of Joachim's Quartett evenings, he writes:—

'Beethoven's *Op.* 130, which is inconceivably great and
solemn, but intensely sad, was clear to me for the first time
to-day. The Adagio was incomparably well played; it is a
wailing dream of lost ideals, perhaps the prototype of Tristan's
Liebestod, a formless surging of infinite melody.'

The year 1876 was that of the first Bayreuth Festival, which
Helmholtz attended with his wife. Both were possessed with
the general enthusiasm which the original and powerful conceptions of Richard Wagner excited throughout the musical
world. 'They ranged themselves among the number of the
Master's inspired friends, and welcomed the new intellectual
and emotional relations, which, helpful and satisfying, became
on both sides one of life's most cherished possessions.' After
Helmholtz had left Bayreuth to recruit in the mountains, his
wife writes to him on August 30: 'No one, save those who
were not present, can deny the power and majesty of the work.
What is original and really great is always uncongenial to the
mediocre; never have I seen anything more pitiful than the
German criticism with its cothurnus and its icy non-recognition.
Happily these gentlemen and their sterility cannot prevent the
accomplished victory.'

Helmholtz's many-sidedness became ever greater, the height
of his grasp and comprehension of new scientific problems ever
more astounding. He followed each new phenomenon with
the greatest interest, and was always ready to give his opinion on
it at length in writing. When Kühne, at the beginning of 1877,
sends him the Optogram, he welcomes the discovery with
enthusiasm, and at once presents it to the Academy; writing
to him on March 13, 1877:—

'I have been immensely pleased with this find; I had always
imagined hypothetically that there must be photo-chemical
action in the retina, but had never supposed one would be
able to demonstrate it. I am curious now about the action
of colour. Boll has already made communications about this
to the Academy, and to the Lincei. Red light ought to rein-

force the red, and blue light to make it paler, but he further distinguishes greenish rods between the red, which should become more intense with green light. Whether the green is anything more than contrast, still appears to me questionable; but that other coloured and uncoloured rods lay between the red, I could see for myself from his demonstrations last summer.'

All this extensive scientific activity did not prevent him, when on the death of Poggendorff in the same year the editing of the *Annalen der Physik u. Chemie* devolved upon G. Wiedemann, from giving a helping hand to the editing (as Wiedemann himself informs us), while he contributed a full written report on every paper of mathematico-physical interest that was sent in.

After his appointment on July 24, 1877, to the Professorship of Physics at the 'Medico-Chirurgical-Military-Academy' (Friedrich-Wilhelm Institut), at which he had received his own education, he gave a discourse on 'Thought in Medicine' at the Commemoration Festival of the Foundation of the Institute in the same year, in which he extolled medical studies as the school 'which had demonstrated more clearly and convincingly than would have been possible in any other case, the eternal principles of all scientific work, principles so simple and yet so often forgotten, so clear and yet so often veiled in obscurity'. He points out that medicine more than any other department of science involves insight; that epistemological questions as to scientific methods might also assume a serious importance, and prove to have a fruitful practical bearing; that if a man work on a perfectly sure basis he loses nothing by an error save that wherein he has erred, but that where everything rests on hypotheses which only correspond with what we should like to hold true the least rift dislocates the entire structure of our convictions. And then in a most brilliant argument he attacks metaphysical systems in natural science, as well those of the spiritualists, who feel themselves elevated above the rest of nature, as those of the materialists, who strive to control the world unconditionally by means of the conceptual forms they have at present arrived at.

He shows by a clear and convincing argument that Kant's refutation of the claims of pure thought had defeated the

spiritualist theory, that his Critique of Pure Reason was a perpetual protest against the use of categories of thought beyond
the limits of experience, and that he detected a tissue of false
conclusions in all metaphysical systems. But inasmuch as
Kant regarded the axioms of geometry as derived from pure
transcendental intuition, pure *a priori* intuition had become the
refuge of metaphysicians, and the expression of this theory in
physiology is the nativist theory. Hence comes the great importance of experiment, to resolve the pure or empirical con-
cépts, the axioms of geometry, the fundamental laws of mechanics,
or the modes of visual perception, into their rational elements.
He warns the younger men of science not to be led away by
the fact that all sects of metaphysicians are up in arms against
it, 'since these investigations put the axe to what seems to be
the strongest support still left to their claims.' Materialism to
Helmholtz is, equally, a metaphysical hypothesis, which may
sometimes have proved profitable to the natural sciences, but
can, as a dogma, be as great a hindrance to the progress of
knowledge.

'Memory, experience, practice, are also facts, the laws of
which can be investigated, and which cannot be decreed away,
even if they are not to be smoothly and simply referred to the
known laws of excitation and conductivity in nerve fibres,
however pretty a playground for fancy may be afforded by the
ramification of the ganglion processes and nervous connexions
in the brain.'

Helmholtz was shaken and wearied in mind and body by the
death of his daughter Käthe, and his incessant scientific work;
he also felt many worries brought on him by envy and malice
more keenly than of yore. His wife, who was at that time
with her children on the Starnberger See, was his comforter
in the best sense:—

'I sit and dream for hours, and think of you, my dear, and
wish you were here and free from all miseries. Nature is a
great teacher, even in matters in which she has otherwise
little enough to do. She brings out the relative value of things
so plainly.'

In the above lecture he had cautioned his pupils: 'One word
more. I would not have you think my point of view affected by
my personal experience. That any one, holding such opinions

as I have put before you, who instils into his students wherever possible the principle, "A metaphysical conclusion is either a fallacy or a masked empirical inference," will not be viewed with much favour by the believers in metaphysics and *a priori* intuition, need hardly be expatiated on. Metaphysicians, like all who have no definite reasons to set against their opponents, are not generally very courteous in their polemic; one's own progress can indeed be estimated by the rising discourtesy of the opposition': and even if he met these discourteous scientific rejoinders with the dignity of a great thinker, the unqualified attacks upon his person and his family had none the less a depressing effect on him, and Helmholtz at this time passed through a critical period.

The entire University of Berlin united solidly with him, as the Philosophical Faculty had on a previous occasion. He, who had so recently joined its ranks, was elected Rector in the year 1876, and this marked witness to the confidence and respect of the many distinguished scientists who belonged at that time to the Berlin University restored his calm and contentment. He went to Switzerland for rest and refreshment, taking long walks over the Grimsel and Eggisch-horn to Belalp, where he stayed with Tyndall, on to Zermatt, and thence with his wife to Stresa, Milan, Spezia, and Rome.

On this journey he composed the discourse which he delivered on October 15, 1877, when he assumed the Rectorate, 'On the Academic Freedom of the German Universities.' It expressed the spirit that was especially cherished and fostered by the Universities of Germany, and which Helmholtz put into words at a much later time in his Congratulatory Address to the Academy on the occasion of du Bois-Reymond's jubilee: 'The younger generation are taught that ideal aims are attainable even in this life, and bring their reward, but only when they are worked for in the right way.' The lecture is of extreme interest, since it reveals the high moral, religious, and political standpoint to which Helmholtz adhered during his whole life, without taking up any public attitude in regard to these questions.

For Helmholtz, the power of a nation lies not merely in its store of provender and money, its cannon and war-ships, but depends, above all, on its political and legal organization as a State, and on the moral discipline of its individual citizens, which determines the superiority of civilized to uncivilized nations. Where there is no firm legal status, where the interests of the majority of the people do not prevail in an orderly fashion, where the political interests of the working classes are not given a legitimate voice in the government, he holds the development of the power of that State to be impossible. For modern Humanity, as he insisted on a later occasion, Science is, in the contests of the more highly developed nations, the sole bond of union that unconditionally makes for peace; in Science, wherever the individual races are educated enough to profit by its fruits, every one is working, not for the good of his country only, but for the whole of Humanity. But it is necessary for the profitable development of the sciences that there shall be an independent conviction of the accuracy of their results, as the consequence of conscientious trial and resolute labour; it is this that becomes the fruitful germ of new insight and the true rule of action. Helmholtz regards Germany as standing in the forefront of the struggle with authority; in the sixteenth century it testified even unto blood for the right of such convictions. He had already pointed out in his Innsbruck Address that there was greater fearlessness of the consequences of the whole entire truth in Germany than elsewhere, while in England and France the many distinguished investigators in natural science had almost always to bow to social and ecclesiastical prejudices, if they were not to suffer in their social influence and activity. In the whole truth he sees the remedy for the disadvantages and dangers of half-knowledge: 'An industrious, moderate, moral people must have the boldness to look truth full in the face: the nation will not perish even if a few premature and one-sided theories are paraded, which may seem to infringe on the principles of morality and social order.'

And yet it is this very love of truth that tempts the Germans to follow out the cardinal questions to their very foundations, without regard to their practical consequences and useful applications. The independent intellectual development of the last three centuries had begun in Germany under political conditions which threw the chief burden upon theological study. Germany had freed Europe from the old tyranny, but in the Reformation intellectual life had lost its former hold and its coherence; everything had to be presented in a new light, and new questions raised for discussion. Since the problems that had to be solved were principally those of morals, aesthetics, and metaphysics, it was in Helmholtz's opinion natural that the learned men of all nations should precipitate themselves upon philosophy. Criticism of the sources of knowledge was initiated, and the German temperament could not break loose from metaphysics, which exerted a dangerous fascination upon it, until there was nothing left to find. Then, in the second half of the Eighteenth Century, the rejuvenated mental life of the nation blossomed into its artistic prime, and all hearts turned from a joyless civic and political existence to the realms of poetry or philosophy. 'The work of the man of science appeared narrow, poor, and unimportant in comparison with the great conceptions of philosophers and thinkers.' Helmholtz recognizes clearly that this movement broke the Napoleonic yoke, and in its great poems set the noblest ideals of the German nation, but 'sanctuary in an ideal world is a false aid of brief duration; it only helps the enemy to his goal, and where knowledge reflects itself repeatedly it becomes objectless and empty, or is lost in phrases and illusions'.

The reaction against this tendency set in not only in the region of natural science, but in history, aesthetics, and in philology also. It was perceived in all directions that facts must be known before their laws can be established.

Helmholtz urges the younger students, in his Rectorial Address, to pursue Science for its own sake, and advances ideas of high ethical import, such as he clothed in beautiful words, with modest but assured self-consciousness, in his famous *Tischrede* in 1891:—

'I will not say that higher ethical motives were not co-operating with scientific curiosity, and sense of duty as an official of the State, in the first half of my life, when I was still obliged to work for my living; but it was harder to be certain of their efficacy so long as egoistic motives drove one to work. The same is the case with most workers. Later, with an assured position, when those who have no inward impulse towards science may cease to work, there is pre-eminently, in those who do work on, a higher conception of their relation to Humanity. They gradually realize by their own experience how the ideas that they have expressed, whether in their writings, or in verbal commerce with their students, acquire a fuller content and more consistent form as they are more thoroughly worked out, bringing new instruction to themselves also. The entire conceptual world of civilized humanity comes before them as a living and growing whole, which in comparison with the brief life of the individual appears to be eternal. Such a one regards himself, in his own small efforts towards the building up of science, as a minister in an eternally righteous cause, with which he is linked by the closest bands of love. Thus, even to himself, his work is consecrated.'

This is the temper which Helmholtz describes to the young students as fostered by the German Universities, and which he holds to be unrealized in other nations, while he does not deny that Germany might well imitate England in her encouragement of a keen sense of the beauty and freshness of antiquity, the refinement and precision of language, and the physical weal of the students. But the untrammelled freedom of the German student, which amazes all foreigners, is a treasure that has to be guarded; it depends on the judgement and reasonableness of those to whom the freedom is granted. Then, and then only, is liberty of scientific teaching necessary and free from danger.

'In the German Empire of to-day, the most extreme consequences of materialistic metaphysics, the boldest speculations on the basis of Darwin's evolutionary theory, can be promulgated as freely as the extreme deification of Papal Infallibility.'

At the close of the same year (November 26, 1877), Helmholtz presented a paper to the Academy, 'On Galvanic Currents, caused by Differences of Concentration; Deductions from the Mechanical Theory of Heat,'—which inaugurated the series of his important researches in electrochemistry. After convincing himself by his electrical work that the Faraday-Maxwell hypothesis for electrodynamics (to the confirmation of which he did not return for two years) was the most probable, he now turned to Faraday's electrochemical theories, of which, as also of their development by Hittorf, Wiedemann, and F. Kohlrausch, he gave a full discussion in the Faraday Lecture delivered some time later in England.

Faraday gave the name of ions to the atoms or groups of atoms that are carried along with the current, calling those that

move with the positive electricity kations, and those charged
with the negative electricity anions; the kation therefore travels
to the electrode to which the positive electricity of the fluid is
directed, to the kathode, and the anion to the anode, whence the
same electricity streams into the fluid. Faraday discovered the
law that governs the whole of modern electro-chemistry, viz.
that there is always equivalence of electrical and chemical
motion in each section of an electrolytic conductor, so that
precisely the same quantity of positive or negative electricity
moves along with each monovalent ion, or each valency of a
multivalent ion, and accompanies it inseparably in all the
motions which it makes through the fluid. Helmholtz called
this quantity the electrical charge of the ion. Assuming that
electricity also is divided into certain elementary quantities, or
atoms of electricity, he concludes that each ion, so long as it
moves through the fluid, must be united with one electrical
equivalent for each of its valencies. Separation can only occur
at the surfaces of the electrodes, so that if these exert sufficient
electromotive force, the ions will give up their previous charges
of electricity, and become electrically neutral. Maintaining
the law of the conservation of energy, as well as the strict
validity of Faraday's law of electrolysis, as fundamental principles,
he finds that if the hydrogen and oxygen of the water could be
dissociated without losing their electrical charges, they would
exert a reciprocal attraction equal to the gravitation of masses
which exceeded them 400,000 billion times in weight. In the
further investigation of the mode in which the motions of the
ponderable molecules are affected by these forces, Clausius had
shown that the electrical forces tend to maintain an even
distribution of the antagonistic ions throughout the fluid, so
that all parts of it are neutralized both electrically and chemically;
but that the least external electromotive force suffices to disturb
the uniformity of this distribution. But when an ion parts with
its charge of electricity, the electrical forces of the battery
encounter a resistance which entails a very considerable
expenditure of work before it can be overcome. This happens
if the ions, as they lose 'their electrical charges, are simultaneously separated from the fluid as gases, or in the form of
solid metallic layers. The chemical association of two elementary
substances of great affinity produces quantities of heat which

are equivalent to a large quantity of mechanical work; the dissociation of the resulting chemical compound requires an expenditure of work corresponding to the amount of the chemical forces lost in the formation of the compound.

'Oxygen and hydrogen when separated contain a store of energy; then if they are allowed to burn to form water, they develop a large amount of heat. The two elements are contained in the water, and their chemical attraction persists, and keeps them firmly united; but it can no longer be utilized, nor produce any positive action. We must reduce the united elements to their first state, and separate them from one another, employing to this end a force greater than their affinity, before we can restore to them the power of producing their original effect. The amount of heat produced by chemical association is at least approximately equivalent to the yield of work of the chemical forces brought into play. The same quantity of work must be employed, on the other hand, to dissociate the compound, and reduce the two gases to a free state.'

In this work 'On Galvanic Currents', Helmholtz was the first to apply the two laws of thermodynamics to electricity. In order to keep up a current of electricity through any conductor it is necessary to expend a certain amount of chemical or mechanical work; the supply of positive electricity in the positive end of the conductor must be perpetually renewed, in order to oppose the repulsive force of the positive electricity there accumulated, and the same holds for the negative electricity at the negative end. In accordance, therefore, with Faraday's law, the electromotive force of the battery must be proportional to the work which can be obtained by the transformations of one equivalent of each of the substances in question. Here, however, it is not merely the great forces of affinity of the elements that unite or separate in fixed proportions that have to be considered, but, further, the lesser molecular forces of attraction exerted by the water and other components of the solution upon its ions, and Helmholtz set himself the task of detecting influences of this kind (which are too feeble to be found by the calorimetric method) by measurement of the electromotive forces. In order to calculate by means of the mechanical theory of heat what influence the concentration of a solution of salt has upon the E. M. F., a current was led through a salt solution, producing on the one hand an equivalent chemical decomposition of the solution, and on the other an alteration of concentration at the electrodes. This alteration was continuously reversed, since, where the current weakened the solution, the excess of water was converted into vapour and removed, while at the points where the solution became more concentrated, the vapour was again condensed. If the water is agitated with the dissolved salt, the temperature being kept constant by an appropriate addition of heat, then with weak currents the whole process may be regarded as a reversible cycle, and the sum of the work gained and lost vanishes; the theoretical conclusions thence deduced agreed satisfactorily with the experimental data previously obtained.

At the close of the year 1877, Richard Helmholtz left the Polytechnic at Munich, where he had been studying for four years; and Helmholtz had the satisfaction of seeing his son established in Krauss's locomotive factory, where in 1880 he became Head of the Bureau for Construction, and in 1887 Head Engineer.

Helmholtz now became more and more occupied with official business.

The time was fast approaching for the delivery of the great Address which he was to give on August 3, 1878, for the Commemoration of the Berlin University, and in which he contemplated a free and untrammelled statement of his philosophical creed. He hesitated for some time as to its title.

'The title must come last,' he writes to his wife. 'I have not yet decided it. Perhaps "What is Reality?" or "All transitory things are but parables", or "An Appeal to the Ultimate", or perhaps merely "Principles of Perception".'

In the end he chose the title 'The Facts that underlie Perception', after his wife had written to him, 'I fear that the Ultimate would be an unknown aim to many.' After delivering this most beautiful and most significant of all his lectures, the contents of which have been already outlined, he announces on August 4 to his wife :—

'I knew it could not be to the taste of the majority. It contained new ideas that were bound to puzzle them . . . not of course Zeller, du Bois, Kronecker, and kindred spirits. But I said to myself that if I had to work, it should be at something that interested me too, for in the long run it is better they should find me too learned, rather than too trivial.'

This left him little time for researches in electrodynamics and electrochemistry, and this year he only published two very interesting points supplementary to his earlier work in acoustics and optics.

The discovery of the telephone was a great surprise to him at first, but he soon grasped its scientific principles.

The thing seemed to him so obvious, he wrote to du Bois, that he had not felt it necessary to form any theory about it; but then of course he had for years gone to bed and got up again with Fourier's series in his mind, and could not reason from himself to other people in this case.

Du Bois had immediately after the production of the telephone explained the appreciation of timbre by this instrument, by saying that he pictured every sound as analysed into its partial tones, basing his opinion on the fact that each of these partial tones was conveyed to the hearer's telephone by the electrical vibrations of the conducting wire, with alteration of phase indeed, but with the same frequency and relative amplitude. Since displacement of phase, according to Helmholtz's earlier acoustical conclusions, is immaterial to the quality of the sound, the timbre of the spoken sounds is not interfered with. Hermann set up an experiment designed for a fresh theoretical verification, in which a current-producing telephone was closed by one wire of a coil wound with two parallel wires, while the second wire, wholly insulated from the first, was either connected directly with the observer's telephone, or with a wire from a second double-wound coil, the other wire of which led to the observer's telephone. Now by the known law of electrodynamic induction, the E. M. F. is proportional to the differential quotients of the current-intensity by the time. But since with the differential quotient of the sine of a linear function of the time, the multiplier of the time participates as a factor in the amplitude, Hermann concluded that in this transfer of electrical oscillations by induction in each of the double coils, the amplitude of the electrical oscillations, which correspond to the higher partial tones of each sound, would increase, as compared with those of the deeper, in proportion to their greater frequency. Since on the one hand the ratio of the intensities of the partial tones emitted by the second telephone must be considerably altered, while on the other hand the quality of sound remains the same, Hermann found this incompatible with the Theory of Timbre which Helmholtz had propounded in his earlier acoustical observations.

Helmholtz then showed, in a paper presented to the Academy on July 11, 1878, called 'Telephones and Timbre', that if the induction of each circuit, not only on those adjacent to it, but also on itself, were taken into consideration the conclusions made by Hermann exactly confirmed his explanation of the timbre. He proved that the intensities of the induced currents were independent of the frequency, while their phases on the contrary were a little displaced, and at the same time explained, from the mathematical expressions he had formulated, what had already been observed, i.e. that the deep tones of a man's voice generally appeared too weak with ordinary telephones. Helmholtz did not take the reaction of the oscillating iron plates in the receiver into consideration, because its oscillation has a much less amplitude than that of the corresponding plates in the transmitter. If the duration of the induction current is prolonged without external disturbance for more than 0·01 second, he finds that with the direct connexion of the two telephones the electric oscillations corresponding with the highest tones and noises do not vary perceptibly in phase, nor in relative strength, from those of the exciting magnetism; the deeper tones on the contrary may be considerably displaced in their phases, and somewhat diminished in strength. Quality of sound is affected not by means of the electrical motions, but only by the co-vibrating iron plates.

After the fatigues of the Rectorial year Helmholtz went to Switzerland for rest, in the first place visiting Boll, who was lying very ill at Davos, and wanted to discuss his theory of light and colour sensation—some notes on which were published after his death in 1881—with Helmholtz. From Davos, Helmholtz went by Samaden to Pontresina, then by the Italian Lakes to Milan, and so by Nervi to Siena, which he had long desired to see. On September 24 he writes to his wife from Siena: 'To-day and yesterday I have been exploring this old and most singular mountain nest. It lies crowded together upon a hill-top, surrounded by great walls, and traversed by narrow streets. The poverty of the present day strikes one acutely in contrast with the mighty remains of former splendours. It has much more character than Pisa; the works of art remind one of the Pisan School, especially the Duomo, the *façade* of which dates from Giovanni Pisano, but is far more beautiful and richer than that of the Duomo at Pisa. It also has black bands, but is covered with a wealth of the finest sculptural ornament, which is well proportioned, with fine red marble inlaid between. Inside there is a pulpit by Niccolò Pisano, father of Giovanni, which recalls the one in the Baptistery at Pisa, but is less finely modelled. The interior, which is also banded, and decorated with fine belts of colour in the roof, is paved with some marvellous *graffiti*, in white marble, with black outlines, and with grey, yellow, and red marble introduced in places. The drawing of these is wonderfully perfect, and the effect is most remarkable, though they have been much damaged in places by people walking on them. Besides the Duomo there are many interesting palaces, nearly all stamped with the black lozenges of the Pitti and Strozzi of Florence. One sees these at every turn. An enormous quantity of pictures has accumulated everywhere, mostly in the ancient style, some badly preserved, so that the colour has perished, and one can only reconstruct them from the quiet, friendly faces. Among the later ones, however, Sodoma and Beccafumi almost come up to Raphael. Of the former, one can only get unsatisfactory glimpses elsewhere: he is skilled in fresco, is less dignified than Raphael, and does not possess his great dramatic power, but his figures might often pass for Raphael's, and have a very pleasing expression. To do justice to Siena, one needs more knowledge of the history of art than I possess at present . . . the Piazza in front of the Palazzo Pubblico is also very characteristic. The Palazzo reminds one of the Doges' Palace at Venice, but is more antique and less stately. The Piazza in front of it has the form and depth of an ancient semicircular theatre, the whole diameter being occupied by the Palace. The rooms inside are very large, and contain a number of pictures, mostly of the early masters, and half obliterated.'

After a short stay in Rome, he hastened on to Naples, which was new to him:—

'I really am in Naples now, and Nature here is incredibly

beautful. The hotel recommended by Bonghi is high up, some 200 feet above the sea, on the slope of the hill, in the new street Corso Vittorio Emmanuele, which is the limit of the inner town. In my room, we have a vertical wall of rock behind us, and a deep precipice in front, so that we can see down to the plain over the roofs of the nearest houses. In the afternoon, when the sun is off my balcony, I need only sit down there in order to have the finest view in the world before my eyes, viz. the most lively part of the strand, above the clusters of the high-roofed houses of Santa Lucia, in the centre of the city, to Posilippo at the end, then the Gulf with the blue-greens and purples of the Mediterranean, and Vesuvius on the other side, with the tongue of land that holds Castellamare and Sorrento, and the island of Capri and open horizon of sea beyond. Vesuvius has lately formed a new cone in its crater. Yesterday evening and early to-day the summit was hidden by clouds; but this evening we saw the column of smoke, which is full of ashes, but looks white by day—red hot from the rift in the mountain below. A fresh outbreak of lava is anticipated. The old streams of lava can easily be recognized from here, making a greyish black trail against the green of the vineyards. I am fortunate in finding the mountain active. The weather is very fine and sunny, with a partly clouded deep blue sky; to-day for the first time it is really warm, but not oppressive, no dust, and the vegetation greener than I have ever seen it in Italy. The elms with thick festoons of vines are touched with brown, but the ground beneath is covered with the freshest green crops. Even at Genoa and Pisa it was much greener than we had seen it elsewhere, but still not so green as this. . . .

'To-day I have made my last mountain expedition for this year, up Vesuvius—to the crater of which I climbed, wandering about on its burning lava, and fortunately returning unconsumed. The crater is covered with this lava at the bottom now, through which the steam has lately forced a new outlet, and is forming a fresh cone of ashes round the hole, where one can see it working all the time. Every now and then the mountain mass, fused by the hot steam, blocks the way, and is then blown out with a noise like cannon, when the glowing remains of the viscous slag are thrown down again in clouds of smoke, fall back upon the cone of ashes, and thus enlarge it. Every five minutes or so there was a similar detonation, and we could get within 100 paces of it, as the glowing slag fell back regularly upon the surface of the new cone. The most recent streams of lava exhibited a very slow and hardly perceptible motion. One could feel it warm to the soles of one's feet, and on pouring water into a crack it hissed out again at once. Some cracks in the newest lava still glowed red. The alpenstocks caught fire, and the guide picked out some of the viscous glowing mass. The old walls of the crater were steaming with a penetrating vapour, and brightly coloured with yellow sulphur, white salt, and green copper. It was in the highest degree interesting and impressive, but also rather fatiguing and expensive.'

From Naples he went by Rome and Trient to see Lenbach in Munich, and thence back to Berlin.

As soon as Helmholtz was free of his Rectorial duties he returned to the electrical work that had been interrupted for a year, starting off with a study of the contact theory of electricity, which appeared in *Wiedemann's Annalen* with the title 'Studies in Electrical Contact-layers'. If, in the theory of the distribution of electricity in conducting bodies, the forces of this agent, as known by their action at a distance, are alone taken into consideration, it is found that in a condition of equilibrium the electricity leaves the interior of the body, and forms an infinitely thin layer upon its surface alone. But if there should be a sudden change in the value of the potential function at the limit of two different bodies, as e.g. at the contact of two conductors under the influence of a galvanic force acting between them, then in this case a double electrical layer will be formed along the surface: Helmholtz denotes the product of the density of the positive electricity into the distance between the two layers as the electric momentum of the layer, where the distance is to be regarded as small, but not infinitely small, since otherwise the work employed in producing the layers would have to be infinitely great.

The supposition of the formation of a double layer, as previously made for bodies electrified by contact, was now extended by Helmholtz to the case of contact between any two bodies. The expressions for the potential difference led him in the first place to explain the production of electricity by friction, and he succeeded in deriving the relations of the series of electrical tensions due to friction, and the theory of the electrical machine, satisfactorily from it. The most important object of the work was, however, to set forth the theory of those phenomena which appear when a fluid is flowing past a solid wall, and to account for the transition between the excitation of electricity by the galvanic opposition of bodies at rest, and by the sliding friction of solid bodies. Starting from the view that the fluid is in galvanic opposition to the wall of the vessel, and that they both form an electrical double layer along their surface ot contact, he succeeded in explaining two phenomena that are very closely connected— the propagation of fluids through narrow tubes, in consequence of the passage of an electrical current through the same, and the appearance of electromotive forces, when fluids are driven through similar tubes by hydrostatic pressure. The theoretical developments and the comparison with the results of G. Wiedemann and Quincke's experiments, however, refer only to capillary tubes, while in wider tubes more complicated phenomena of motion appear at the point at which the current enters. In this paper, as in the Faraday Lecture later, and in a series of subsequent electrical researches, Helmholtz comes back repeatedly to the close connexion between the electrical and the chemical forces, as well as to the explanation of Volta's fundamental experiment.

He assumes that electrical and chemical forces are essentially the same, and supports the view that the presence of the forces, which when unchecked set up chemical processes, suffices to call out the corresponding electrical distributions, even before the appearance of the chemical combination; it does not seem to him necessary that a complete chemical process must invariably be the precursor of Volta's charges. Helmholtz is here at one with Faraday, who assumed the identity of the forces of chemical affinity with electricity, and expressed the view that the atoms adhere to the electrical charges, and the opposed charges again to each other, without thereby excluding molecular forces, which act directly from atom to atom.

Helmholtz regards Volta's much-contested experiments as unimpeachable; if a momentary metallic connexion be made between a copper plate and a zinc plate, at minimal distance from each other, and well insulated by bars of shellac standing opposite one another like the plates of a condenser, and if they are then moved farther apart, the copper will be negatively, and the zinc positively charged.

The necessary experimental laws had already been expressed by Helmholtz in the 'Conservation of Energy', to the effect that, so long as only conductors of the first class are involved,—i. e. conductors which undergo no electrolytic dissociation during conduction,—and so long as these conductors are at the same temperature and at rest, the passage of the electric current always tends to equilibrium of the electricity; it is only when the conductors are moved by an external force that electrical currents, or concentrated accumulations of electricity, arise. This class of experiments further comprises those with dry metal plates, which are connected by dry and insulated metal wires. Since in this case, with each new arrangement of such conductors at the same temperature, the electric motion soon produces equilibrium, we must assume its cause to be forces of a simple character, which obey the law of the conservation of energy. In this essay Helmholtz brought forward the view that these phenomena arise from forces of attraction, which the different substances possess in different degrees for the two electricities, and which only act at perceptibly small distances. When two pieces of copper and of zinc are in contact, and the zinc attracts the positive electricity more strongly than the copper, it flows to the zinc, and charges it positively, while the copper remains negative, until the electrical attraction produced by this charge, and acting at a distance, which draws the positive electricity back to the copper, restores equilibrium with the attraction of the zinc.

Moreover the *vis viva* which a particle of positive electricity acquires from the influence of the zinc and copper alone, in its transfer from copper to zinc, will be equivalent to the *vis viva* lost by the same electric particle through the attraction of the negative charge of the copper, and repulsion of the positive from the zinc, in the same way. This last magnitude calculated for the unit of positive electricity is, however, termed difference of electrical potential-function between the copper and the zinc.

This theory thus demands that the electricity contained in the copper and zinc when they come into contact shall be so distributed between the two that the difference of electrical potential shall be of a definite magnitude, determined by the nature of the metals. From this it is at once obvious that conductors of this sort must be subject to the laws of the galvanic tensional series, and that chains consisting of three or more conductors of the first class at the same temperature can never produce an electric current, since the attractive forces of the metals for the electricities can only cause the electricity to assume the state of equilibrium, which is imposed by these forces of attraction. Volta assumed a separating force residing in the surface of contact, and believed that the positive electricity, having once entered the zinc by the surface of contact with the copper, could flow out again without further obstacle into any conductor in which it was not opposed by any new force of separation at the contact surfaces; in Helmholtz's opinion, on the contrary, the positive electricity was held fast in the zinc by attraction, and this attraction must be overcome by a corresponding expenditure of work, before the positive electricity can be removed from the zinc again by any other natural force. Electrolytic conductors, however, do not follow the tensional series, because they are dissociated by each electric motion, and cannot, of course, while this dissociation is proceeding, arrive at a state of resting equilibrium. Helmholtz confirmed his theory by a long series of elaborate experiments, which he performed with the help of W. Thomson's quadrant electrometer.

In his earlier critical work on the Theory of Electrodynamics, Helmholtz had evinced more and more disposition to adopt the Faraday-Maxwell hypothesis, but he had always insisted that a complete understanding of the theory of electromagnetic phenomena, and an ultimate decision as to the claims of the several hypotheses, would only be possible after an exact investigation of the processes that obtain for unclosed currents of very brief duration. Weber had, indeed, endeavoured to minimize certain difficulties and contradictions in his electrodynamic hypotheses, by attributing to electricity a certain amount of inertia, such as pertains to heavy bodies; Helmholtz, however, very soon recognized that true inertia would be proportional to the mass of the electricity in motion, independent of the position of the conductor, and that this would be manifested in the retardation of the oscillatory motions of the electricity, as appears with sudden interruptions of the electrical currents in wires of high conductivity.   Since it was to be expected that it would be possible by this means to determine an upper limit to the value of this inertia, Helmholtz, when he had to set a prize subject in physics for his students at the end of the summer term, gave them the task of devising experiments which should demonstrate the strength of extra-currents, 'with the certain and subsequently confirmed expectation' that Heinrich Hertz, who by von Bezold's advice had been working in the Physical Laboratory of the University under Helmholtz's direction since the autumn of 1878, and whom the latter had recognized even in the elementary course as a student of quite extraordinary promise, would interest himself in it, and attack the problem successfully.

The magnitude of the extra-current was to be used in ascertaining an upper limit for the mass in motion; and the extra-currents from double-wound coils with their branches traversed by the current in opposite directions were specially recommended.   The precise answer given by Hertz showed that at most $\frac{1}{20}$ to $\frac{1}{30}$ of the extra-current in a double-wound coil was due to the inertia of the electricity; investigations of the influence of the centrifugal force of a rapidly rotating plate upon the motion of the electrical current flowing through it led the gifted young investigator to a far lower superior limit of the value of inertia in electricity.

These researches of Hertz, the results of which were plainly foreseen by Helmholtz, gave substantial support to the Faraday-Maxwell hypothesis of the nature of electricity, and confirmed Helmholtz in his opinion of the accuracy of Faraday's conceptions.   The phenomena of diamagnetism were explained in the simplest manner, on the assumption that diamagnetic bodies are such as are less magnetizable than the surrounding media with which space is filled, so that even the space that is free from all ponderable masses, or the luminiferous ether contained in it, must be magnetizable.   According to Clerk Maxwell it was, however, of essential importance for Faraday's Theory of Dielectric Polarization and the elimination of action at a distance, to know whether the origin and passage of dielectric polarization in an insulator would give rise to the same electro-dynamic action in its neighbourhood as a galvanic current in a conductor. In order to obtain evidence for this, Helmholtz made it the subject of one of the great prize competitions of the Academy, by which Hertz was led to his remarkable discoveries. These afforded the direct proof of the accuracy of the hypothesis which Faraday and Maxwell had advanced as highly probable, i. e. that the oscillations of light are electrical oscillations in the ether that occupies space, and that this in itself possesses the properties of an insulator and a magnetizable medium.

'There can no longer be any question,' says Helmholtz later in his classical preface to Hertz's *Principles of Mechanics*, 'that the luminous vibrations are electric vibrations in the ether that fills space, and that the latter itself possesses the properties of an insulator and a magnetic medium. The electric oscillations in the ether represent an intermediate stage between the relatively slow motions produced by the elastic and resonant vibrations of a magnetic tuning-fork, and the enormously swift vibrations of light, but it can be shown that their rate of propagation, their character as transverse oscillations, and the concomitant possibility of polarization phenomena, and of refraction and reflection, correspond completely with those obtaining in the case of light and heat rays. The electrical waves are only lacking in capacity to affect the eye, like the dark heat rays, since their frequency is not sufficiently high. It was verily a great achievement to acquire absolute proof that light, that mysterious and powerful force of nature, is so nearly related to a second equally mysterious and perhaps still more potent force, that of electricity. For theoretical science it is perhaps even more important to understand how what appears to be action at a distance can be propagated by translation of action from one layer of the intermediate medium to the next. The mystery of gravitation indeed remains, since we cannot yet logically explain it otherwise than as due to a true action at a distance.' But it took Hertz nearly the whole of the last decade but one of the Nineteenth Century to establish and work out his mighty conception, which is to-day the foundation of the whole modern doctrine of electricity.

In the Easter holidays Helmholtz visited Ludwig at Leipzig, and wandered through the Schwarzathal in Thuringia, and at the close of his Rectorial year, wearied with incessant official and scientific work, he went for three weeks to Pontresina, where he had been used to refresh himself in body and mind by long visits.

'Although Helmholtz grew older,' writes Blaserna to the author, 'and began to feel trouble in his respiratory organs, he did not give up climbing. He looked on mountaineering as a cure, when properly administered. Thus he told me one day that he intended to climb the magnificent Piz Languard. I offered myself as his companion; but for a long time he would not hear of it, as he thought I should go too fast for him. It was only when I promised to keep behind, and give him no opportunity for talking, that he accepted my company. It is notoriously an ascent with a good path, which a strong climber can do in three hours, a moderate walker in four. We took quite six hours over it: but Helmholtz arrived in good condition, spread out his map, and studied all the different mountains, and after we had rested there an hour we started down again, and returned safe and well to Pontresina. In the last years of his visits to Pontresina he gave up the mountains, but he made two little ascents with great regularity every morning and afternoon, up the Muottas da Pontresina or da Celerina, or up the Schafberg. The iron regularity with which he accomplished his two walks every day was amazing. They were unfortunately his last. A few years later, Pontresina lost, as one might say, by his death its distinguishing scientific character.'

After he had left Pontresina, and had spent some weeks with his wife at Interlaken, he wrote from Thun on September 15, 1879, to his friend Knapp at New York: 'Relatively speaking, things have gone better this year than previously in Berlin. I have at last learned how much I can get out of myself in work and pleasure, and am stubborn and unresponsive to people who try to take up my time when I am tired.'

In the Easter holidays of 1880, he took a journey of several weeks in Spain, going as far as Tangier in Africa. His full letters to his wife give us a lively account of the impressions made on him by art and nature; a few short extracts may be cited :—

'*Barcelona, Palm Sunday, March* 21. From Nîmes we made

an expedition to the Pont du Gard, a strong bridge over the
torrent, constructed for a Roman aqueduct in the time of
Augustus, in a solitary mountain valley, as high as the highest
cathedral. Rousseau is reported to have said of this that it
was the only thing he had seen in his life that had exceeded
his anticipations. The expedition takes at least five hours, and
we discussed whether it were worth devoting the day to a
fragment of Roman aqueduct when we had seen so many.
But we felt like Rousseau, save that it was not the first time
we had had such an experience. . . .

'Here we have spent two very pleasant days, with a Passion
Play in the Theatre, which was very remarkable, with a great
Procession, and so on. . . . The Theatre is a vast building for
four thousand spectators, well proportioned and comfortably
arranged, so that our northern Court Theatres would be put
to shame by it. The old Passion Play was given in the
Catalonian dialect, which of course we could not understand,
since we are much in the same plight with modern Spanish.
It was cleverly staged with all modern accessories, and
frightfully realistic in every detail, so that the whole performance succeeded in impressing one as the reading of it
never does. . . . The Procession on Palm Sunday was escorted
by a troop of Roman warriors in costume, with a band and a
captain. . . . There was a great crowd of people,—long processions
of Catholic Guilds, students and young men in strange costumes
of shiny black linen, cut with trains like women's clothes with
gauffred frills, dragged the figure of the Christ, which was
drawn along on boards, and represented the bowed Christ of
the Mount of Olives. . . . L. urged us to visit his friend, the
Professor of Chemistry, Don Ramon Manjarez, in his laboratory, and allow him and the other professors to take us round
the new University buildings. I had the satisfaction of finding
my acoustical apparatus fairly complete.'

'*Madrid, Good Friday, March* 26. The Escorial, gigantic
burying-place of the Spanish Kings, lies some distance from
Madrid in a rocky waste among the mountains, and gives
a certain idea of serious grandeur and artistic taste in the
fanatical Philip II which raised him above his childish
successors. One can see that he was in terrible earnest over
what he wanted, and what he designed for himself is simple

to a degree, and almost meagre. The church, on the other hand, is of vast proportions, erected with taste and simplicity by Neapolitan architects, something after the model of what S. Peter's in Rome might have been if the rococo style had not spoiled it. What Philip's successors added is merely childish, with the exception of some beautiful Gobelins after Teniers' sketches, for which indeed the finest pictures of Raphael and Titian were sent to the lumber-room, whence they were rescued for the Museum. Taken as a whole it is an historical monument, testifying to the spirit of its age, even if that was antagonistic to us. . . . The Picture Gallery is imposing; the collection of people whom Velasquez counterfeited is so extraordinarily fresh and full of expression, that they seem to be our contemporaries. . . . Yesterday I went early to Toledo, the former Palace; a crowded mountain nest, surrounded on three sides by the Tagus in a deep gorge, a natural fortress with all kinds of Ostrogothic and Moorish remains; these are insignificant, but the Gothic Cathedral is so pure, fine, and luxuriant in form, with such elegance of stone- and woodwork, in which the influence of the Alhambra School seems to survive, that it overshadows everything I have previously seen in Gothic churches. Besides, it has been comparatively little spoilt by later additions from the Jesuit period. It is far more characteristically and consistently Gothic than the Cathedral at Milan, and therefore makes an even purer impression of perfect beauty of form and dignity. . . . Unfortunately the exterior is almost invisible. . . .'

'*Cordova, Tuesday, March* 30. Here then is the great mosque, the Cathedral of to-day, a wonder of architecture, exotic and fabulous, an immense flat tent-roof supported by more than 1,000 pillars, united by fantastic double arches, originally open everywhere to the orangery of the fore-court, with the chapel for the preservation of the Koran behind, adorned with wondrous marble work and mosaics, all in carpet patterns. Not far off is a similarly decorated chapel, the place of prayer of the Khalif. Unfortunately they have closed it in as a church, separating it with walls from the court, and have erected a high choir in the baroque style, so that one can only imagine how airy, and clear, and cool, and light it must have been before they made a church out of it. The question is forced upon one, how this highly developed civilization came to an end. The Moors took none of it back to Africa, and what the Spaniards may have learned from them disappeared within the next hundred years, save for the great system of irrigation, which made the land fertile so far as it extended. . . . Next day we took a walk to the slopes of the Sierra Morena north of the city, whence we had a good view of the fertility of the country. Little runlets of water come down from the hills, and are carefully distributed. The orange-trees are like forest trees in their growth. I never saw any like them in Italy, and they were more covered with fruit than any apple-tree I ever saw, while among the fruit were fresh buds and wreaths of blossom; wild roses, irises, spireas, violets, all in full bloom, as one sees them in Germany on the sunniest days of June. Among them are solitary date palms, shooting gracefully heavenwards.'

'*Granada, Friday, April* 2. And now we have really seen the Alhambra, which is as marvellous in reality as it has been described in books and pictures. Marble in the most elegant carved work, with a superfluity of wondrous patterns. . . . After luncheon there was a bull-fight, the first in a new arena, a great festival for the people. As regards the spectators it was extremely interesting. The arena is constructed exactly after the old pattern (it is true that the upper part is of wood); the public behaves exactly as was described by the Roman authors. The crowd is seized with a raging intoxication; the shouting is uninterrupted, now applause, and now hisses. It is necessary to get there an hour before the time, otherwise one has no chance of a seat. During this time we were entertained by a feeble jet of water that was supposed to sprinkle the Square, and by the orange-sellers who flung their fruits up to the purchasers in the top rows of seats, and were paid in the same way, to the entertainment of the public. Each good throw was applauded, each bad one hissed. The elegant ladies for the most part, unfortunately, were above us; those we could see were in picturesque national costumes, pretty to look at, but very bold in colouring: one was dressed like a toreador. These last are fine fellows, slim, agile, dexterous and reckless, so that it is a pleasure to see them moving about in their splendid and elegant costumes. The banderilleros especially, who let the bull charge them without cloak or weapon, and then leap aside at the moment when he threatens to impale them, and fix the barbed plumes of feathers and ornaments on his neck, are incomparably skilful. Immediately after, indeed, the bull is diverted by waving a cloak in front of him, to prevent him from repeating his attack. The fate of the bull is really a subject for congratulation ; he falls in battle instead of in the slaughter-house. It is true that the animal, by the time the matador advances alone to give him the death thrust, is in the last degree exasperated and distraught, and for the six bulls that were immolated this *coup de grâce* was successful at its first delivery in two cases only. But what really shocks one is the way the horses are treated, not merely in the arena but every-where else, like those destined for death that are ridden against the bull with bandaged eyes by the picadores, and are driven by goads to the attack so long as they can carry them ; and the way the public yells for new horses, *Caballo ! caballo !* when only one or two survive; this is the really horrible part of the spectacle. If it were only an exhibition of human courage one could forgive an element of savagery. But in reality they tire out the bull by letting him rush repeatedly at the defenceless horses, which he hates more than men, and it is only when he is utterly exhausted that the men take part in the encounter.'

' *Malaga, Tuesday, April* 6. Malaga is not particularly characteristic. A fine Renaissance Cathedral, the tower of which we climbed to get a general view of the town, is fairly large and elegant. The sea-winds are injurious to vegetation close to the town, but wherever shelter is afforded by the mountains, there are huge groves of oranges, plantations of sugar-cane, and the like. . . . We find Wattenbach's book a great treasure; it is more useful than Murray, Gautier, and Amici. He has distinct talent as a Baedeker, and his prose is not unworthy of Spain.'

' *Tangier, Tuesday, April* 13. We spent a very interesting day in Gibraltar; one of the English officers, Col. Lemprière, whom we met in the Ronda, gave us an order for the Galleries where the cannon are posted round the northern side of the rock, and we roamed from 10 till 4 through the tunnels of the battery. . . . It is impossible to express all the astonishment one feels here in Tangier, on being suddenly plunged into the midst of the Mohammedan world, as it is presented to eye and ear. The variety of costumes and of nakedness is indescribable. The turbans, which are only worn by the Moslems, are kept scrupulously clean, and make a good effect . . . as also the white, or black and white striped burnous, with the extraordinarily characteristic eyes and sharp features of the older men beneath them. The women, so far as they appear in the streets, are veiled in not over clean and coarse rough sheets, which they are not too particular in drawing over their faces.'

Helmholtz then returned by Seville, Bordeaux, and Paris to Berlin, where he immediately resumed his lectures.

At this time he was already occupying himself with the arduous work in thermodynamics which stood in the closest relation with his later discoveries in the principles of mechanics, but was not published for another two years. He was, however, obliged seriously to consider his health a little more in his enormous undertakings. Even in Seville a slight fainting fit had alarmed his travelling companion, and again after the fatigues of the summer session, a few days before the holidays, he met with an accident by slipping, due probably to a sudden swoon, which might have had the most serious consequences.

By August 8, however, he was able to announce to Ludwig that he was so far better that he should begin the journey to Munich with his wife in a few days by easy stages, and would come first to Leipzig, to rest there a little. The projected journey was carried out, after which he went for a few weeks' rest to Switzerland, returning then to Berlin to resume his thermodynamic work. In the meantime Hertz had been appointed his Assistant in the Physical Institute, and remained there till the year 1883. Helmholtz was also working out certain points that were intimately connected with his earlier researches in electrodynamics and electrochemistry.

The fact that a certain distribution of magnetism occurs in the molecules of soft iron in the vicinity of a magnet, so that the soft iron itself attracts and repels small magnetic bodies, was known not to be peculiar to iron. Faraday had shown that this effect is visible in almost all bodies, and that similar phenomena, indicating a distribution of the opposing kinds of electricities in the molecules of electric insulators, are called out by electric forces. The phenomena were treated mathematically for the motions of rigid magnets and magnetizable iron by Poisson;

W. Thomson had extended this theory to the motions of rigid bodies in magnetizable fluids, and shown them to be related to Faraday's diamagnetic experiments. So soon as the molecules of magnetic or electrically polarized media can be displaced in relation to each other, molecular action necessarily comes into play as well as the original forces acting at a distance. Faraday had assumed a state of tension in the magnetically or dielectrically polarized media in the direction of the lines of force, in consequence of which these tend to shorten, while a pressure acts at right angles to these lines, which tends to drive the substance out in that direction. After W. Thomson in 1843 had proved that forces of this nature could produce the same effect as direct action at a distance on Coulomb's theory, Clerk Maxwell had made this assumption of Faraday the basis of his whole theory of electricity and magnetism. The remarkable effort of electric insulators to expand transversely to the direction of the electrical lines of force had already been established by experiment, when Helmholtz, in his communication to the Berlin Academy (Feb. 17, 1881) 'On the Forces acting on the Interior of Magnetic or Dielectrically Polarized Bodies', proposed a complete theory of the phenomenon that insulators tend to alter their shape under the influence of dielectric forces.

He shows that the tensions which produce an expansion perpendicular to the lines of electric force are (without any special assumption as to the internal constitution of dielectric media) a necessary consequence of the law of conservation of energy, and of those laws which by Poisson's theory regulate temporary magnetism, and are directly transferable to dielectric polarization. By supposing that the constants in Poisson's equations may alter, on the one hand, in consequence of the altered density of the medium, on the other in virtue of the actual displacement, he arrives at another distribution of the potential, and thus at a calculable alteration of energy. But since the equivalent of these is the excess of work which the ponderomotive forces must accomplish to produce the displacements of the points, beyond what is required when no dielectric tension is present, he was able to calculate these forces where the change of energy is determined. The discussion of how far the calculated forces may be resolved into molecular forces shows that it is possible to replace them by a pressure that acts within a dielectric upon a surface-element, the normal to which forms a given angle with the direction of the lines of force, and a tension that is effective in the direction of the same. Helmholtz finally concludes from the expressions for the forces, that the two views—that, namely, which postulates forces acting at a distance, and that of Faraday-Maxwell, according to which there is only polarization of the media—may thus exist side by side.

At the same time Helmholtz published a brief notice in *Wiedemann's Annalen* on 'An Electrodynamic Balance', which he had constructed with the object of avoiding, in the measurement of galvanic currents in absolute measure, the disturbances which the changes in the direction and intensity of the earth's magnetism produce by their electromagnetic action. At the ends of the beam of a small chemical balance, he suspended two coils of copper wire, the height of which is equal to their internal diameter, the axes being vertical; two coils of the same height and greater radius were held in a fixed position somewhat above the movable coils by a horizontal metal bar, fixed by its centre to the pillar that carries the balance. The connexions of the wires are so arranged that one of the movable coils is attracted and the other repelled by the fixed coils; the attracted coil rises, the repelled sinks, when current is passed through the circuit, each of the movable coils being connected with the wires that carry the current by two strips of brass foil. The total action of both coils is maintained in equilibrium by appropriate weights, so that the force which opposes the electrodynamic force, and measures it, is subject to gravity alone, with no variations, such as affect the earth's magnetism.

In the Easter holidays of 1881 Helmholtz went to London with his wife at the invitation of the Chemical Society to give a Lecture in the place 'in which the great investigator Faraday, whose memory was to be honoured, had so often surprised his admiring audience by his revelations of the unsuspected secrets of nature'.

His discourse on 'The Recent Development of Faraday's Ideas on Electricity' (delivered in English, after Roscoe had read it through and altered a few expressions) ranks from its form and content among the most beautiful and profound of his Addresses.

'His Faraday Lecture,' writes his wife, 'was a brilliant success.

The subject was incomprehensible to me, as he discoursed for the most part on atoms, and the influence of electricity on chemical properties: but the enthusiasm when he entered, and the cheers whenever he expressed his own conclusions or opinions, were delightful.'

Commencing with an historical review of the development of Electrodynamics, which culminated in a brilliant exposition of the Faraday-Maxwell Theory, he for the first time gave a connected account of the relation between electrical and chemical forces, as we have followed it above in his separate publications. To arrive at an understanding of the relations between electrical forces and chemical affinity, he shows from the phenomena of electrolytic dissociation how we are to picture the ponderable atoms as bound up with electricity. He concludes from the assumption that ions are charged with electricity, that a wandering group of atoms invariably carries the same charge of electricity with it, and that electricity itself is composed of definite elementary particles which behave like the atoms of electricity. An essential factor in chemical affinity is formed by the attractions of the opposite electricities for each other in the compounds. When a unit of positive electricity in an atom is held by the unit of negative electricity in another atom, these electricities will be externally inactive, and the atoms will adhere together with saturated affinity.

In Hertz's opinion this theory gives us a consistent representation of the nature of valency, and this alone he considers a sufficient proof of the weight and significance of the conceptions evolved by Helmholtz of chemical processes. When, on his seventieth birthday, Hofmann spoke of his researches in the interpretation of chemical processes as the inauguration of a new era in chemistry, by means of which new light had been cast upon entire regions, and these had been brought essentially nearer to our comprehension, Helmholtz expressed his thanks in the most modest words :—

'I am exceedingly grateful that you recognize and feel an interest in my amateur efforts in chemistry, and are so good as to tell me so.'

After delivering the Faraday Lecture in London, Helmholtz went on to Cambridge, where he was made Doctor of Laws ; stayed some time in Glasgow with his friend W. Thomson ;

and then returned direct to Berlin, to prepare his thermo-dynamic work for publication.

The Faraday Lecture had made quite an unwonted stir among English men of science, and Sir William Thomson in consequence approached Helmholtz with the request that he would give some popular lectures in England in the autumn of that same year. Helmholtz replied on July 15, thanking him, but declining:—

'Best thanks for your friendly invitation to return to Glasgow. But I find myself incapable of acceding to your offer. In the first place, I know too little of the public I should have to address, and am not usually very successful in my attempts at giving popular lectures to a large audience from mixed classes; in the second place, the preparation of a lecture in English takes up too much of my time, and there is every reason why I should husband it, seeing that I am sixty years old this year, and still have much work that I want to accomplish.'

After recuperating as usual from the fatigues of the summer session in August at Pontresina, where he celebrated 'the solemn day on which he parted with the fifties' by a tiring twelve-hour expedition to the Diavolezza, he went on September 15 to Paris for the Electrical Congress, which again tried his working powers sorely, but afforded much that was interesting and stimulating.

'I went with du Bois to the Opening Meeting,' he writes to his wife. 'The *Ministre des Postes* is President, three other Ministers are the Vice-Presidents selected for France. The foreigners were still to be chosen: Sir W. Thomson, Professor Govi of Turin, and your husband were elected. We took our seats along with His Excellency M. Cochery, amid great ac-clamation. The session itself was merely a formality; there are a great many interesting people at the Meeting. . . . In Congress we have had session after session of sections, com-missions, sub-commissions, and private committees, to decide the question of electrical units of measurement, as between Germany and England. It seems now to be happily settled. I made three or four speeches in French each day, which it was fortunate you could not hear. Sir W. Thomson and an English lawyer Moulton are the chief speakers on the English side. For the rest I am happy in the approval of my audience, and therefore go on flinging my bad French in their faces.'

From Paris, Helmholtz returned by Florence and Vienna (where he and Sir W. Thomson visited the Electrical Exhibition) to Berlin, and proceeded to report on the decisions of the Paris Congress in written memoirs and addresses to various Scientific Societies. Before the end of the year he entered more precisely into the results of the proceedings in a lecture to the Electro-Technical Union, ' On the Electrical Units as determined by the Electrical Congress assembled in Paris, 1881,' and in another given the following year to the Physical Society in a ' Report on the Proceedings of the International Electrical Commission ', which were summed up in his article ' On Absolute Systems of Measurement for Electrical and Magnetic Magnitudes ' in *Wiedemann's Annalen* for 1882.

Helmholtz had now practically finished his fundamental researches in thermodynamics, and was engaged on the difficult problem of preparing them for publication. At the same time he was directing various pieces of experimental work, which were of especial theoretical interest to him in establishing his chemical views.

On November 3, 1881, he presented a paper to the Academy ' On the Galvanic Polarization of Mercury, and some new Experiments of Herr Arthur König relating to the same,' which König had carried out in the University Laboratory under Helmholtz's direction. Their purpose was to determine the capillary tension of galvanically polarized surfaces of mercury, in which the disturbing influence of the alterable adhesion of the two fluids to the glass walls was eliminated. The optical difficulties in measuring the difference in level between the top and the maximal circumference of a quiescent drop of mercury were also avoided, and the measurement of the surface-tension of the quicksilver was obtained by observing the curvature of the summit of a drop of mercury, which could be determined with the greatest precision by the ophthalmometer. The drop projected from the upper circular opening, 9 mm. in diameter, of a glass vessel, and was surrounded by the electrolytic fluid contained in a wider vessel. By a special arrangement the top could be more or less protruded from the mouth of the narrow vessel, and arranged in such a way that the curvature was greatest at the vertex. The experimental series coincided in showing that the surface-tension reaches a maximum at a moderate degree of polarization, which differs for different fluids. Helmholtz now assumed that the forces under the influence of which equilibrium is produced at the polarized surface, between the molecular and electrical forces acting at the summit of the drop, are conservative, and finds on this assumption that there is no difference of potential between the mercury and the fluid in the state of maximal surface-tension, and that the surface presents no trace of an electrical double layer. In conclusion he showed further, by using the mercury as an electrode, that Faraday's electrolytic law, by which, where no electrolysis is possible, there can be no transference of electricity from the metal to the electrolytes, or vice versa, is only in apparent contradiction with the experiments on the galvanic currents that can be excited by the successive immersion of two similar electrodes in the same fluid.

The year 1882 brought high honour and distinction to Helmholtz and his family: he was elevated by the Emperor William I to the ranks of the hereditary nobility. The appearance of Vol. I of his *Wissenschaftliche Abhandlungen* ('Scientific Papers'), followed in the next year by a second volume, had brought the astonishing extent of his great scientific achievements before the eyes of the world.

A year of hard work brought him to the conclusion of his profound investigations in thermodynamics, and these at once formed the starting-point of his remarkable theory of the statics of monocyclic systems, culminating eventually in the fundamental researches into the principle of least action with which he was occupied to the end of his life. On September 18, 1882, he writes to Thomson:—

'After ten months of work I was longing for undisturbed rest, for which I always find Pontresina one of the best places in the world. On October 16 I have to go to Paris as a Member of the International Commission of the Electrical Congress. My Faraday Lecture put me on to electrical researches: I hope you have received my first note on this subject, "On the Thermodynamic Value of Chemical Actions." A second has just been published, a comparison of the chemical energy of solutions, &c.'

Since the loss of mechanical energy by friction produces heat, while gain of mechanical energy produces loss of heat, and since further the sum of energy lost and gained is proportional to the sum of the heat gained or lost, heat must be regarded as a form of energy, and it follows that every particle of a warm body must always be moving in a constantly varying direction, so rapidly that it undergoes little or no alteration of place in the body. But if so, a part of the energy of a warm body must be in the form of kinetic energy, and since every mode of energy can be transformed into heat, it follows that the energy can be measured in the form of heat. But from the law of the conservation of energy it is impossible to determine whether work can be unconditionally transformed into heat energy, and the latter, conversely, into work, and the same for all the other natural forces. Helmholtz accordingly turned in the first place to the determination of these important theoretical and practical relations. He endeavoured to ascertain how large a portion of the heat developed in a galvanic cell by chemical processes reappears as current energy, and arranges the forms of energy in different grades, according as they are more or less completely capable of conversion into mechanical work.

In the fundamental papers on 'The Thermodynamics of Chemical Processes' (communicated to the Berlin Academy on February 2 and July 27, 1882), he develops in mathematical form the relations between the laws of heat, of electricity, and of chemical phenomena, from which an identity of chemical valencies and electrical potentials of the atoms appears probable, so that the electrochemical processes would seem to be an ordered motion of the atoms and molecules, directed along the co-ordinates of space, while heat is a similar process, but unordered.

The question as to the connexion between the electromotive force of batteries with unpolarizable electrodes, and the chemical changes which take place in them, led Helmholtz to the more general question as to what portion of the energy present in a body can be converted into other forms of work, and carried him on to his work on the thermo-dynamics of chemical processes, which again were only the prelude to his great researches on monocyclic systems. Owing to the introduction of potential energy, which Helmholtz had designated earlier as quantity of tensional force, the analytic development of dynamics had been essentially simplified and generalized. As a rule, however, alterations of temperature had not been taken into consideration in the application of this conception, either because the forces of which the work-equivalent was to be calculated, e. g. the force of gravity, did not depend on temperature at all, or because the temperature during the processes under investigation might be regarded as constant, or as a function of definite mechanical alterations, viz. in sound-waves, as a function of the density of the gas. But if the physical constants occurring in the value of the potential energy, such as density, and the like, vary with the temperature, which would make that energy a function of the temperature, then the integration constants comprised in the value of such potential energy would require a purely arbitrary determination for each new temperature; the transition from one temperature to the other would not be possible.

Previous investigations of the work-equivalent of chemical processes referred almost exclusively to the quantities of heat that appear or vanish when compounds are formed or decomposed, whereas most changes are connected with alteration of the state of aggregation and density of the bodies. These, however, produce or consume work under two forms, as heat, and as unrestrictedly transformable work. A supply of heat is not unrestrictedly convertible into other work-equivalents, but can only be partially transformed, and only on the condition of a simultaneous transference of the remainder of the unconverted heat to a body of lower temperature. Since in most chemical processes the changes of melting, evaporating, &c., also attract heat out of the environment, it is necessary to inquire in what proportions mechanical and thermal energy are obtained in these cases also. When we further consider that chemical energies *per se* may produce not merely heat but other forms of energy as well, without any alteration of temperature in the combining bodies being required, proportional to the work done, as e. g. in the work produced by galvanic batteries, it is evident that there must in chemical processes also be a distinction between that portion of their forces of affinity which is capable of free conversion into other forms of work, and the portion which is manifested as heat only.

Helmholtz now designates these two portions free and bound energy. He shows that the processes which appear spontaneously in a state of rest, and at a constant and uniform temperature, and are maintained without help from external working force, can only progress in such a direction that the free energy diminishes. Among these are included the chemical processes that begin and continue of themselves at constant temperature, and, if the Law of Clausius held without limitation, it would be the value of the free energy, not that of the total energy indicated by the evolution of heat, which would determine the direction in which chemical affinity can act.

Helmholtz next undertook a general inquiry into any compound system of masses having all the same temperature, and all being subject to the same alterations of temperature, and assumed that the state of the system was completely determined by the temperature and by a number of independent parameters. In a series of brilliant mathematical deductions he arrived (by means of the two equations of Clausius) at the result that it is only necessary for the representation of thermodynamic equations to obtain the differential quotients of the so-called ergal, which is absolutely determined as a function of temperature. This ergal, for all alterations occurring at constant temperature, coincides with the value of the potential energy for the unrestrictedly convertible quantity of work, and he calls it the free energy of the system, while the difference between the total internal energy and the ergal is termed the bound energy. The quotient of the restricted energy by the temperature is the entropy of Clausius.

In order, further, to distinguish what had till then been known as *vis viva*, or kinetic energy, in theoretical mechanics from the work-equivalents of heat (which indeed was for the most part regarded as the *vis viva* of invisible molecular motions), Helmholtz proposes to call the former the *vis viva* of organized motion. As a general definition of organized motion he gives that in which the velocity components of the masses in motion may be taken as the continuously differentiable functions of spatial co-ordinates. An unorganized motion, on the contrary, is that in which the movement of each separate particle exhibits no sort of similarity with that of its neighbours. Heat motion may very probably be included in this mode, and in this sense he defines the magnitude of the entropy as the measure of disorganization.

'For our instruments (which are coarse in comparison with molecular structure) it is organized motion alone that is freely convertible into other forms of work; whether such transformation is actually impossible in view of the fine structure of living organic tissues appears to me still to be an open question, the importance of which in the economy of nature is plainly obvious.'

By simple mathematical calculations Helmholtz arrived at the result that in all changes in which the temperature remains constant, work is only done at the expense of the free energy, while the bound energy alters at the expense of the in- and out-going heat. In all adiabatic alterations work is produced at the cost of free as well as of bound energy, so that the entropy remains constant. In all other cases external work is done at the cost of the free energy, all production of heat at the cost of the bound, while with each rise of temperature in the system free energy is transformed into bound.

Observations on galvanic cells agreed with these general conclusions. Here too it appeared that the bound energy increases at the cost of the heat supplied, and with rise of temperature at the expense of the free energy, so that free must always be transformed into bound energy, and not vice versa. Neither is the free work in isothermal changes expressed in irreversible processes by the heat developed, when the initial and final temperatures are the same, since this heat is derived from the free and the bound energy, while free work depends upon the former only. The fact that, apart from alterations of temperature, the vanishingly small alteration of free energy is not positive, or is *nil*, may be taken as the condition of the system remaining in its present state, but if a point be reached by rise of temperature, at which this becomes negative, dissociation will ensue. Thus all chemical compounds below the temperature of dissociation give out heat, if they are formed by reversible processes.

Helmholtz then employed his new concept of free energy in calculating the connexion between the E.M.F. of a cell and the vapour tension.

In a paper communicated to the Academy (May 3, 1883), 'On

the Thermodynamics of Chemical Processes: Conclusions relating to Galvanic Polarization,' he applies the thermodynamic theorems previously developed to the theory of galvanic polarization, ascribing great importance to them in this connexion, 'because they show that the surplus of the free energy of the mixture of oxygen and hydrogen over that of the water depends largely upon pressure, while the development of heat in the compound is almost independent of it. So long as it was believed that the electromotive force of polarization must be calculated according to the latter (as I did myself in my earlier work) it appeared to be an almost unalterable quantity, and this made certain processes in the polarization of a voltameter almost inexplicable. But if the electromotive force is calculated according to the free energy, it is then found to be exceedingly liable to alteration according to the gaseous saturation of the layers of liquid lying next the electrodes, and this essentially modifies the interpretation of a large proportion of the phenomena of polarization, so that most of those which were previously inexplicable can now be understood.'

Helmholtz had showed in his earlier work of 1873, that the gases dissolved in the liquid, oxygen in particular, have a great influence on the intensity of the current, for the unlimited duration of which, with weak E.M.F., no explanation had been found, and had then explained the origin of the convection currents dependent upon them; experiments undertaken with the view of removing the last trace of dissolved gases were unsuccessful. The opposing force of polarization, too, increased steadily with the increased E.M.F. of the galvanic battery, where there had been a prolonged evolution of gas. Helmholtz now believed that he had solved these difficulties by his thermodynamic theory, since it was plain from this that the resistance of the chemical forces to the electrical current increases steadily with the solution in the liquid of the gases given off at the electrodes. Finally he also applied his theory to the formation of gas bubbles after the saturation of the layers next the electrodes with gas, and calculated the work corresponding to the diffusion of the gases through the liquid.

He ascribed great importance to thermodynamic researches in the scientific development of chemistry, saying in an interesting letter in 1891:—

'Nernst has thrown himself zealously into the newest applications of physical chemistry, as worked out by the Dutchman Van't Hoff, and advocated with great vigour by Professor Ostwald of Leipzig in his *Journal*. These theories have already proved to be of great practical utility, and have led to a multitude of demonstrably correct conclusions, although they imply some arbitrary asumptions which do not seem to me to be proven. The chemists, however, make use of this hypothesis (of the dissociation of a portion of the compound molecules of the dissolved salts) in order to form a clear conception of the processes, and they must be allowed to do this after their fashion, since the whole extraordinarily comprehensive system of organic chemistry has developed in the most irrational manner, always linked with sensory images, which could not possibly be legitimate in the form in which they are represented. There is a sound core in this whole movement, the application of thermodynamics to chemistry, which is much purer in Planck's work. But thermodynamic laws in their abstract form can only be grasped by rigidly trained mathematicians, and are accordingly scarcely accessible to the people who want to do experiments on solutions and their vapour tensions, freezing points, heats of solution, &c.'

In a sketch which was probably designed in 1883 to be the Introduction to the Third Part of his 'Thermodynamics', Helmholtz set forth clearly and intelligibly the reasons that led him to adopt the expressions 'free' and 'bound' energy, showing at the same time how he had plotted out the continuation of his investigations, had he not been led by the generalization of all these considerations to far more comprehensive problems.

'Thermo-chemical researches have till now been directed almost exclusively to the quantities of heat evolved during chemical processes, when the forces of chemical affinity are given free play, so that the association of the combining substances usually takes place with more or less disturbance. In such cases heat is as a rule the only work-equivalent of the chemical forces produced, or at best there is only an insignificant proportion of other forms of work, among which the overcoming of atmospheric pressure plays, relatively at least, the most frequent part. In thermochemical researches the attempt is usually made to show how much heat has been given off, or taken up, by the end-products of the chemical process, when they have returned to the temperature of their initial state, before the chemical process began. The heat-equivalents of any further work that has been done or absorbed (i. e. done negatively) must if necessary be added.

'By this method is obtained the heat-equivalent of the excess of the whole store of energy which the substances involved contained in their initial state, over that of the final state. This is the foundation of Thermochemistry, firmly established by countless arduous and most valuable investigations, and corresponds to the general Law of the Conservation of Energy.

'The work done by the chemical forces for the most part appears only in the form of heat, but under special circumstances we can directly obtain other forms of work, mechanical or electrical, from it. Heat, according to Clausius's stricter interpretation of Carnot's law, plays a peculiar part as compared with the other work-equivalents. While the others can be transformed freely and with no perceptible remainder *inter se*, the convertibility of heat is limited, so long as we are confined to the attainable limits of temperature. At all times it is only a fraction of the heat present that we are able to convert into other forms of work, while the remainder of this part is reduced from a higher to a lower temperature. If we take θ_0 to denote the lowest absolute temperature (that is, temperature measured from $-273°$ C. as the zero-point) at which we can get our store of heat to flow away, θ_1 being the initial temperature, we must allow the fraction θ_0/θ_1 to pass away unconverted, in order to convert the remainder $(\theta_1 - \theta_0)/\theta_1$ into work. Hence the higher the temperature θ_1, the larger the fraction of the heat present that can be transformed into mechanical work.

'In order to describe this antithesis briefly, seeing that it is of essential importance in the question of the efficiency of chemical forces, I have adopted the expression 'free energy' to describe the work-equivalents of the different natural forces that are freely convertible *inter se*, with no necessary remainder, denoting the heat store on the other hand as 'bound energy'. To the former, for instance, belong the energy of a raised weight, of a stretched elastic spring, the *vis viva* of a mass that is moved as a whole, an accumulation of electricity at rest in a conductor, &c. To say that these are interconvertible 'with no necessary remainder' merely signifies that when the process is carefully conducted, the remainder which is lost in, e.g., friction, elastic after-effect, electrical resistance, and so on, and converted into heat, may be made minimal. Conversion without remainder can only be an ideal limit for our terrestrial conditions, to which we can approximate more or less closely. Still there is a great difference between these losses of the freely convertible energy and those which we encounter in heat, where an important fraction, which cannot be diminished by any precautions known to us, necessarily remains over in the form of heat.

'We already know that chemical forces can develop not merely heat, but mechanical work also, either immediately or by setting up electric currents. This brings in the question, to what part of their work the free energy corresponds, and what other part on the contrary appears exclusively in the form of heat. It is well known that an extraordinary number of chemical changes in the state of aggregation occur; in these also heat may become free or bound. Of this heat we already know that it is subject to the limitations of Carnot's law. Moreover, it has long been known and proved in thermochemical work that this binding and loosing of heat plays its part in the alteration of the state of aggregation; and that we may even have chemical processes that are self-initiated and self-developed, as in the mixture of ice and salt, which engenders cold, and in which external heat must be introduced before the initial temperature can be reinstated. Here then the salt solution that results has more internal energy than the dry salt and snow had previously.

'Further it is clear that the sudden alterations of the state of aggregation represent only the most striking cases of such binding and loosing of latent heat. We are equally justified in regarding the cooling which occurs when a gas expands as a binding of heat; it is true that with slow expansion this will in the latter case be reconverted wholly or almost entirely into mechanical work, but even the latent heat of steam includes the work done in overcoming the pressure on the steam. In the sudden expansion of a gas without resistance, as in Joule's experiments, there is indeed no cooling, but this is only because the initial work performed in producing the *vis viva* of the violent motion of the gas has been retransformed into heat by friction. But if heat becomes latent under such slight modifications as the alteration in the volume of a gas, we must expect corresponding latency and disengagement of heat in all the countless alterations of aggregation and density that occur in almost all chemical processes. And it appears no more uncertain than in the case of the latent heat of steam, that all the quantities of heat as here described must be referred to the bound energy comprised under Carnot's law, and are therefore to be regarded as heat, which was present as such in the initial states of the substance, but has no place in the final states at the same temperature, and is evolved. But the opposite process may equally well occur. The final states may require a greater quantity of latent heat at the same temperature, and the initial temperature may be reinstated only at the cost of the heat contained in the surrounding bodies. In the former case the ' heat toning ' (purely chemically developed heat) will appear to be increased, in the latter to be diminished.

' If we want to determine the largest quantity of free energy that can be obtained by chemical processes, the same general considerations hold good as were laid down by Carnot. Precautions must be taken to ensure the reversible character of the entire process : i.e. the working forces must be held at equilibrium by other forces which are under the control of the observer, so that the entire process shall take place slowly and quietly, without development of violent disturbances, in which the *vis viva* might be converted by impact and friction into heat. All friction, inelastic impact, and transfer of heat between bodies of different kinds must be entirely avoided. The reversibility of the process is conditioned by the fact that with perfect equilibrium of internal and external forces, the observer has it in his power to reverse the process by a slight reinforcement of the latter.

' Nor is it only in the practical task of obtaining motive power for other purposes by means of chemical forces that this separation between free and bound energy plays an essential part : it obtains in the region of chemical phenomena also. A chemical process cannot appear of itself, or go forward, unsupported by external motive forces, without diminution of the total sum of free energy in the co-operating bodies.'

In 1883 the Prussian Board of Education, at the request of Helmholtz, invited his Assistant, Heinrich Hertz, to receive the degree of Dozent in view of his approaching call to Kiel; and he took over from Helmholtz, whose activities were now devoted entirely to other fields, the task of further exploring the difficult and still unsolved problems of the doctrine of electricity, on the principles of the Faraday-Maxwell hypothesis.

Hertz had begun an investigation in Helmholtz's Institute at Berlin which he concluded in this same year at Kiel, and published as 'Experiments on the Glow Discharge'. It was concerned with the form of discharge occurring in vacuous vessels, which is accompanied by the phenomena of the cathode rays, and of the striated positive light. Hertz finds that the cathode rays do not deflect a magnetic needle, and so do not produce the electrodynamic effect of a current; and he therefore regards them as being only the accompaniment of a current, and not as themselves constituting a current.

On July 29, 1883, Helmholtz writes to Hertz:—

'I have read your investigation on the Glow Discharge with the greatest interest, and cannot refrain from writing to say Bravo! The subject seems to me to be of very wide importance. I have been considering for some time whether the cathode rays may not be a mode of propagation of a sudden impact upon the Maxwellian electromagnetic ether, in which the surface of the electrodes forms the first wave-surface. For, as far as I can see, such a wave should be propagated just as these rays are. Deviation of the rays through magnetization of the medium would accordingly also be possible; longitudinal waves could be more easily conceived, and might exist if the constant k in my electromagnetic researches were not zero. But in that case, transversal waves could also be produced. You seem to have the same idea, but, however that may be, do not hesitate to make use of my suggestion, for I have no time at present to work it out. Besides, these thoughts arise so readily in reading your investigation, that they would be bound to occur to you soon, if they have not done so already. One objection to your experiments, however, occurs to me which you may perhaps be able to remove better than I, and which in any case must be mentioned. This is that if the cathode rays are electrical currents, according to the earlier view, they must necessarily have another invisible returning portion, somewhere in the region of the wall of the tube. This is a point which I have often discussed with Dr. Goldstein. In that case they could no more have external magnetic action than closed currents proper, within the tube, since they would form ring magnets. In the rectangular vessel there would still be the possibility of giving such a form to the invisible returning currents that the observed effect should occur. Such an interpretation to me appears hardly probable, since the cathode rays form a concentrated beam, and personally I do not believe in its probability, but I fear it is an objection that will occur to many readers.'

To this letter Hertz made a full and most interesting reply, in which he discusses the views and criticisms of Helmholtz:—

'My warmest thanks for your kind letter. Your words are the strongest and most agreeable spur to activity that could be given me. May I make a few observations in reply? I do not want to inflict myself on you, but write in case you care to read them. I had, as a matter of fact, considered the ideas you express, but was inclined to think that the cathode rays are produced by the longitudinal waves, which correspond to the transverse vibrations of light. For it seems to me as if the longitudinal waves, in a medium in which the plane of polarization of the transversal waves rotates, must be propagated along curved lines, and thus the direction of rotation for light and for the cathode rays would be identical. Then, if the arrow xy gives the direction of the positive current, produced by a magnetic field, the plane of polarization for all gases hitherto investigated will be turned in the direction of this arrow,— that is, a force is produced which acts along AB, and produces a displacement at an angle to this, as CD. There must also be longitudinal impulses propagated in a curve that is deflected to the right hand. But an elastic wire in which a positive current was flowing to the cathode would also be deflected to the right hand, and so a confusion between the two phenomena would be possible. The question no doubt is whether these simple considerations will hold good for the more exact application of the theory. I have not attempted this, because I had imagined, perhaps erroneously, that the theory was not yet sufficiently perfect.

'The following seems also to point to a correspondence between the two phenomena. The more the tube is exhausted, the less does the magnet act upon the rays, and the more rigid they become, as Dr. Goldstein expresses it. This may show (although there is another possible interpretation) that the magnet can only act indirectly upon the cathode rays, as it does upon light, that is, by means of the ponderable matter. In this case, the action of magnetic matter must be enormously stronger upon the cathode rays than it is upon light, but since the same difference undoubtedly exists in regard to absorption, this is the less to be wondered at.

'Generally speaking, the cathode rays excite the same fluorescence in solid bodies as does light. But I do not therefore hold it necessary to assume that they are directly converted into optical rays. One would be more inclined to interpret the phenomenon in the opposite sense. For as the transverse rays of light break up inside the bodies, they will give rise to longitudinal waves, and it is quite natural according to our view that these again should immediately disappear with the production of the same light as is produced by the long cathode rays in the vacuum.

'I have also tried to induce phenomena of diffraction, by sending thin cathode rays through a grating, but obtained no result. At the same time the experiments were not of a nature to prove anything. These are the kind of ideas which I have on this subject. Up to the present I have not entertained any hopes of utilizing the phenomena in electrodynamics, as for the determination of the constant k, since the only effect that can be measured exactly, the action of the magnets, appears to be essentially conditioned by the ponderable substances. I will reflect upon this point, and upon the objection you pointed out. The latter, I think, may be entirely refuted, if we succeed in obtaining more certain proof that cathode rays are possible in the absence of all electrostatic differences.

'It now only remains, *hochverehrter Herr Geheimrath*, to repeat my sincerest and warmest thanks, and I remain, with deepest respect,

'Your devoted H. HERTZ.'

On June 20, 1883, Helmholtz writes to his wife, who had gone to Paris in the middle of May for the funeral of her uncle Julius von Mohl:—

'Geheimrath Herzog was here yesterday, and brought me an invitation to join a sixty-seven days' journey to the Pacific and back, from August 15 to October 22, for the Opening of the Northern Pacific Railway, as the Company's guest; thirty distinguished men are to be invited from Germany, and they say Count Lerchenfeld, the Minister Krüger, Georg Bunsen, Gneist, and the Reichstags-Präsident von Levetzow, are going. Herzog promises princely accommodation on the journey, and receptions. If one is to see America in this life this would perhaps be the best opportunity imaginable. For this reason I have not yet declined, although there are many obstacles in the way, and it is really not essential that one should see America, at any rate not for what I have to do in the world.'

His wife did not approve of his undergoing the fatigues inseparable from this journey; accordingly he declined the invitation.

'I have no particular wish to make a journey at present,' he writes to her again on August 1, while she was still detained at an English watering-place by the protracted illness of their son Robert. 'Just now I have some interesting experiments on hand, that are beginning to go well, and have received my new magnetic balance admirably made. But I notice signs that I am getting worked out, so it can't go on much longer, and the climate of Pontresina admits of no delay.'

During this time Helmholtz had great pleasure in carrying on a scientific correspondence with his son Robert, who was pursuing his studies in chemistry, physics, and mathematics with the utmost zeal. On October 20 he writes from Rome:—

'As to your experimental inquiries, I should recommend you to find out if electrified air gives a double layer at the surface of a conductor. Take a Kohlrausch condenser with carefully cleaned plates, and test the tension between them. Then charge one of them temporarily with an electrical machine, and discharge it by a small flame that gives no deposit of moisture; then bring it back to the condenser, and see if the difference of potential remains unaltered. Then do the same with the opposite electricity. The experiments

you describe would require an extraordinarily exact control,
to show that the dependent plate remained symmetrical to the
electrical sphere.'

With the winter of 1883-4 Helmholtz entered on a period of
great mathematical exertion in attempting to discover a unifying
principle governing Nature, which occupied his thoughts during
the last decade of his life, and down to his closing hours.

His work in thermodynamics had led him to general researches upon monocyclic systems, and the deeper significance
of the principle of least action; but the difficulties of working
out his ideas had soon accumulated, and his time was much
taken up by various official duties.   Nor was it only his
experimental and mathematical lectures, the management of
the Physical Institute, and the lectures at the Military Medical
Academy that hindered him from immersing himself in his
own ideas.   Technical Reports of the most varied character had
to be sent in, since his opinion was claimed on all sides as that
of the most competent authority.   In different places we find
reports on the position of lightning conductors for the protection
of powder magazines surrounded with earth, on the results of
ballooning, and an infinity of other things ; besides, there were
musical interests, and all kinds of artistic interests from which
he could not and would not separate himself,—yet despite all
this the profound and fruitful ideas which we shall endeavour to
trace in subsequent pages were developing in rapid succession.

On January 7, 1884, he writes to W. Thomson :—

'I myself am still engaged upon the subject of monocyclic
movements, and have now discovered some far-reaching
generalizations, which are connected with a universalized form
of Hamilton's Law of Mechanics.   You had better wait for the
later paper before you go on with the monocyclic system; you
will get it in a more convenient form.'

Even before the Easter holidays he was able to lay a portion
of the results of his researches before the Berlin Academy,
but was obliged on account of his health to break off his work,
and go to England with his daughter Ellen, directly the session
was over.

After seeing Tyndall, Herbert Spencer, Sir John Lubbock,
Huxley, and Hooker, the Director of Kew Gardens, he spent
some very stimulating days with Sir Henry Roscoe in

Manchester, 'with whom he had much to discuss in regard to his latest work on the relations between heat and chemistry.' In Glasgow, his old and well-loved haunts were open to him in the house of Sir William Thomson, whom he found absorbed in regulators, and measuring apparatus for electric lighting, and for electrical railways.

'On the whole, however,' he writes to his wife, 'I have an impression that Sir William might do better than apply his eminent sagacity to industrial undertakings; his instruments appear to me too subtle to be put into the hands of uninstructed workmen and officials, and those invented by Siemens and Hefner v. Alteneck seem much better adapted for the purpose. He is simultaneously revolving deep theoretical projects in his mind, but has no leisure to work them out quietly; as far as that goes, I am not much better off!' And he adds immediately after: 'I did Thomson an injustice in supposing him to be wholly immersed in technical work ; he was full of speculations as to the original properties of bodies, some of which were very difficult to follow ; and, as you know, he will not stop for meals or any other consideration.'

His wife replies: 'I am delighted to think of your being with dear Sir William; how you will revel in the fundamental concepts of things. If only one was not pulled up by the great query at the beginning and end of life, and obliged to content oneself with that! That is where you are so fortunate; the things that lie beyond our limits do not weigh upon you, and there is enough of Eternity for you outside our little human existence.'

From Glasgow Helmholtz went on with Thomson to the University festivities in Edinburgh, where he was assigned the honourable task of replying for the foreign guests at the great banquet, and of making a speech on a similar occasion at a reception of the students, where he was received with loud applause.

On November 10, 1884, his daughter Ellen married Arnold Wilhelm von Siemens, the eldest son of Werner von Siemens, who was born on November 13, 1853. After nearly forty years of close friendship this link brought great joy into the lives of both men.

Helmholtz's 'Studies in the Statics of Monocyclic Systems' (published in the Proceedings of the Berlin Academy, March 6,

March 27, and July 10, 1884), his 'Generalization of the Theorems of the Statics of Monocyclic Systems' (ibid. December 18, 1884), and his 'Principles of the Statics of Monocyclic Systems' (*Crelle's Journal*, 1884), are in the closest connexion with his memoir 'On the Physical Significance of the Law of Least Action' (*Crelle's Journal*, 1886). An important supplement to these articles was given in the Note published in the Berlin Proceedings for March 10, 1887, on 'The History of the Law of Least Action,' and developed in more detail in an address to the General Meeting of the Academy on January 27, 1887, the full publication of which was suppressed, because Helmholtz subsequently learned that Adolph Meyer of Leipzig had already published a complete and fundamental discussion of the Law of Least Action in his Inaugural Address. Helmholtz's lecture, remarkable both for its matter and for its style, was incorporated after his death, with his wife's consent, in the *History of the Academy* (Vol. II, Documents and Deeds), issued in 1900, on the 200th anniversary of its foundation.

The fundamental researches set out in these memoirs (which gave Hertz the idea and the starting-point for his *Principles of Mechanics*, and of which the enormous importance, partly from the difficult nature of the problems attacked, partly from the succinct character of their statements, has not yet been widely recognized by scientific men) are entirely mathematical; at the same time the purely mathematical problems that occur during the generalization of mechanical principles are, according to Helmholtz's invariable practice in his mathematico-physical work, dealt with only in so far as is required for their application to physical questions. Since all mathematical expressions have to be avoided here, it is only possible to give a general outline of these papers.

'A law which is to comprise the total sum of alterations in Nature must necessarily deal with concepts of the most abstract kind, from which everything has been eliminated that refers to the particular properties of the natural bodies known to us; for the most part it is necessary, indeed, under such conditions, to form new abstract concepts for the purpose, which, when any one hears them defined for the first time, shall evoke no previous concepts or experiences,—that is, in popular parlance, make him think of nothing.'

Leibniz had defined the work-equivalent as whatever in Nature could be employed as motive force, or (to give us at the same time a measure of it) could lift a weight ; and he gives as the measure of work the product of the weight, and the height to which it is raised. We call this the potential energy of the weight, because in falling it is able to do this work ; it is in this way, as was said above, that potential energy is reckoned for all other forces and any given path of the body affected, only that the force must be replaced by its component in the direction of the path. Leibniz, however, had already pointed out the second principal form of the work-equivalents of ponderable bodies, namely the *vis viva* of the moving masses, or the kinetic energy, and finds its value equal to half the product of the mass into the square of the velocity.

The Law of the Conservation of Kinetic Energy stated that in any given aggregate of natural bodies, on which only such forces act as proceed from fixed centres, the sum of the actual, or kinetic, and the potential energy is constant. It was only when men began to investigate the work-equivalents which must be gained or lost if imponderables are to be brought into play, that Robert Mayer and Helmholtz became convinced of the universal validity of the Law of Energy for all natural processes of the non-living as of the living world, and thus arrived at the Law of the Conservation of Energy. But it is the task of physics to refer the phenomena of nature back to the simplest laws of mechanics, which gave rise to the important question how mechanics itself is constituted in its simplest presentation, and what, as Hertz expresses it, are its ultimate and simplest laws, which every natural motion obeys, which admit of no motion that is excluded by our present experience, and from which, as from the true principles of mechanics, the whole science of mechanics can be purely deductively developed without further appeal to experience.

The discovery of the Law of the Conservation of Energy made a coherent structure of theoretical mechanics possible. The concept of force retreated into the background ; mass and energy emerged as the given indestructible physical quantities. The energy present proved to consist of two parts, one of which, the kinetic energy, bears in all cases the same relation to the velocities of the masses in motion ; the other, the potential energy, is determined by the relative positions of the masses, but in every case can only be ascertained by a knowledge of their particular nature. The discussion of the different forms of energy as well as the condition of its conversion from one form into another represents, according to Hertz, the subject-matter of the whole of physics and chemistry.

From the Law of the Constancy of the Sum of Kinetic and Potential Energy, the important consequence followed immediately that, if a system of bodies is at rest in any position, from which every movement compatible with the restrictions of the system tends to a position with higher potential energy, no *vis viva*, and therefore no motion of the bodies, can arise; there must accordingly be stable equilibrium in any position at which the potential energy is at a minimum. The Law of the Conservation of Energy, however, tells us nothing in the case of motion, as to the succession of positions which the system has to traverse, in order to get from a given initial to a given final position: it is this which is elucidated by the principle of least action.

Leibniz had already asked himself what work can be done by the inertia which distinguishes space filled by mass from geometrical bodies; he found that the work was the greater, in proportion to the magnitude of the mass in motion, the length of the path through which it moves, and the velocity with which it is moving. The amount of the action was thus the product of mass, distance, and velocity, or, what amounts to the same, of *vis viva* and time. We thus arrive at a law that completely embraces all possible motions of any given number of material bodies under the influence of conservative forces, in part exerted reciprocally, in part suffered from fixed centres, —as is summed up in the law of least action. According to this, when such a material system passes with free and undisturbed motion from a given initial to a given final position, with a definite energy-value, the action has a limiting value, and for short phases of the motion this is a minimum. Accordingly, with given values of energy, the inertia must always bring the masses in motion to their end by a path which, at any rate for short distances, exacts the least amount of work. To define the mathematical conception of the limiting value Helmholtz says:—

'When a traveller wants to cross a mountain ridge, the height of the pass is of course the maximum height to which he must rise, while if he crossed at any other point he would have to climb still higher. This is called in mathematics a maximo-minimum of height, and all such values, as well as the complete minima and maxima of variable magnitudes, are known as limiting values.'

So long as this principle was applied only to the obvious motions of ponderable bodies, it seemed to have no other real content than that contained in Newton's equations of motion, but it soon acquired much greater significance, when the investigation was extended to bodies within which persistent concealed motions were proceeding. Helmholtz ascribes a fundamental theoretical interest to the formulation of the Law of Least Action, in relation to the course of all natural processes, inasmuch as the energy components, with which mechanics was originally concerned, entirely disappear from the problem, and 'the question is now reduced to the two chief forms of energy, the total value of which is unalterable and eternal, but which fluctuate to and fro in the most complex forms of manifestation in natural bodies. By this law the ebb and flow of energy is brought under a brief but all-embracing rule, whereby everything that happens in the world is resolved simply and solely into a question of the distribution of energy in time'.

As the first and most striking example of the application of the law of least action to the investigation of bodies, in the interior of which concealed motion is proceeding, Helmholtz cites the 'originally mysterious and incomprehensible laws of the mechanical theory of heat' of Sadi Carnot, Clausius, and Boltzmann; he points out that F. E. Neumann expressed the law of the electromagnetic action of closed galvanic currents in the same form as results from the law of least action, and remarks that all the hypotheses advanced by W. Weber, Clerk Maxwell, Riemann, C. Neumann, and Clausius, for the resolution of the reciprocal actions of many electrical masses into elementary actions, have resulted in forms of calculation which correspond to the law of least action, although what corresponds to *vis viva* and inertia in electricity is expressed in a different form from those used for ponderable bodies. The validity of the law appears to Helmholtz to be limited in the so-called irreversible processes of conduction of heat, production of heat by friction, electrical resistance, and so on, only because we are unable either to follow the unorganized motions of the individual atoms or to bring them together practically in any congruent direction. He tried, in his work on monocyclic systems to show that the most diversified classes of internal motions are subordinated to the law of least action.

The hypothesis that Helmholtz here puts forward and is constantly elucidating, to the effect that all phenomena come about uniformly through the action of concealed masses, by concealed motions and rigid combinations, was subsequently stated by Hertz (as a corollary to this fundamental idea of Helmholtz, which stands for the most significant advance that has been made by modern mechanics) in correct language in the somewhat wider assumption : ' that the complexity of the real world is greater than that of the world that lies open to our senses ; we admit that an unknown agent is at work, but we deny that this agent has a specific character, like the concepts of force and energy ; the unknown must still be Motion and Mass, distinguished from the visible not by its own nature, but simply in relation to us, and to our normal modes of perception. . . . Force and Energy are no more than effects of Mass and Motion which are not always perceptible to our senses.'

In his Address to the Academy, Helmholtz gave a striking account of the historical development of the law of least action, tracing it back more particularly to the works of Maupertuis, who was ' essentially what we term a genius, with all the qualities and failings which that implies '. He indicates what is indefinite and obscure in the views of Maupertuis, who holds that this law satisfies the demand of metaphysics, that Nature should invariably employ the simplest means to produce her effects, and thinks himself called upon to ascertain what quantities are minimal in natural processes, since these will be those which Nature tries to economize ; so that we can discover the objects which Nature pursues. Maupertuis even goes so far as to assert that the law of least action, as discovered by himself, is the first binding and incontrovertible proof of the existence of God, as an Intelligent Governor of the Universe.

With regard to this metaphysical assumption of Maupertuis, Helmholtz jestingly remarks in one of his papers, in allusion to the distinction which he had laid down between limiting value and the minimum: 'If inertia is to be personified, as in this formula, it would be proper to make it shortsighted, and concerned with the immediate moment only.'

The credit of the first, even if it were a wholly indefinite, formulation of the principle is ascribed by Helmholtz to Maupertuis, but he justly accuses him of obscurity and want of strict deduction.

'He grossly neglects the old Socratic demand that every philosopher, i. e. man of science, should be clear in his own mind as to what he knows. He must have been aware that the law which he brought forward as incontrovertible could neither be verified nor clearly applied in many classes of instances. Immersed in self-admiration he held himself justified in merely announcing his discovery like a prophet, a tragic instance of how a mind that was highly gifted at the outset can be led away by vanity and the lax discipline of so-called metaphysical thinking, to border-lands where even the faculty of reasoning becomes dubious. Yet even if he were only guessing at the truth, the truth it was, none the less. And his fixed belief in the possibility of finding a universal law of nature was rooted in a proper confidence in the uniformity of nature, i. e. in the Law of Causation, which is the ultimate basis of our thinking and acting.'

In his paper 'On the History of the Law of Least Action ', Helmholtz criticizes the evidence given for it by Lagrange, Jacobi, and Hamilton. He shows that if, on comparing the adjacent paths with that actually followed by the system, we assume for the others not only the conservation of energy, but also the same value of the energy constants, then in order to maintain the validity of the law the same initial and final positions may be postulated for the contrasted motions of the system, but not the same period of time. The time must accordingly be taken as a variable factor in the analytic derivation of the principle.

Jacobi's proof is physically valid for every complete, self-centred material system. Hamilton's form of the law (to be discussed below) allows us, on the contrary, to extend the equations of motion to such imperfectly closed systems as are affected by variable external influences, if we can regard them as independent of any reaction of the moving system, as e. g. in the case of the forces proceeding from fixed centres.

'In any case the universality of the law of least action appears to me so far assured that it may be assigned a high value as a heuristic principle and guide in the attempt to formulate laws for new classes of phenomena.'

Helmholtz then, with a view to more exact investigation, sets out from the law of least action in the form proposed by Hamilton, according to which the negative mean value of the difference in potential and kinetic energy (of the kinetic potential), calculated for each time-element, is minimal in the actual path of the system, and has a limiting value over a longer portion as compared with all adjacent paths leading in the same time from the initial to the final position. Without separating kinetic and potential energy, he develops the analytical expression for this law with the utmost freedom for the nature of the kinetic potential, and derives the form of Lagrange's equations of motion from it, showing that already in the mechanics of ponderable masses (under special conditions, and with the elimination of single parameters of the problem) these more general forms may arise, in which the two energies are not separated. Even under this most general assumption he deduces the law of the conservation of energy, and finds that it is not true conversely that in every case in which the conservation of energy obtains, the law of least action holds good also. 'The last expresses more than the first, and it is our task to find out what more it expresses.' He shows, on the assumption of the validity of the law of least action, how it is possible from the complete knowledge of the dependence of energy upon the co-ordinates and the velocities to find values for the kinetic potential, and therewith for all the laws of motion of the system. In the mechanics of ponderable bodies the kinetic potential is a homogeneous function of the second order of the velocities; yet under certain conditions, with elimination of co-ordinates, Lagrange's equations of motion may stand for the remaining co-ordinates in exactly the same form as for the kinetic potential, in which case the velocities are also linear. In correspondence with this analogy from the mechanics of ponderable bodies, Helmholtz designates other cases of physical processes, in which the kinetic potential contains terms which are linear in the velocities, as cases of concealed motion ; these cases differ essentially from those in which the kinetic potential involves velocities only in the terms of the second degree, inasmuch as the motion cannot under similar conditions be reversed unless the concealed motions be simultaneously reversed.

He then considers, under the above general assumptions, the reciprocal relations between the forces which the system simultaneously exerts in different directions, and its accelerations and velocities, which embrace a series of highly interesting associations of physical phenomena, such, e. g., as the law of thermodynamics : if increase of temperature raises the pressure of a material system, then its compression will raise the temperature ; further, if heating of any point in a closed circuit produces an electric current, the same current will produce cold, if the heat due to the resistance be disregarded ; and many others. After deriving the necessary conditions for this extension of kinetic potential from the extended form of Lagrange's equations, he enunciates the theorem that these conditions are moreover adequate for the existence of the kinetic potential, but reserves the proof of this for another occasion. In his posthumous papers we find more about the method of proof which he had chosen for this, but in regard to this point he came to no satisfactory conclusion. On April 25, 1886, he writes from Baden-Baden to Kronecker :—

'I have received your card from Berlin with the address you give for my manuscript, and your letter of the 21st inst. from Florence finds me here. As a matter of fact most of my MS. already has the pages numbered, but I am still hung up over one point as to which I must consult a paper by Lipschitz, which was sent on to me here by Königsberger. Pray, however, do not delay the printing for me; that would distress me very much. I can appear just as well in the third or the fourth part. In the attempt to reverse my propositions, I have been led to the theory of polydimensional potential functions, where one has to walk very warily, and I have not decided whether to make this discussion a digression in the main essay, or to treat it separately. Even in the second case, however, I must first get my excursus worked out. . . . Boltzmann's essay opens with some very interesting observations, with which I also occupied myself at one time without coming to any right conclusion; still I am content, for I see that Boltzmann could not get much farther either.'

Hamilton had replaced Lagrange's equations of motion by a system of total differential equations of the first order, which present the total differential quotients taken according to the time of the free co-ordinates, and a like number of quantities deduced from *vis viva* (momentum of motion), as the partial differential quotients according to these magnitudes of the energy supply. Helmholtz, for any given form of the kinetic potential, generalizes the form of the corresponding differential equations of Hamilton. He then proceeds to apply the above theory to the laws of reciprocity that govern the changes in the forward and backward motions consequent on small impacts, after the lapse of a certain time. He terms the motion of the system reversible, when the sequence of positions which it has taken up in its forward motion can also be traversed in the opposite direction without the action of other forces, and with the same time-intervals for each pair of similar positions. He thus arrives at reciprocal laws, of which those which he had long before established for sound and light (though only for systems at rest) are merely special cases. Just as the forces of heat had at an earlier period been referred to the concealed motions of tangible masses, and Clerk Maxwell had recognized in electrodynamic forces the action of concealed masses in motion, so Helmholtz now proposed in general to admit the motion and energy of these concealed masses in the treatment of physical problems, since in the invisibilities that lie behind phenomena, he saw only motion and mass that are incapable of being demonstrated to our senses. And thus he selected the law of least action for the expression of the total motion, since this law admits that the mechanical system—the internal forces of which can be represented as the differential quotients, independent of time, of the force-functions of the visible co-ordinates of the system—is also affected by external forces that are dependent on time, the work of which must be specially calculated, which therefore do not belong to the conservative forces of motion, but are conditioned by other physical processes.

Helmholtz had been led to these universal considerations by his investigation of the form of the kinetic potential, as required by Maxwell's theory of electrodynamics. In this the velocities of electricity appear in a function of the second degree, the coefficients of which are not, however, constants, as are the masses in the value of the *vis viva* of ponderable systems, while linear functions of the velocities moreover come into play, so soon as permanent magnets are introduced. Since the phenomena of light can essentially be explained on the hypothesis that the ether is a medium of similar properties to the solid elastic ponderable bodies, and as the law of least action must in any case be held valid for the motion of light, Helmholtz even at this stage regarded the validity of the principle of least action as far transcending the limits of the mechanics of ponderable bodies, and held it to be highly probable that it was the universal law of all reversible natural processes.

In this connexion it must be mentioned that Boltzmann had, as early as 1866 (in a memoir, ' On the Mechanical Significance of the Second Law of Thermodynamics,' that remained comparatively unnoticed and was unknown even to Clausius), formulated a law for the mechanics of ponderable masses, which is as analogous to the Second Law of Thermodynamics as the Law of *Vis Viva* is to the First, and that, as Boltzmann wrote to Königsberger in 1896, he had, as early as 1867, been presented by Stefan to his colleague Loschmidt as ' Herr Boltzmann, the discoverer of the physical significance of the law of least action '. The scope and weight which Helmholtz attributed to this principle in every department of physics, and actually established by rigid mathematical deductions, appear with increasing clearness from his earlier as well as from his subsequent papers ; the almost simultaneous work of J. J. Thomson was directed to the same object.

Helmholtz was led to these universal investigations, which aimed at the widening of the principles of mechanics, by special cases, whence he had shortly before obtained a similar though less extensive generalization, published in 1884 in the above-mentioned memoirs on the principles of the statics of monocyclic systems. By monocyclic systems he understands mechanical systems which exhibit internally one or more stationary motions returning upon themselves, but which, supposing there to be several, depend in their velocity upon *one* parameter only, while systems with several independent parameters are termed polycyclic. A stationary motion is one in which (as expressly pointed out by Helmholtz in reply to a criticism made by Clausius, who had erroneously attempted to prove that his conclusions were incorrect) the homogeneous moving particles exhibit constant velocity at the same spot, as in the motion of a rotating disk, or in a current of frictionless fluid in a ring-shaped canal. It was further assumed that the forces that act between the bodies of such a system are conservative, and that the problems to be attacked are statical, in the sense that altera-tions in the state of the system, while not excluded, go forward so slowly that the system never perceptibly passes out of the state in which it might remain : which hypotheses are also tacitly accepted by Clausius as the basis of the whole system of laws which he has laid down for the reversible changes of heat. Helmholtz insists that heat-motion is not, strictly speaking, monocyclic, since each individual atom apparently alters its mode of motion perpetually ; but inasmuch as in an enormous number of atoms all possible stages of motion are represented, the me-chanical features of monocyclic motion obtain, even if the several steps are performed now by one atom and now by another.

He then defines as the object of his investigation the proof that there is a class of motions that are perfectly intelligible from the mechanical point of view, in which there are the same limitations to the conversion of work-equivalents as are pre-dicated by the second law for the motion of heat. Helmholtz protests against Clausius's objection to the effect that he had claimed to have provided an explanation of the Second Law of Thermodynamics ; in choosing instances of monocyclic motion he was concerned merely with their complete mechanical intelligibility.

'As a rule,' he says on a later occasion, 'I have only felt it necessary to reply to a criticism of scientific laws and principles when new facts could be brought forward or misunderstandings cleared up, in the expectation that when all the data were given, my scientific colleagues would ultimately form their judgement without the discursive explanations and sophisticated arts of belligerents.'

Helmholtz in the first place developed the general equations of motion of mechanics for polycyclic systems ; under the foregoing assumptions, and on the hypothesis that one or several of the external forces that act on the system are persistently *nil*, he succeeded, as was indicated above, by the elimination of single co-ordinates, in finding other exact equations for the remainder according to Lagrange's formula, and names the system resulting from the elimination of those co-ordinates the imperfect, in opposition to the original perfect system. These investigations were then specialized for the general case of monocyclic motion, in which several velocities are present, which, however, all depend upon one of the same. Helmholtz imagines fixed associations acting in such a way that they have no influence on such motions as take place of themselves under the play of the effective forces, in correspondence with the equations of the combination, but that they oppose to any incipient deviations such forces as are necessary in order to check this deviation; the forces exerted by fixed associations contribute no work to that done by the forces acting from without. He terms the system after the introduction of these fixed associations, the restricted system. Two equations (analogous to the two relations of Carnot-Clausius in the Theory of Heat) are derived from the relation that the work applied to the acceleration of motion in the restricted system is equal to the sum of work expended for the same alterations of velocity in the unrestricted system. The first of these states that the heat that enters the system during a vanishingly small alteration of the absolute temperature and the parameter, as measured by its work-equivalent, is equal to the increase of total energy and of freely convertible work not transformed into heat, which the system gives off externally on alteration of the parameter,— provided that alteration of the temperature without alteration of the parameter induces no intake or output of any form of work other than that of heat:—the second finds this quantity equal to the product of the temperature and the increment of a quantity which Clausius had called entropy, while Helmholtz terms the factor which here is temperature, or a function of it, the integrating denominator.

Precisely the same relations obtain for the monocyclic systems, with all the correlative inferences as to limited convertibility. Since in the Theory of Heat, temperature, which represents the integrating denominator, is (in accordance with the kinetic theory of gases) proportional to the *vis viva* of the internal motion, and since Helmholtz considers the hypothesis of Clausius and Boltzmann (that this is the case for all other bodies also) to be highly probable, he next inquires into the conditions under which *vis viva* becomes the integrating denominator for monocyclic systems with fixed associations of the moving elements—as is the case for simple monocyclic systems. He finds that it is a condition that the entropy of the restricted system should be a homogeneous function of the first degree of the momentum of the unrestricted system, whence it results that if the complete system of parameters is kept constant, the total momentum and the velocities of the restricted system must increase in proportion to the resulting momentum and the resulting velocity of the internal motion. It was shown that all cases known to us at present of the mechanical coupling of any pair of cyclical motions fulfil the conditions under which *vis viva* is an integrating denominator in the compound monocyclic system. He further succeeded in defining the special mode of these fixed associations between the moving parts of the system more exactly. When two monocyclic systems originally independent of each other are transformed by a proper adjustment of external forces into a state corresponding with this particular kind of fixed association, it is possible to bring them into this fixed association without disturbance of the motion present; and they can then, upon further alterations of energy, continue their motion while maintaining this fixed combination,—which is again analogous to the motion of heat, in which two bodies of equal temperature can be brought into conducting contact without alteration of their internal motions, so that during new and sufficiently slow changes they maintain a constant temperature. This state of temporary fixed association is termed by Helmholtz the coupling of the system. He points out, as especially interesting, the case in which a mechanical association is set up between two systems which have equal values for one of their integrating denominators, in such a way that, so long as this association persists, the equality of this denominator will be maintained, as is the case in the contact of two bodies at the same temperature, where the temperature is the integrating denominator. Helmholtz calls this kind of association an isomerous coupling. It is found universally that if monocyclic systems only admit of inter-associations, in which the two preceding characteristics of heat motion obtain, then the third essential characteristic of heat as expressed in Carnot's Law, its limited convertibility, holds good also, and in accordance with these conditions Helmholtz develops the corresponding characters of the coupling.

In conclusion he discusses another and hitherto neglected general law, which affects the character of all associations that can be set up by means of ponderable natural bodies in the case of bodies in motion. Wherever, in the older discussions of mechanical problems, fixed associations are referred to, the expression covers only the inalterability of given spatial measurements, but here it implies fixed relations between velocities. At an earlier point Helmholtz only used for the establishment of the equations of the problems associations which had no influence, so long as the motion was already proceeding in and for itself in a way that corresponded with them, and which accordingly neither performed nor destroyed work; but in considering the question of the cases in which *vis viva* becomes the integrating denominator of the compound monocyclic system resulting from the associations he was led to distinguish those cases which he terms pure kinematic associations. He refers this distinction back to still more general considerations, arriving *inter alia* at the interesting proposition that no kind of attraction of cyclical motions conceivable between physical bodies can avoid the admission of any desired proportional increase of all the velocities, the relations of these velocities to one another remaining unaltered, so long as the value of all the co-ordinates is constant. The problem of finding analytical expressions for such associations as make a polycyclic system monocyclic had been attacked by Kronecker quite generally from a purely analytical point of view, as an appendix to Helmholtz's first paper. Helmholtz here gives merely the integration of the equations of restriction for any physical system, and compares the results with those of Kronecker.

The simultaneous preparation of the new edition of *Physiological Optics* brought Helmholtz a little respite from these arduous and exhausting labours. Part I appeared in 1885, Parts II and III in the following year, Part IV in 1887, Part V in

1889, Parts VI and VII in 1892, Part VIII in 1894, and the conclusion not till 1895, after his death. During this time he evolved many developments and improvements of his earlier theories, and again exchanged a lively correspondence with many learned scientific men. On March 2, 1885, he writes to Lord Rayleigh:—

' I have never doubted that our colour-system depended on three variables, and no more. In regard to colour-blindness, the recent observations of Donders and of my assistant Dr. A. Koenig show that this defect cannot be referred simply to the lack of one of the fundamental colours, but that two of the primaries (red and green) appear to acquire a more even distribution in the spectrum, so that now one and now the other makes a more vigorous impression ; in other words, the resulting curve approximates now more to the red, and now to the normal green sensation. In addition to this we have every shade of lessened power of discrimination. Consequently different individuals require very different mixtures of lithium and thallium light, in order to make up sodium light. . . . I am much excited over the electrochemical equivalent of silver, having occupied myself during the last winter with the attempt to construct good methods of absolute measurement for galvanic currents. . . . I confess that I am getting heartily sick of giving lectures. It is possible that we may be going to have a scientific Physical Observatory here, as a gift from Dr. Werner Siemens, with no teaching attached to it, the Direction of which has been offered to me. But the matter moves all too slowly for my age, which is sixty-three.'

The close of the year 1885 brought great joy to the Helmholtz family. After long anxiety over the health of their son Robert, he was able, on December 23, to take his doctor's degree in Berlin, with a highly commended thesis on the ' Investigation of Vapour and Fog, particularly those of Solutions '. His essay on ' The Alterations of the Freezing-point as calculated from the Vapour Tension of Ice ' was published the next year, followed a few months later by his ' Experiments with a Steam-Jet ', published in the *Annalen d. Physik u. Chemie*, which was very well received in the scientific world.

Helmholtz also wrote an interesting ' Report on Sir William Thomson's Mathematical and Physical Papers ' for *Nature*, in

1885, in which he speaks with the greatest admiration of the issues of his friend's genius. He places the great value of Thomson's scientific methods in the fact that he followed Faraday's example in avoiding hypotheses as to unknown matters as far as possible, and took pains in his mathematical treatment of the problems to express simply the law of the observed phenomena. This limitation of his field enabled Thomson always to bring out the analogy between the different processes of nature far more clearly than would have been the case had it been complicated by widely divergent ideas in regard to the internal mechanism of the processes.

At the close of this year Helmholtz received an intimation from Donders that the Ophthalmological Society had voted him the first medal struck in remembrance of Albrecht von Graefe, and that it would be presented to him the following autumn in Heidelberg. He replies to Donders on January 31, 1886: 'I am greatly flattered at being the recipient of the Graefe Medal, the more so as long years have gone by since I recalled myself to the memory of the ophthalmologists. ... On the whole we are well; if I am aware of certain infirmities of advancing age, I cannot complain of deficient working powers; I only wish I had more free time. One of the causes which lost me nearly a day a week for many years, the *migraine*, has almost entirely disappeared. They always told me it would wear out with old age. The main point really is to learn what one can do, and to respect one's limitations.'

At the close of the Summer Session of 1886, Helmholtz went alone (his wife being detained by the illness of their son) to Heidelberg, for the celebration of the 500th anniversary of the University, where he delivered a stirring discourse in its honour at the Banquet on August 4, in the presence of the Crown Prince of Germany, the Grand Duke of Baden, and the Rector of the University.

Immediately after this, Helmholtz was presented with the Graefe Medal, on August 9, at a solemn session of the Ophthalmological Society in Heidelberg. He replied to the fine address of the President, Donders, with expressions of profound gratitude, and ended his long oration with the words:—

'And now you must permit me to express my conclusion in allegorical language, so as to wound no feelings of personal modesty. Let us suppose, since an allegory does not bind us to historical accuracy, that up to the time of Pheidias no one had a chisel hard enough to work on marble with complete mastery of form. At most they could knead clay or carve wood. Then a clever smith discovered that the chisel could be tempered. Pheidias rejoiced over the improved tool, fashioned his divine statues with it, and manipulated his marble as none had done before. He was honoured and rewarded. But great geniuses are, I have observed, most modest, just in that wherein they excel all others. That particular thing is so easy to them that they hardly understand why others cannot do it as well. With the highest endowments there is always associated a corresponding sensitiveness to the defects of the artist's own work. Accordingly, Pheidias in an access of noble modesty says to the smith: "Without your aid I could not have done all this. Yours is the honour and the glory." The smith can but reply: "I could not have done it with my chisel; you without any chisel would nevertheless have modelled wonderful works in clay. I must decline the renown and glory if I am to remain an honourable man." Then Pheidias was taken away from the world; his friends and scholars, Praxiteles, Paionios, and others survived him. They all used the chisel of the smith; the world was filled with their works, and the glory of them. They determined to honour the memory of the deceased with a wreath, to be bestowed on him who had done most for art, and in the art of statuary. The beloved master had often praised the smith as the author of their great successes, and at last they decided to award the wreath to him. "It is well," replied the smith, "I consent. You are many, and among you are clever people; I am only one. You declare that I have been of great service to you, and that there are sculptors in many places who adorn the temples with copies of our divine statues, which without the tools I gave you, would have been less well fashioned. I must believe you since I have never chiselled marble, and I thankfully accept what you award me. I myself should have voted for Praxiteles or Paionios."'

While Frau von Helmholtz was tied by one of the long and wearisome illnesses of her son Robert, Helmholtz planned a few days at Interlaken with his daughter Ellen, but became seriously ill as soon as he arrived there, in consequence of the undue exertions which he had undertaken in Heidelberg. On August 22, his wife, who had hastened to him, writes to Robert: 'I found your father weak and ill, and very depressed. He is convinced that he is on the point of death, and is altogether in a curious state. The doctor found himself superfluous in the face of your father's theories and his very limited obedience, and seems to give in to him.'

In the early days of September he was able to move from Interlaken to Rigi-Kaltbad, and from there went with his wife to visit the Minghettis and Blaserna at Selisberg.

The painful attacks and mental depression, however, soon reasserted themselves. 'Your father must return home,' writes his wife. 'He wants proper watching and treatment, must have special nourishment, and have done with this hotel life. If we cannot give him mountain air at home we can at least see that he has rest and care, which is something to the good.'

First, however, they went to consult Kussmaul at Strasburg. 'He listened with great attention, asked clear and precise questions, and then said to me: "I am really unable to find anything amiss, but I would not therefore treat his condition lightly; we can't find out everything by auscultation. Positively ill he is not, but neither is he well. You must take the utmost care as to his diet."'

After a rest of some weeks in Baden he recovered almost entirely.

During his stay on the Rigi, Helmholtz made a series of observations which were the starting-point of his subsequent and fundamental work in meteorology. On October 22, 1886, he sent a brief report to the Physical Society, 'On Clouds and Storm Formation,' describing a phenomenon he had witnessed there. One September morning the view of the Jura from the Känzli on the Rigi was clear, while at a somewhat lower level a layer of light clouds indicated the upper edge of a horizontal layer of dull and heavy air, travelling from North to South, which formed the primary cyclone, by the disturbance and rolling up of its edges. In the course of the day the clouds increased, till by the evening they had formed great masses, in which the separate currents rising from the lower layer could be distinguished, and which were ultimately equalized by the electrical discharges.

For the time being Helmholtz gave no explanation of the phenomenon; it was necessary first to arrange his observations scientifically. 'I thought it useful,' he said at a later time, 'as far as I was able, to introduce rigid mechanical concepts into meteorology, and to see what could be determined by that method.'

'I cannot conclude this letter,' Bezold writes, on October 9, 1902, 'without especially referring to the loss I have sustained in the death of the two great physicists Helmholtz and Hertz, who did not consider meteorology a low form of science, but contributed to it themselves, and were deeply interested in it.'

Before the end of the year Helmholtz was made Vice-Chancellor of the Friedensklasse of the Order *Pour le Mérite*. He resorted to Menzel, the Chancellor, to learn what his obligations were, and Menzel replied: 'I can only say to you what Ranke replied to me in his time, "As Vice-Chancellor you have nothing to do but to wait for my death to become Chancellor."'

In December, 1886, Hertz sent Helmholtz the continuation of the experiments begun in Berlin and resumed at Kiel, which already gave promise of the rich significance of his discoveries. In a letter from Karlsruhe, Hertz remarks: 'I take this opportunity of communicating certain experiments in which I have been successful, because I was in hopes when I undertook them that they might interest you. I have succeeded, unmistakably, in showing the inductive action of one open rectilinear current upon another open rectilinear current, and I venture to hope that this method will eventually yield the solution of one or other of the questions associated with this phenomenon.' Helmholtz, who already recognized the full significance of this work, was greatly excited by the more detailed account of its progress; he took no further part in the development and organization of these experiments, but handed the whole subject over to his great pupil Hertz.

'I am proud,' he said later, 'to think that my ideas will survive and develop in future generations, when my individual life is at an end, and you will understand that just as a parent cares most for the welfare of his own sons and endeavours to promote it, so I have a special predilection for the children of my brain, and you will also understand that as an individual I can only follow

my own convictions, and lay most stress on these, rejoicing if
the progress of science should tend in the same direction. Then
again I am beset with doubts as to whether my own ideals are
not too narrow, and my own principles in individual points too
incomplete, to satisfy the cravings of Humanity for all time. . . .
One banner only do I uphold, that it is the aim of science to
comprehend reality, and to grasp the transitory as the phenomenal manifestation of the intransitory—that is, of Law.'

It had become absolutely necessary for Helmholtz either to
give up his teaching altogether, or to limit it materially, in order
that he might devote the greater portion of his working time
and energy to the investigations which occupied him almost
exclusively henceforward to the end of his life, and a fortunate
turn of the wheel soon enabled him to satisfy his inclinations.

'The moment arrived,' says du Bois-Reymond, 'at which our
distinguished friend Werner von Siemens prepared to found
a Physico-technical Institute at Charlottenburg, partly at immense personal expense, which only he could afford. We
knew that Siemens always deplored the amount of time and
energy that Helmholtz was obliged to devote to his duties as
a teacher, instead of to the prosecution of his incomparable
researches, and it was no secret to us that he designed the post
of Principal of the Institute for him, as one that would relieve
him of all but his scientific occupations—a post such as an
academic could only regard as the ideal of his dreams.'

The first proposals for the erection of a State Institute to
be devoted to the advancement of exact science and technical
instruction had been mooted as early as July 30, 1872, by
Schellbach, supported by Helmholtz, du Bois-Reymond,
Paalzow, Bertram, and Förster, and were warmly welcomed by
the Crown Prince, afterwards the Emperor Frederick. In
consequence of this movement, General Field-Marshal von
Moltke, as President of the Central Directory of Survey in the
Prussian State, appointed a special Commission towards the
end of the year 1873, which in January, 1874, made 'Proposals
for the Improvement of Scientific Mechanics and the Instrumental Sciences'. Herein it was urged as the first duty of the
State, that it should in future, along with provision for immediate needs, devote its attention to the supervision of technical
instruction—systematically, and not merely on occasion.

Further discussions in 1875-6 led to the resolution that the earlier Industrial Academy should be supplemented by the foundation of an Institute for Scientific Mechanics, a project which was supported by the Ministers of Trade and of Finance. It could not, however, be carried out exactly in this form, since the Industrial Academy was just then replaced by a Technical High School, which was to incorporate all the different Technical Institutes, and the building of which was at once begun.

Meantime the proposal to found a Mechanical Institute was again suggested in 1879 to the Minister of Education (to whose department the Technical High School had meantime been transferred), by the Central Board of Survey in Prussia, and by the Mechanics' Union, in consequence of which Conferences were held at the end of 1882 in the Education Office, and it was decided to supplement the Technical High School by an Institute of this kind. The results of these deliberations, in which Helmholtz, Reuleaux, Förster, and Werner Siemens (all members of the former Commission) took part, were collected in a Memorial of May 23, 1883. In a special report Helmholtz pointed out the necessity of combining a scientific department with that of technical mechanics.

In a further Memorial of June 16, 1883, the earlier scheme for the foundation of 'an Institute for the Experimental Promotion of Exact Science and the *Technique* of Precision' was proposed, with important additions, and accompanied by a draft of the proposed organization. Of the comments which Helmholtz appended to this Memorial the following may be cited:—

'I should like to emphasize still more strongly the fact that there is a whole series of important problems on the side of pure science, which cannot be undertaken with the private means of individual workers, or in the Laboratories of the University, which are founded for purposes of instruction, since their accomplishment demands costly accessories of space and instruments, and the unhampered working time of experienced and capable observers, beyond what can as a rule be obtained without assistance from the public funds. Till now it has been almost exclusively Astronomy which has been taken under the protection of the State in Institutes dedicated primarily to scientific research, and only secondarily to teaching—the Observatories. Despite the apparent remoteness of the objects of this science from any aims of terrestrial utility, the old rule has held good here, that all serious scientific work must eventually find its practical application, even where this might previously have been least expected. Apart from the fact that astronomy has brought about a total revolution in our conception of the world, in consequence of the ideas it has given us of the construction of the Universe, our navigation and the determination of civil and historical chronology depend essentially upon it; and the art of practical optics, of the higher branches of clockmaking, and all refinements of longitudinal and angular measurement, have developed directly out of its problems. Lastly, it would be of the utmost importance for higher scientific education if a small and select number of young men who had already proved their capability for experimental work could be admitted as Assistants or Volunteers at such an Institute, and thus have opportunity to learn the application of the most perfect methods and instruments possible.'

Helmholtz then enters in detail into the reasons why the establishment of a scientific department of the Physico-technical Institute along with that of technical mechanics would be desirable. He had already outlined the duties of the scientific department of the proposed Physico-mechanical Institute as follows:—

'1. The exact determination of the intensity of gravity, and the comparison of this force at different parts of the Earth's surface.

'2. The absolute measurement of gravitation, or the determination of the mean density of the Earth.

'3. The continuation of the exact determination of the velocity of light at terrestrial distances, with the object of reducing cosmic distances to terrestrial measures of length.

'4. In the theory of the magnetic actions of electrical currents a velocity, which appears to be exactly equal to that of light, and which W. Weber characterizes as *critical*, ... seems to play a fundamental part. Its identity with the velocity of light appears to me to indicate an essential and intimate relation between optical and electrical processes. We seem hereby to acquire a clue to the mysterious aspects of electromagnetic phenomena, which probably may lead us to their deepest foundation.

'5. Determinations of electrical units of measurement.

'6. Measurements of pressure and density of gases and vapours at different temperatures, and the measurement of the amount of heat consumed in these processes.'

He further points out that the foundation of a scientific department 'would also make it possible for the older and accredited physicists of Germany to carry out special researches for which the apparatus is not to hand in their own neighbourhood'.

'It is unworthy of a nation that has acquired by its power and intelligence, and has to maintain, a position in the front rank of civilized peoples, to leave the provision for such fundamental knowledge to other nations, or to the accidental tastes of certain fortunately situated private individuals. Germany has already taken the lead by the institution of University Laboratories for Chemistry, Physics, and Physiology; these have rapidly grown and multiplied, and have been imitated in all the surrounding countries.'

When it was seen that the immediate fulfilment of the project was delayed by financial difficulties, and more particularly by the question of finding a suitable site, Werner Siemens made an offer to the Minister of Education of a site in the Marchstrasse in Charlottenburg, one hectare in area, as a gift to the Prussian State. In consequence of certain objections made by the Minister, and in view of the national significance of the plan, as also in the hope of its being carried out on a larger scale and with more complete equipment, Siemens resolved to repeat his offer, as previously made to Prussia, to the whole Empire, on May 20, 1884, in a gift of half a million marks, including the value of the land, for the endowment of an Institute of Scientific Research for Technical Purposes. 'The class-rooms and laboratories in our Universities and Schools, which are set apart for teaching,' said Siemens, 'are not suited for the installation of definite scientific researches, any more than are the professors in charge of them. Besides the leisure for intellectual absorption in their researches, the teachers lack suitable accommodation and means for procuring the right instruments and apparatus. The Institute we wish to found would thus contribute to the elevation and maintenance of the scientific achievements of our nation, and secure for us a post of honour among civilized peoples.'

The Commission convened in 1884-5 to discuss the organization of the Institute insisted that the proposed foundation, which later received the name of *Physikalisch-Technische Reichsanstalt*, must comprise a scientific and a technical department, the vigorous co-operation of which would be of great value, and would further the national interests to the utmost.

Even before the Imperial Budget for 1887-8 had officially sanctioned the necessary expenditure, Siemens, with the consent of the authorities, had begun the building of the Institute as early as 1886 at his own risk, and the Director's House and the buildings for the staff were accordingly ready for occupation by 1889, though the engine-room and observatory were not completed till 1890-1.

In April, 1887, Helmholtz was formally invited by the Geh. Ober-Regierungsrath Weymann, on behalf of the State Secretary of the Interior, to become President of the new Physico-technical Institute. He accepted on April 4, provided he were compensated by the salary and the official residence attaching to it for his income from the Berlin University and the Friedrich-Wilhelm Institute for Medicine and Surgery, which he would have to give up, and on the understanding that his position at the Academy of Sciences in Berlin was in no way altered.

When the Treasury had guaranteed these conditions Helmholtz drew up a scheme for the organization of the scientific department of the Reichsanstalt, and detailed statutes defining the power of the Director of the Physical Section, as well as the co-operation of the Management in the annual schedule of work. The President of the Institute would reserve the right of initiating and carrying on other researches. The working constitution was ratified on July 26 by the Secretary of State for the Interior.

Meantime the Philosophical Faculty of the University, so soon as they heard of Helmholtz's intention to resign his Chair, had applied to the Minister with the request 'that he would graciously make provision that Herr von Helmholtz should remain a teacher of the University and a Regular Member of the Faculty. As is known to your Excellency, Herr von Helmholtz's master-genius extends to many subjects, his profound knowledge to all—mathematical and scientific, as well as philosophical and literary. The judgement of this one man is accordingly of consummate value, and cannot be replaced by any combination of judgements from individual professors, since the questions brought before the Faculty are nearly always those of the rival claims of the interests of the several departments; and any one who combines all these, and deliberates on them in his single mind, is the more capable of solving such weighty and complicated problems correctly and completely.'

Upon the pressing request of the Minister, that upon these grounds, and from considerations referring to the salary, Helmholtz should remain in connexion with the University, he declared his willingness to give a public lecture of two or three hours in each term, 'provided he were relieved from the duty of taking part in the executive work of the Faculty and the Examinations.'

On April 4, 1888, his appointment as President of the Physikalisch-Technische Reichsanstalt was consummated.

Despite the inevitable burden of organization Helmholtz felt thoroughly happy and contented in his new post. He found ample compensation for the many administrative duties (in which he was assisted by a distinguished body of younger men) in the stimulus of the innumerable problems that arose in the scientific department of the Institute, and in the freedom from the frequent repetition of experimental lectures and demonstrations, which had absorbed so much of his time and energy.

During the last year before he definitely took over the Presidency of the Physico-technical Institute, Helmholtz had been profoundly stirred by the work of Hertz, who sent regular reports of his experiments to his former teacher.

By the end of the year he was able to communicate his well-known experiments on the interference between the effects propagated along wires, and through the air, without at that time being able to demonstrate a finite velocity of propagation for these latter. Far greater surprises, however, were in store for Helmholtz in Hertz's letters of the early months of the ensuing year, 1888; his delight finds expression in the frequent repetition of the words 'Bravo! Best congratulations' at the end of his short answers: and when he sent to du Bois-Reymond, for the Academy, the memoir in which Hertz proved that the electrodynamic waves are reflected from solid conducting walls, and that with vertical incidence the reflected waves interfere with the incident, and give rise to stationary waves in the air, he concludes his letter with the words, ' Hertz's work is the work of a genius.'

Helmholtz's desire to conclude a series of hitherto unfinished investigations had led him back in the summer of 1887 to the subject of electrolysis. On July 28 he made a communication to the Academy ' On Further Investigations on the Electrolysis of Water', which he linked on to his first paper ' On the Thermodynamics of Chemical Processes', written in 1883, giving experimental proof of a number of the results therein deduced theoretically. He had previously discovered in theory that the electrolytic dissociation of water must occur with less electromotive force according as the quantities of oxygen and hydrogen dissolved in the proximity of the electrodes are smaller, and that no inferior limit other than zero could be given to the smallest electromotive force capable of dissociating perfectly gas-free water. The experimental determination of this law, however, had presented great difficulties, inasmuch as the platinum anode, or both electrodes, contain occluded hydrogen or combustible gases, with which the oxygen conveyed by the current combines, so that a much lower E.M.F. can liberate bubbles of hydrogen at the cathode. The construction of a special apparatus and most accurate measurements now yielded a satisfactory reconciliation of theory and experiment.

Helmholtz was also contemplating the extension and definite conclusion of his thermodynamic and chemical researches in a paper of the widest scope which was to be entitled ' Thermodynamic Considerations as to Chemical Processes'; but of this only a few fragments remain, in particular the Introduction, designed for a large circle of readers, which summarizes the researches of Berthelot and other workers, and is of great interest on account of its clear historical exposition of the theories of physical chemistry that had come so prominently forward in the last ten years.

The parting of Helmholtz from the great society of Members and Associates of the Berlin University, to which, properly speaking, he belonged only as an honorary member from this time forward, is marked in the history of his untiring scientific activity, by the essay on Natural Philosophy entitled 'Numbers and Measurements treated from the Epistemological Point of View', and dedicated to his friend Eduard Zeller for the fiftieth year of his doctorate. This paper was an important amplification of the empiricist theory which he had previously put forward, that the axioms of geometry can no longer be regarded as propositions incapable of and not requiring proof, and also established this theory with respect to the origin of the arithmetical axioms, which stand in the corresponding relation to the conceptional forms of time.

The five well-known axioms of arithmetic—(1) when two magnitudes are equal to a third they are equal to each other; (2) the associative law of addition, $(a+b) + c = a + (b+c)$; (3) the commutative law of addition, $a + b = b + a$; (4) if equals be added to equals, the wholes are equal; (5) if equals be added to unequals, the wholes are unequal—were then examined in regard to their independence of each other, and in their relation to experience. While he derives numbers from the fact that we are able to carry in our memory the sequences in which the acts of consciousness have followed one another in time, the theory of pure numeration is for him merely a method built up on psychological facts, for the logical application of a system of signs, unlimited in its extension and possibility of refinement, with the object of representing the different modes of association of these signs, all of which tend to the same ultimate result. After the definition thus obtained of the ordered series of the positive whole numbers and of the unequivocal character of their succession, he established the concept of the addition of pure numbers, in the first place explaining the signs by saying that if any number be designated by the letter a, the next following in the normal series shall be $(a + 1)$, while the definition of $(a+b)$ is that number of the principal series which is reached by counting One for $(a + 1)$, Two for $[(a+1)+1)]$, and so on, until one has counted up to b. And then he shows how this idea of the addition of pure numbers confirms the arithmetical axioms of the equality of two numbers in relation to a third, the associative law of addition, and the commutative law merely by the agreement of the result with that which can be derived from the numbers of external enumerable objects. Figures are to him arbitrary signs, to establish the time order of a series, and all enumeration is the arrangement of the things enumerated in a time-series; he regards the composition of fractions of time into magnitudes of time as the primitive type of addition. He further proposes definitions for objects in general; the definition of equality is that if two things are equal to a third thing they are equal to each other: permutation (combination) is the association of different things, in which the order of association is not indifferent; addition is the combining of homogeneous things, independent of the order of association; multiplication is (at least in all its applications), as he sets forth in a note, the combining of heterogeneous magnitudes, for which the order of association is indifferent—since units of any kind are multiplied by abstract figures, or horizontal by vertical lines, or distances by masses. In the other mathematical operations the order is not an indifferent matter. Lastly, he regards magnitude as an additive combination of homogeneous units or parts: equal magnitudes are composed of pairs of equal parts; while a sum is the additive combination of magnitudes.

While therefore objects which are equal in any definite respect, and are enumerable, are termed units of numeration, their number is termed a denominated number, and the special kind of unit which they comprise is the denomination of the number; the concept of the equality of two groups of denominated numbers of similar denomination is established by their having the same number. If the objects, or the attributes of objects, which when compared with others admit of the distinctions of greater, equal, or less, are termed magnitudes (as to which only empirical knowledge of certain sides of their physical reactions in coincidence and co-operation with others can decide), and if we can express these magnitudes by a certain number, we term this the value of the magnitude, and the method by which we find the given number we call measurement. Thus we measure a force either by the masses and motions of the system by which it is exerted, or in dynamic measurement by the masses and the motions of the system on which it acts, or lastly by the static method of measurement of force, by bringing the force into equilibrium with known forces. There remains only one question to be answered: when may we express magnitudes by denominated numbers, and what actual knowledge do we gain by doing so? To answer this,

Helmholtz proceeds to the questions that are so important and interesting in physics, of physical equality, and the commutative and associative laws of physical relations, defining addition in a somewhat extended form as a relation of magnitudes of the same kind, the results of which do not alter by exchanging the terms for equal magnitudes of the same kind. So that Helmholtz maintained for arithmetic, or for the transcendental conception of time in relation to its axioms, the same standpoint which he took up in opposition to Kant in his investigation of space.

Helmholtz's house had been for more than ten years the centre of the most enlightened minds of the new capital of the Empire: here, to their mutual advantage, both mental and spiritual, the most profound thinkers met the most talented artists, not on neutral ground, but on a soil ripe to receive all that was good and beautiful. Moltke's pupils and Bismarck's disciples came together under the Olympic peace of the great investigator and his distinguished wife, who here developed her transcendent gift of bringing the most unlike minds into contact. External position counted for little with her if it were not accompanied by intellectual distinction or a fine artistic temperament:

' I have set myself all my life against a low level of social environment, and kept it away wherever it was not imposed upon me. I have held good manners, and a mental equipment superior to my own in some aspect, or interesting at the least, to be the first requirement of social intercourse. In this respect one cannot afford to be modest, unless one means to drop into mediocrity.'

The migration to the new Presidential dwelling in Charlottenburg did but provide a 'more intimate and perhaps even more harmonious setting for these social relations'.

CHAPTER XI

HELMHOLTZ AS PRESIDENT OF THE PHYSIKA-LISCH-TECHNISCHE REICHSANSTALT
1888-1894

DURING the closing winter months of 1887 and the whole of the following summer Helmholtz gave his entire thought, time, and energy to the arrangement and organization of the Reichs-anstalt, more particularly in regard to the scientific and technical questions with which it had to deal; and with the valuable assistance at his disposal everything was brought into order with surprising rapidity.

After some months of uninterrupted work he was, however, compelled to pause on account of his health, and to abate his activity. At the beginning of August, 1888, he went with his wife to Bayreuth, and gave himself up once more to the enjoyment of 'the incomparable charm of the *Meistersinger*'; and his wife did but interpret his emotions, when she wrote to her daughter:—

'Bayreuth, dear ones, was icy cold, and its enjoyment purely intellectual . . . that, however, was immense, and it is beautiful to be able to put earthly considerations so entirely into the background. What the *hohe Frau*, as Robert calls her, has accomplished in these marvellous representations passes imagination. Her great artistic will stands behind all her fellow workers, and her taste prevails everywhere. All the artists are at one, and all are good friends.'

From Bayreuth, Helmholtz went on once more to Pontresina, to seek the refreshment it never failed to bring him. The warm tone of his letters betrays his delight that his son Robert should have made a name for himself, oy his various experimental researches, among the physicists, and that his inclination was increasingly directed to the study of mathematical physics. On August 18, he writes to him from Pontresina:—

'As regards your problem, I know the astronomers have discussed the question whether time is required in gravitation. I do not know how far its exact determination is possible. They assert that observation goes against this hypothesis. In any case it is useless to attack a problem of this kind until one knows what observations are possible, and how they should be carried out in order to decide it.

'The thermoelectric currents in the body of the Earth present a complicated problem. An arrangement of different concentric shells in the Earth's crust would only yield currents corresponding with closed ring magnets, with no external action. Our present methods of measuring gravity are not exact enough to enable us to measure the gravitation of the Moon. Meantime the geodesists are seeking for better methods, and an Academic prize-question has been set on the influence of the suspension of the pendulum on its vibration-period (elasticity of the support, form of the knife-edge, or, on the other hand, length and elasticity of the spring by which it is suspended). For my own part I have learned whatever I know of mathematics merely from the problems I have tried to solve, and have never been able to grasp anything from purely abstract study unrelated to problems. But you must first choose simpler tasks, either in mechanics, or the theory of potential functions, electrical distribution, or the distribution of electrical currents. The theory of the pendulum, for instance, suspended by an elastic watch-spring would be a good example. This kind of suspension is far less subject to friction than that from a knife-edge.'

Helmholtz spent his birthday as usual in Pontresina, in the company of his wife, and had the accustomed number of respectful congratulations; this first birthday in his new post brought him a letter from the mathematician L. Kronecker on August 28, which is interesting both in its style and its contents :—

'In a few more days, on the last of this month, you will complete the 67th year of your prolific life, by which light has been thrown on innumerable fields of activity. I send you my warmest congratulations. . . . I am happy in the conviction that your present phase of exclusive devotion to mathematical physics will be succeeded by a phase in which you will turn to pure mathematics, and bring the light of your intellect to bear on that also. You have already attacked it at many points, and it is (as I have long felt) only the consequence of the remarkable development of your scientific life, which is unique in the history of the sciences, that it should, beginning at the right hand with the most practical scientific medicine, advancing through physiology to experimental and theoretical physics, arrive finally at the extreme left of the abstractions of "pure" mathematics. The wealth of practical experience, of sound and interesting problems, which you will bring to mathematics, will (like the work of the astronomers in the last century) give it a new direction and a new impulse; whereas the one-sided mathematical speculation that returns upon itself only leads to sterile regions. Therefore come over to our side, honoured friend, and impress the imperishable traces of your bold and original progress upon the paths of pure mathematics, so that the lines of the future may be indicated in this direction also.'

At this very time Helmholtz was already midway in his great mathematical investigations of monocyclic systems and the principle of least action.

The new edition of *Physiological Optics* compelled him at the same time to examine a whole series of difficult optical problems, and restate the answers to them. On November 2, 1888, he made a brief communication to the Physical Society 'On the Intrinsic Light of the Retina', published in an expanded form in 1890 in the *Zeitschrift f. Phys. u. Psych.*, with the title 'The Disturbance of the Perception of the Least Differences of Brightness by the Intrinsic Light of the Retina'. Helmholtz finds that the intrinsic light is not equally distributed over the fundus of the retina, but always appears to us in irregular patches, and that what we generally perceive of this internal retinal excitation, under normal conditions, with weak external illumination, is only the local differences of brightness in the patches; and it is only under exceptional circumstances that we can estimate the mean brightness of the fundus by comparison with still darker fields. Helmholtz adduces a number of highly interesting experiments, which show that the patchy character of the intrinsic light is the chief obstacle to the perception of very weakly illuminated objects, especially if they are small, since these disappear between the patches of the intrinsic light, and are confounded with them. His experiments also elicited the interesting fact that a large *resting* surface, emitting weak light, may disappear entirely in the intrinsic light of the retina, while still sending out sufficient light to render visible the *moving* objects which it illuminates.

The further development of the theory of electricity on the lines of the Faraday-Maxwell hypothesis had, as we have seen, been handed over entirely by Helmholtz to his friend and pupil Hertz. The latter wrote on November 30 to Helmholtz:—

'When you asked me in Berlin if I had made any further experiments on electric waves, I had nothing important to tell you, but I have now made a farther advance, by which the relation between light and electricity seems to me to be firmly established, and I am anxious to tell you about it.

'In the first place, I discovered by a happy accident that it is not only possible to produce waves several meters in length, but that one can also work with much shorter waves, which is infinitely more convenient. I have been able to confirm and in part to improve on my earlier results with waves 33 cm. long in air. I have also repeated the experiments with these short waves of sending the force by means of concave mirrors to a distance, and thus producing a beam, and with the best results.

'I place my primary and secondary conductor in the focal line of a parabolically curved tin-plate 2 m. high by 2 m. wide, and then obtain a well-defined beam some 1½ m. in width from the mirror, which is perceptible in a second concave mirror up to a distance of 16 m., and apparently even farther. The beam can be directed by rotation of the mirror, and one can demonstrate rectilinear propagation and the formation of shadow perfectly by its means. If, for example, a man crosses the path of the beam, the stream of sparks in the induced mirror will entirely disappear. Yesterday I also succeeded in showing the regular reflection of the beam more plainly than I could have hoped. When I put the concave mirrors side by side, there was no effect from *A* to *B*; but if a plane metal screen was placed in front of the concave mirror, sparks passed in *B* which were still perceptible when the screen was removed 10 m. from the mirrors. I was also able to establish the reflection at 45°, by employing two adjacent rooms. Shutting the wooden doors between them in no way hindered the appearance of the secondary spark. On the other hand the sparks ceased when the plane reflecting screen was rotating as little as 5° to the one side or the other of the right position : this proves the reflection to be regular, and not diffuse.

'You will pardon my impatience, in giving you such prompt information about these matters. I intend to repeat and extend my observations, and then to put them together in a report for the Academy, and hope you will be good enough to receive it, though doubtless you are already overcrowded with such things.'

Helmholtz replied most genially :—

'I am much delighted with your last results. I have puzzled for years over the possibility of getting at these things, so that I am familiar with the whole train of thought, and its immense importance is obvious to me.'

In 1885 Hertz had been appointed Ordinary Professor of Physics at the Technical High School of Karlsruhe, and he was subsequently, on the death of Kirchhoff and Clausius, offered the choice, through Helmholtz, of Berlin or Bonn, when he decided for the latter, because 'he preferred the Chair at Bonn, which was an experimental post, to the great honour the Faculty of Berlin had designed for him'. Helmholtz writes on December 15, 1888 :—

'Personally I am sorry that you are not coming to Berlin, but, as I have already told you, I believe it is for your own interest to go to Bonn. Those who have still much scientific work in view are better away from big cities. At the end of one's life, when it is more a question of utilizing the points of view one has arrived at for the education of the coming generation and the administration of the State, the case is different.'

The prosecution of his meteorological studies during the ensuing winter, and the consequent limitation of his public lectures and addresses to Scientific Societies, was only once interrupted with the express intention of doing justice to the great scientific merits of his quondam friend and subsequent opponent, R. Clausius.

On January 11, 1889, Helmholtz delivered a memorial lecture to the Physical Society of Berlin, which emphasized the great services rendered by Clausius, notwithstanding many points of past controversy between these eminent men. His own investigations in recent years into the modern development of the mechanics of chemistry had all been based, so far as they were certain and established, upon the so-called Second Law of Thermodynamics, which (at first stated by Sadi Carnot in a restricted form that applied only within the narrowest limits of temperature) had been extended and generalized in the strict interpretation given to it by Clausius. 'This is not merely one of the most important, but also one of the most surprising and original achievements of ancient or modern physics,' because it is one of the very few principles whose absolute universality can be predicated independent of all dissimilarity of natural bodies. At the close of his laudatory appreciation of the work of Clausius, Helmholtz states that it had now for the first time become possible to obtain a concept of absolute temperature, independent of the characteristics of any particular natural body. Still more important was the fact that it had established the specific character of the motions of heat, by which the latter were differentiated from all other force-equivalents. While the others can be converted and reconverted indefinitely among themselves, this is only possible to a very limited degree for heat, so long at any rate as we are unable to go back to the zero of absolute temperature.

What Helmholtz himself thought in regard to these difficult questions appears from the preceding account of his mono-cyclic studies, in which he distinguishes between organized motion, defined as a continuous function of the co-ordinates and the time, and unorganized motion, in which the motions of the neighbouring particles have no kind of mutual similarity. He regards the motion of heat as being also unorganized, but refers the difficulty of converting it into organized motion solely to the limitations of the methods at our disposal; if we could but overcome this obstacle, all processes would necessarily be reversible. Moreover, as he repeatedly indicates, there are vegetative processes in many plants, where no source of energy is visible, and the question presents itself whether these may not in some sort be the organization of heat motion.

During the Easter holidays Helmholtz heard of the death of his faithful old friend Donders, and writes on March 27 to Engelmann: 'Your announcement of the death of Professor Donders was a quite unexpected blow, and a great shock to me. I knew no other scholar and distinguished investigator in whom the consciousness of working for ideal aims was so keen and so inspired. To be in contact with him always gave one the sense of extraordinary benevolence and cordiality.'

After moving in 1889 from the official quarters which he had previously occupied in Berlin to the residence assigned to the President of the Physikalisch-Technische Reichsanstalt, in the Marchstrasse, in Charlottenburg, Helmholtz temporarily laid aside all other scientific work, in order to devote himself, as far as was compatible with his duties at the Reichsanstalt, to meteorological research. On May 31, 1888, and on July 25, 1889, he communicated two papers to the Academy 'On Atmospheric Motion', the contents of which were in part, and in a somewhat altered form, the subject of a lecture given in September, 1889, to the Heidelberg Congress of Natural Science, 'On the Movements of the Atmosphere.'

In the first place, Helmholtz applied to Euler's hydrodynamic equations for a fluid subject to friction the consideration of which he had so frequently availed himself, viz. that its particular integrals held good also for the case in which the co-ordinates, the time, and the friction-constants were multiplied by an arbitrary factor n, while the forces, the pressure, and the components of velocity remained unaltered. It was found that the motion proceeded analogously, only more slowly, if in the motion of the magnified masses the friction-constants were correspondingly magnified. But if the value of these last be unaltered, the influence of friction upon the magnified mass will be much less, and the large mass will have the effects of inertia much less affected by friction. Since the density and the potential remain unaltered, and the forces, inasmuch as the entire process takes n times as long, must be reduced to the nth part of their previous value, Helmholtz concludes that the different densities of the air at different heights cannot be reproduced in reduced models, since we cannot alter gravity proportionately.

He showed by special cases how extraordinarily insignificant the effects of friction at the surface of the earth, which would ensue in the course of a year, must be for the upper air-layers. The destruction of *vis viva* by friction can only occur at the surface of the earth, and at the separation surfaces of vortex motions. So too for heat exchange: hardly anything except radiation and convection of heat comes under consideration in the motions of the air, save at the limits next the earth's surface, and the internal surfaces of discontinuity, where indeed changes of temperature might take place between the warmer and colder layers, by the actual conduction of heat, and diffusion of the molecules that are in motion. It was shown on the basis of Maxwell's friction-constants for air, that a motion delayed by friction at 0° would fall to half its velocity in 42,747 years, if the interval between the two layers is 8,026 m., the mean height of an atmosphere of constant density; and the lower temperature of the upper layers still further diminishes the effect of friction. In the same way, the conduction of heat may reduce the difference of temperature in the upper and lower surfaces of an atmosphere of 8,026 m. to one-half in 36,164 years.

'For meteorology,' says von Bezold, 'the researches of Helmholtz into the integrals of hydrodynamic equations will be of enormous importance in time to come.'

When, at the end of July, Helmholtz communicated Part II of his Meteorological Investigations to the Academy, his colleagues found him markedly depressed. Sorrow and trouble weighed upon his family. It was increasingly certain that the bodily affections of his younger son Fritz must permanently hinder his mental development, although the malady of the elder son Robert appeared for the time at least arrested, and his parents hoped that a long life might lie before him. His scientific work had found general recognition, his cheerful disposition made him the life of the house, and he was always surrounded by a set of talented young people, who shed 'the sunshine of their youthful candour' on the Helmholtz household.

'Even if Robert Helmholtz,' writes the Assyriologist Professor Lehmann from Berlin, 'at all times represented a somewhat unattainable standard to his friends, this was due in part at least to the sincerity of his disposition. What was a striking trait in both parents had descended to their son. He reminded one of the mother, whose features he bore, in his frankly outspoken yet never depreciatory criticisms, and his no less generous appreciations. His father's immense scientific veracity extended to his judgements of all human relations, so that Frau von Helmholtz justly observed, " My husband has no confidence in any one who does not follow out his own scientific conclusions logically and faithfully to the uttermost; such persons are incomprehensible to him"; and this veracity translated into life was characteristic of Robert also. The strikingly condensed and pregnant style of his papers and letters was in his father's opinion due to the necessity of economizing his forces. "It seemed," Helmholtz once said, "at last, as though he were sparing even of his words." Robert's energy concentrated itself on the expenditure of his extraordinary talents in indefatigable scientific work in defiance of his bodily weakness. After his death his father showed that he had doubtless anticipated that only a short time was left to him, and had tried to complete as much as possible. He always looked up with admiration to his father's eminence, recognizing clearly and unreservedly that it was something quite unattainable. "We average beings cannot compare ourselves with genius; ours is quite another standard."

'Perhaps nothing is more characteristic of Robert as a friend than the fact that he never referred to his own ill health or infirmity unless it were to encourage some friend who was less used to pain, and less patient of it.'

Even down to the spring of 1889 he was engaged in most difficult experimental researches, his prize essay 'On the Radiations of Light and Heat in Burning Gases' being crowned by the Verein für Gewerbfleiss in Berlin with the prize of 5,000 marks and a medal; and until the first months of summer he was carrying on important experimental investigations in Bonn and Berlin in co-operation with Richarz, when there came a sudden collapse of the frail body that had been doomed from birth. He had just surprised and delighted his father (who knew nothing of the matter) by his appointment as Assistant at the Reichsanstalt, when his strength forsook him. On his deathbed he prepared his prize work for publication; he died on August 5. The introductory words with which Helmholtz prefaced the posthumous publication of the memoir ran as follows:—

'When the first proof-sheets of the following essay arrived, its author was already lying on his death-bed. The sad duty has devolved on me, his father, of preparing it for publication. He had hoped to work through the second part of the essay again, and to enlarge it, and had already begun experiments with other combustible substances.   Much of the rest also is incomplete, because the time-limits of the competition obliged him to be content with temporary determinations of certain points, which he could with more time have worked out more carefully and accurately: these cannot now be altered.   Nor again am I sufficiently sure of his views in these matters, for he worked quite independently, and seldom asked my advice. It was only when the problem was down on paper that he used to show it to me, and discuss it.   I must therefore confine myself to the alteration of any obvious errors on the part of the copyist, and the modification of a few points that are not clearly stated, where I can be certain that the author himself would have altered them in the same way, if he had looked through the proof-sheets.'

The loss of their son was paralysing to the sorely-tried parents, and Helmholtz, who was quite broken down, went to Switzerland in the middle of August, to recuperate in mind and body amid new impressions.

'Do not write too much,' he writes from Munich to his wife; 'try to sleep as much as possible both day and night.   Since we both have work to do in the world, and may not yet lie down and give it up, we must take care to remain fit for it.   We must not leave Fritz just yet, but the future has become frightfully indifferent to me.   I shall continue to do my work, but whether it is for a long or a short while begins to be all one to me now.'

His letters show that Nature had a beneficial effect upon him in Pontresina: he took long walks, climbed the Piz Languard, which he had shrunk from for four years, and began once more to occupy himself with various and complicated problems.   At the end of September he attended the Scientific Congress in Heidelberg, at which Hertz delivered the Address that has become so famous for its lucid simplicity and its profound content.

'I came across the whole Siemens family, and Edison and his wife, the first evening in the Schloss Garden.   Mr. Edison is a beardless individual somewhat resembling Napoleon I, but far kindlier, with an almost childlike expression and clever eyes, but he is very hard of hearing.   In reply to our questions he gave us much interesting information about his way of working. To-day we had the address from Professor Hertz; it really was extraordinarily good, very finished in style, tactful and tasteful, and called out a storm of applause.'

A quarter of a century had passed since Helmholtz had heard Kirchhoff, in his admirable Pro-Rectorial Address, in the Great Hall of Heidelberg University, announce that the discovery and logical development of the Law of the Conservation of Energy had been the greatest achievement of the century in natural science: and now he was in the front rank of the auditors of the lecture given by his great pupil Hertz, who had taken his stand upon Helmholtz's earlier criticism of the different electrodynamic theories, accepting his interpretation of the Faraday-Maxwell hypothesis, and had thereby arrived at his own fundamental discoveries.

'When in the present century the reactions between electrical currents and magnets became known, which are infinitely more complex than those of gravitation, and in which motion and time play such an important part, it became necessary to increase the number of actions at a distance, and to improve their form. Thus the conception gradually lost its simplicity and physical probability. It was sought to regain this by seeking for comprehensive and simple forms, the so-called elementary laws. Of these the celebrated Weber's law is the important example. Whatever may be thought of its accuracy, this attempt as a whole formed a closed system full of scientific charm: those who were once attracted into its magic circle remained imprisoned there. If the path indicated were a false one, warning could only come from an intellect of the highest originality, from a man who would look at the phenomena with an open mind, and without prejudice, and set out again from what he saw, and not from what he had heard, learned, or read. Such a man was Faraday. . . . To him the electric and magnetic forces became the actually present, tangible realities: while electricity and magnetism were things whose existence was disputable[1].'

In April, Helmholtz went to Cap d'Antibes to make scientific observations upon the movement of the waves of the sea, and

---

[1] Hertz, *Miscellaneous Papers*, English Translation by D. E. Jones, p. 315.

communicated his theoretical conclusions, and the comparison of them with his observations, to the Academy of Berlin, on July 17, 1890, with the title 'The Energy of the Waves and Wind', as the continuation and completion of his two earlier works on atmospheric motion.

In his earlier investigations Helmholtz had shown that a level surface of water, over which a wind is blowing evenly, will be in a state of unstable equilibrium, and that the origin of the waves of water must be ascribed to this very circum-stance. Further, the same process must occur at the border of layers of air of different densities that slide over one another; but will here assume much greater dimensions, and has an essentially causative significance in the irregular phenomena of meteorology. This determined him to investi-gate the relations of energy, and its distribution between air and water, more exactly in his memoir on the energy of waves and wind, while still confining himself to the case of stationary waves, in which the movements of the water particles can only proceed parallel to a vertical plane. He refers the laws of stationary rectilinear waves back to a minimal problem, in which the potential and kinetic energy of the moving fluids are the variables, and is able to formulate conclusions as to the increase and decrease of the energy, and the difference between stable and unstable equilibrium of the surface of the water. In this difference of the state of equilibrium, the masses in question are no longer at rest, but are in persistent, though stationary, motion.

Till now it had proved impossible to lay down any general law for moving systems, comparable with that for resting bodies, as expressed in the statement that stable equilibrium involves a minimum of potential energy. Helmholtz finds the minimal law for stationary waves with constant amounts of current to be that the variation of difference between potential and kinetic energy disappears, so that stable equi-librium of a stationary wave-form corresponds under all possible variations of such a form with a minimum of such a difference. If, on the other hand, the same magnitude becomes a maximum with another form of curve, the con-dition of equality of pressure on either side of the limiting surface is at least temporarily fulfilled, but any disturbances, however small, of the form of equilibrium will be augmented, and the equilibrium will become unstable, as appears with real water-waves in the foaming and breaking of the wave-crests. With increased force of wind, and propagation of the waves along the water, the absolute minimum must eventually cease to exist, and the equilibrium becomes labile, so that with increasing currents stationary waves of given wave-length become impossible. It follows that stationary waves of prescribed wave-length are only possible in the case of current velocities lying below certain limits, while the value must also exceed certain minimum limits. One velocity of current determines the rate of wave transmission along the water, the other the velocity of the wind relative to the waves. The application of the analytical expressions thus determined shows, in conformity with experience, that wind of constant intensity which impinges upon a quiescent surface produces faster, that is longer, or higher, waves when it has been blowing for some time upon the waves first produced, and has accompanied them for some distance along the surface of the water: with constant wind, the waves can only increase if the wind goes forward in the same direction more rapidly than they do themselves. From observations made at Cap d'Antibes in April, with a small portable anemometer for measuring the strength of the wind, he was, generally speaking, able to confirm the theoretical statement that so long as the wind outruns the waves it augments the total energy and the momentum of the wave-motion. So long as the energy calculated for stationary waves diminishes, and produces a still lower minimum, the tendency towards the form of minimal energy, under the influence of all the little disturbances produced by the other concurrent waves in actual cases, also co-operates. This eventually tends to a maximum value, and the breaking of the crest, if this can be reached at the given velocity of the wind.

Helmholtz now became engrossed in his work at the Reichsanstalt. On December 13, 1890, he published a 'Memoir of the Work hitherto accomplished at the Physikalisch-Technische Reichsanstalt', to be laid before the Reichstag, which bore witness to the zeal and energy with which he had endeavoured to fulfil all the duties of his position. The physical portion of the memoir covered the fundamental work in electricity and in thermometry, capillary deviations, barometric determinations, and estimations of expansions. The technical portion dealt with the testing of clinical thermometers, of which some 25,000 had been examined and guaranteed at the Institute during the three years of its existence, thermometers for scientific work, photometric determinations with a view to establishing a fixed unit, the manufacture of standard tuning-forks, and an infinite series of other technical tasks.

'Is anything more needed,' says du Bois-Reymond, 'to show how erroneous was the assertion that he had been favoured in his productive output by the quiet and uniform nature of his professional duties?'

He was also, as a Member of the Commission convened by the Prussian Minister of Education, contributing to the discussion of the questions of higher education: his 'Remarks on the Training preliminary to Academic Studies' being published in the following year. When Königsberger asked in October, 1888, at the request of a colleague, if he would sign the memorandum then circulating in academic circles in favour of the Gymnasia, he replied:—

'I do not propose to sign the memorial. In the first place I do not approve of these public manifestoes by private individuals, since, so far as I know, they are always without effect; and in the second place I hold that our Gymnasia have been conducted on false lines, even if I do not want to see Greek struck out of our first-class schools. Having no professional inducement, I therefore see no necessity for entering the lists with a voluntary and spontaneous declaration in favour of the present trend of classical study at the Gymnasia, without at the same time expressing my objections to the system.'

He defines his position in these matters, in accordance with the views already expressed in his Rectorial Address at Heidelberg, in noble and characteristic language:—

'The education of civilized nations has till now centred in the study of languages. Language is a great instrument, the possession of which essentially distinguishes man from the lower animals; by means of it the knowledge and experience of his contemporaries, and of past generations, are at the disposal of each individual; without it every one would, like the lower animals, be confined to instinct, and to his own individual experiences. It is obvious that the development of language was the first and most necessary task of the adolescent peoples, just as now the finest possible development of its significance and its proper application is and must be the cardinal requisite in the education of each individual.

' Historically, the culture of the modern nations of Europe is especially connected with the study of classical literature, and thereby immediately with linguistics. And linguistic studies are in relation with the study of forms of thought which language expresses. Logic and grammar—that is, according to the original meaning of the words, the art of speaking and the art of writing, taking both in the highest sense—have thus hitherto formed the natural corner-stones of intellectual culture.

' Granted, however, that language is the means of transmitting and preserving the truth when it is once known, we must not forget that its study is no guide to the discovery of new truths. Logic, for instance, teaches us how to draw conclusions from the universal proposition which forms the major premise of a syllogism, but tells us nothing as to the derivation of such a proposition. Any one wishing to convince himself independently of its validity must on the contrary begin with the particular cases comprised under the law, which, later, when it has been established, may no doubt be regarded as its consequences. It is only when the knowledge of the law has been handed down that it actually precedes the cognition of the premises, and it is in such cases that the prescriptions of the old formal logic acquire their indubitable practical significance.

' All these studies, accordingly, fail to lead us to the true source of knowledge, nor do they bring us face to face with the reality which we seek to know.

' They even contain an undeniable danger, inasmuch as that knowledge is transmitted by preference to the individual, of the origin of which he has no right conception. Comparative mythology and the criticism of metaphysical systems can tell us much as to the way in which metaphorical expressions have subsequently acquired a literal significance, causing them to be cherished as the tradition of a mysterious and primaeval wisdom.

' Thus, while fully recognizing the high significance to the intellectual development of the human race of this subtly elaborated art of transmitting and receiving the accumulated wisdom of others, and with all deference to the importance of the classics in the evolution of the moral and aesthetic sense, and in the development of an intuitive knowledge of human sensations, ideas, and conditions of civilization, we must nevertheless insist that this exclusively literary and logical method of education fails in one essential point. This is the methodical training of the faculties, by which we subject the unorganized material, governed apparently more by chance than by reason, which we encounter in the real world, to the organizing concept, after which it is capable of linguistic expression. The methodical development of this art of observation and experiment has hitherto been confined almost exclusively to the natural sciences ; any hope that the psychology of individuals and of nations might be directed to the same goal, along with the practical sciences of education and of social and political organization which should be based upon it, seems for the present to be relegated to a distant future.

'This new task, pursued by scientific workers along new ways, resulted promptly enough in new, and, after their kind, unprecedented consequences, a proof of what achievements the human mind is capable when enabled to traverse the entire path from the facts to the complete knowledge of the law, under favourable conditions,—self-conscious, and itself testing all things. The simpler relations, those of inorganic nature in particular, permit us to obtain such an exact and penetrating knowledge of their laws, such far-reaching deductions of the consequences to which these lead, and then again to test and confirm these deductions by so exact a comparison with reality, that the systematic evolution of these concepts (e. g. the deduction of astronomical phenomena from the law of gravitation) can be compared to no other product of human thought, in respect at once of consistency, certainty, exactitude, and fecundity.

'I only refer to these facts in this connexion in order to point out in what sense the natural sciences have become a new and essential element in human civilization, of indestructible significance to its whole future development, so that the complete education of the individual, as of the nations, is no longer possible without a combination of the former literary and logical tendencies with those of modern science.

'The majority of educated people at the present time were instructed on the old lines, and have scarcely come in contact with scientific ideas, or at most with a little mathematics. It is men of this school who are directing our State, educating our children, maintaining the standard of morality, publishing the wisdom and knowledge of our forefathers. It is they who must organize the changes in the mode of education of the rising generation, wherever such changes are essential. They must be encouraged in this task, or compelled to undertake it, by the public opinion of all classes throughout the whole nation, whether men or women, who are competent to judge.'

Despite all the obligations resting upon him, Helmholtz continued to work at his difficult problems of mathematical mechanics, while in the next year he published some amplifications of his earlier work in optics.

The issue of the new edition of *Physiological Optics* had led him to some very interesting researches, the first of which was published under the title 'An Attempt to enlarge the Application of Fechner's Law in the Colour System', in the *Zeitschrift f. Psych. u. Physiol.* in 1891. He starts with the assumption that the totality of colours perceived by the human eye is a triple complex, like that of position in space, and that Newton's Law of Colour-Mixture depends upon this, by transferring the less easily perceived relations of colours to the composition of geometrical lines and the construction of centres of gravity. Just as we may use the most dissimilar measurable spatial magnitudes in order to determine any position in space, so we may employ very dissimilar magnitudes to define a colour. In order to obtain direct measurements of the field of sensation, Fechner confined himself to the alteration of light intensities with unaltered mixture of light, whereas further determinations are requisite as to the size of the distinguishable graduations in colour-tones, and in the saturation of colours, without or even with simultaneous alteration of brightness, as well as of the dependence of these gradations upon the physically definable alterations in the exciting light. Helmholtz designates his own communications as hypotheses, which must be tested more precisely, but believes that such an attempt must be made, in order to obtain the preliminary orientations in a new department.

If the brightness of two somewhat differently coloured lights be compared together, a point is arrived at with gradual alteration of the intensity of one of them, at which the perceptible colour difference reaches a minimum of clearness; the ratio of light intensities corresponding to this point is then regarded as the ratio of equal brightness. Helmholtz next proposed to himself the task of ascertaining this point of least recognizable difference for a series of mixed colours, obtained from the same colour-elements by admixture upon the colour disc. He found in the first place that the effect of an increment of any colour upon the brightness was essentially diminished by the amount of that same colour already present in the mixture; it follows from the experiments that if, starting from a highly saturated colour, we determine a series of mixed colours of equal brightness (by always comparing two very closely connected members of the series with one another), the total quantity of mixed light in such a series of colours cannot remain unaltered. If we begin with the most highly saturated red, we shall diminish the brightness far less by subtracting a small quantity of red than we strengthen it by adding an equal quantity of blue. The comparison thus effected between two approximately equal and highly saturated colours is essentially different from the case in which the brightness of two very differently coloured fields is compared together. A long series of experiments led in the first place to the result that the recognizability of low gradations of the intensity of coloured light is far less affected by the simultaneous presence of a second and quite dissimilar colour in the field, than it is by the presence of an equally bright quantity of the same colour.

The extension of the form of the psycho-physical law to complexes of more than one dimension had led Helmholtz (while Fechner's law referred merely to alterations in light intensity with unaltered mixture of the light) to the quantitative determination of the nature of a colour-sensation in dichromatic eyes by two independent variables, in trichromatic eyes by three variables. In these two papers (one published with the title 'Attempt to apply the Psycho-physical Law to the Differences of Colour in Trichromatic Eyes,' in the *Zeitschr.*

f. Psych. u. Physiol., the other, ' Shortest Lines in the Colour System,' communicated to the Academy on December 17, 1891), Helmholtz returns to the conclusions laid down by himself and Riemann, that all the characteristics of our particular form of space can be derived from the fact that the value of the distance between two adjacent points may be expressed by the corresponding increment of the co-ordinates, and accordingly requires that the interval between any two points of a rigid body should be completely given by the position of its terminal points, and remains the same in all possible displacements and rotations of the rigid body. Starting from the fact that each special colour may be represented by the combination of the corresponding measured quantity of three appropriately selected fundamental colours, which take the place of the co-ordinates, he finds in the sharpness of the distinction between any two nearly related colours, a quantity which is analogous to the distance between points in space, and proposes a very simple analytical expression which he hopes will play the same part in the region of colour-sensation as the formula for the length of linear elements in geometry.

This expression gives the degree of clear distinction between any two colours, which are at the same time different in the fundamental colours that blend in their composition, that is, which differ both in brightness and in quality. In analogy with the shortest line between two points in space, he defines as the shortest colour-series, those series of transitional colours between two given terminal colours of different quality and quantity for which the sum of the perceptible differences is a minimal.

Helmholtz next applied these results to the solution of a weighty but very difficult problem. Newton's Law of Colour-Mixture referred the entire complex of possible colour-sensations to three co-existent modes of exciting the nervous apparatus of the eye, but left undecided which colour-sensations correspond with these three elementary excitations. Helmholtz once more attacks the question of determining which are the three physiologically simple colour-sensations. The investigation yielded the following results, with some degree of probability, for the three fundamental colours : spectral red is a whitish, slightly yellow modification of a ground colour, which must therefore be a highly saturated carmine-red; spectral violet is a pale red modification of the third ground colour, which may therefore be compared with ultramarine in its tone, while the second fundamental colour corresponds more or less with the green of vegetation. These results are contradictory to Helmholtz's own earlier opinion, that dichromatic subjects are simply wanting in one of the fundamental sensations of the trichromatic eye. But Helmholtz now gave up this view (as he had already informed Lord Rayleigh), and adopted the position that coloured lights which appear equal to the normal trichromatic eye must do so to the dichromatic eye also. If Newton's Law of Mixture is applicable to the colours of the dichromatic system, it follows that (granting every plane, the rectangular co-ordinates of which represent the values of the prime colours of the trichromatic system, to be available as a colour table) all the isochromatic planes in a dichromatic colour system must pass through a line of intersection. It further follows that in the colour table constructed after Newton all isochromatic lines of a dichromatic system intersect at a point beyond, or at the limit of, the trichromatic colour triangle. He concludes the investigation with a comparison of sensitiveness to differences of brightness, and to differences of colour.

After the heavy afflictions that had befallen Helmholtz and his family, the second half of the year 1891 brought a flood of ovations from the scientific, and indeed from the whole learned world, such as have seldom fallen to the lot of any scholar.

After taking up the Presidency of the Test Commission at the International Technical Exhibition in Frankfurt-a-M., and again devoting the summer to optical problems, he went with his family to Campiglio in the middle of August, to avoid the excitement and exertion incident on his seventieth birthday, and only returned to Berlin when the anniversary was over.

Both at Campiglio and subsequently at Feldafing, he received innumerable congratulations from the whole world. On September 21 he writes to Ludwig:—

'Best thanks for your kind—in my opinion far too kind—appreciation of my labours. When two friends are working in somewhat different directions, it is natural that one should occasionally be able to help the other, and I am glad if I have

sometimes been able to do this for you. On the other hand
I have received much from you in return, especially while
I was engaged in physiology, where you were always my chief
authority.   For the last fortnight I have been sitting three
hours daily as a model to the sculptor Hildebrand, who is
reproducing me in marble.   My health has been very good
so far, and I am prepared for the Berlin Commemoration.
Naturally the thought of one's seventieth birthday is a mixed
joy, and hardly a festival; but I must confess that the amount
of tokens of sympathy, and of respect and gratitude, which
have poured in on all sides, and the greater part of which
must be meant in a right spirit, since they were quite un-
solicited, has something solemn and elevating.   Apart from
all questions of vanity, it is legitimate for one of us, who has
worked hard all his life, to ask, 'Is what you have done useful
and worth having?' and this can only be answered by others,
who have found it useful and profitable. . . .'

On the Emperor Frederick's birthday he was made Wirk-
licher Geheimrath, with the title of 'Excellency', by patent
granted on October 12, 1891, by the Emperor William II in
Potsdam.

November 2 was the date of the ovation to Helmholtz in
Berlin, which was a memorial not only to him, but to the investigators of every country, in its ungrudging recognition of
his immense services to science, and of his fine and noble
personality.   It will suffice to quote the words of du Bois-
Reymond, from the legion of testimonies borne by Ministers,
Academies, Scientific Corporations, and individual Students:—

'We issued an appeal, as international as is science, reaching
beyond all bounds of Chauvinism and of politics, to the learned
men of whatever category, to physicists, mathematicians, physicians, physiologists, all of whom must perforce acknowledge
themselves as your admirers, and your pupils: and the result
of this appeal is shown in the list I herewith hand you, containing some 700 names (I have not counted them exactly),
among which, however, are Societies which in themselves
include a vast number of signatures.   The appeal has been so
successful that it has provided us with ample funds for realizing
several tokens of our homage.   Yonder bust is known to
you already, since you sat for it.   We return our thanks to the

sculptor, Adolf Hildebrand, who has so admirably preserved your features for the coming generations. But since such a bust is a ponderous possession to many, even as a plaster cast, we have commissioned Jacobi's etching pen to make your features more generally accessible in the guise of this picture. Even this did not content us, and we were fortunately able, with the large funds at our disposal, to go much further. We resolved to endow a foundation at the Academy of Sciences in your name, and from time to time to bestow a medal bearing your portrait and your name on some distinguished scholar and worker in one of the innumerable fields of your activities. I have the pleasure of handing you the first copy of the medal.'

The great banquet, which brought 260 friends and admirers of Helmholtz together at the Kaiserhof on November 2, excited deep and universal interest, on account of the speech made by him at the dinner, which became widely known in the course of the year, and is usually regarded as autobiographical. One extract only can be given here. ' My results have been of value in my estimation of myself, only in so far as they have given me a standard of what I might attempt to investigate farther; they have not, I hope, led me into self-adulation. I have often enough seen how injurious megalomania may be for a student, and so have always tried to prevent myself from falling into the clutches of this enemy. I knew that strict criticism of one's own work and one's own capacities was the best palladium to protect one against such a catastrophe. After all, one only needs to keep one's eyes open for what others can do and oneself cannot. I do not think the danger is very great, and as regards my own work I doubt if I have ever finished the last corrections of any paper, without finding some points twenty-four hours later which I could have made better or more complete.

' I know how simply everything I have done has come about, how the scientific methods developed by my predecessors have led me logically to the point, how at times a favourable accident or lucky circumstance has helped me. But the chief difference lies here: what I have seen slowly growing from small beginnings through months and years of tedious and often enough of tentative work, from invisible germs, has suddenly sprung out before your eyes like the armed Pallas from the head of Jupiter. Your judgement was modified by surprise, mine not: it may indeed, if anything, have been depressed by the fatigue incident on work and by annoyance at all the many irrational steps that I had made by the way.'

Almost before the festivities were over, Helmholtz immersed himself once more in problems of the most heterogeneous kind, turning in the first place to those complex mathematical problems which were to set the Principle of Least Action at the head of the laws of Nature.

On Feb. 26, 1892, he writes to Hertz: 'I too am writing another little electrodynamic paper, viz. a transformation of Maxwell's equations in the form of the Principle of Least Action, since, as you have already remarked, the derivation of the pondero-motive forces might otherwise conceivably be imperfect. But it results from the above-mentioned principle in a manner agreeing perfectly with the older derivation from energy.'

Hertz replied on Feb. 28 that he was not acquainted with any irreproachable connexion of the pondero-motive forces based on Maxwell's equations, for the general case of any alterations whatsoever.

Helmholtz (after spending a few weeks in the North of Italy and fetching his wife from her sister's home in Abbazia) communicated these researches to the Academy of Berlin on May 12, 1892, with the title 'The Principle of Least Action in Electrodynamics'. He set himself the excessively difficult problem of ascertaining whether the empirical laws of electrodynamics, as expressed in Maxwell's equations, could be reduced to the form of a minimal law.

In a system of ponderable bodies, the internal forces of which are conservative, it is known, as a rule, which quantities denote co-ordinates and which velocities, and it then becomes possible, up to a certain point, by means of the relation which Helmholtz had earlier discovered between the total energy and the kinetic potential, to develop the latter from the former. There only remained undetermined, as previously stated, a linear homogeneous function of momentum, which has to be added to the value of the kinetic potential, because such linear terms are eliminated from the value of the energy supply. This cannot, however, be carried out, unless we are able to see which of the internal changes of the system correspond to alterations in the position of individual parts, and which on the contrary are alterations in velocity of unknown internal motions, or even possibly of changes in momentum. And in this case we find ourselves in the region of electrodynamics; here we have to deal with electrification and magnetization of individual bodies and substances, both which conditions may persist permanently. Electrical currents evoke magnetic forces, magnetic alterations evoke electrical forces. And here, unless we depend upon that relation between energy and the kinetic potential, and can establish the principle of least action by calculation of the latter, we are compelled to see whether the empirical laws of electrodynamics, as expressed in Maxwell's equations, can be brought under the form of a minimal law, and what analogy this form has with that established for ponderable bodies.

Helmholtz now set out from the consideration that if we want to form conceptions as to the mode of electrical and magnetic forces, and the nature of the material substratum that carries them, we only know in the first place that both come under the law of the conservation of energy. But we cannot separate the two forms of energy from one another for certain, and, further, we do not know if they participate in the other general properties of all the conservative motive forces of ponderable substances, which find their briefest expression in the principle of least action, and, as Helmholtz pointed out in the mechanical papers previously alluded to, are the expression of a series of special laws of reciprocity between the forces of different origin in a system of ponderable masses. The principle of least action holds good (as Helmholtz had already pointed out) in so far as the laws of potential determined by Neumann and extended by Helmholtz apply to closed currents, in which the intervening spaces are free from magnetic and electrical substance. The further question remained, whether the principle could also cover the more complete equations of electrodynamics, as proposed by Clerk Maxwell, and completed by Hertz, with explicit development of the terms which depend upon the motion of the medium.

Apart from theoretical questions as to the nature of the fundamental forces, there were other problems relating to the observed phenomena. The values of the pondero-motive forces in electromagnetic systems had so far been derived from the energy value only. Helmholtz, however, had previously shown that in cases where the kinetic potential contains terms which are linear in respect of the velocities, these disappear from the energy value, so that the forces due to them cannot be ascertained from the energy. Such linear terms are in fact present in the kinetic potential according to F. E. Neumann, so soon as permanent magnets and closed currents act upon each other. The question whether there may not be others of the same kind cannot be determined without special investigation. Helmholtz actually succeeded in formulating a kinetic potential of such a kind that the variation, assumed equal to zero, of its integral, taken between two points in time, gave the Maxwell-Hertz equations, while the pondero-motive forces were shown by the minimal principle to be in complete agreement with Maxwell's theory. Unlike the known forms of the problem, it was found here that quantities which were ultimately characterized as momentum, were treated in the variation as independent variables in accordance with his earlier general investigations, in which the velocities were in the same way treated as independent variables, and the signification of these quantities first appeared from their variations. There are many cases of which it is unknown whether they are states or alterations of velocity of states; similar investigations occupied Helmholtz at the close of his life.

On June 11, at the General Meeting of the Goethe Society at Weimar, Helmholtz delivered the address on 'Goethe's Anticipations of Coming Scientific Ideas', to which reference has already been made. On his return from Weimar, he found an intimation from Paris that he had been elected 'Foreign Associate on June 13, 1892, in place of Don Pedro II D'Alcantara, Emperor of Brazil'; as also his nomination to be Honorary Member of the German Chemical Society of Berlin. On the other hand he had the immense pleasure of communicating a high mark of distinction to his old friend Lord Kelvin. On July 4, 1892, he writes (in English) to Kelvin: 'I don't know if you have already received the information that on last Thursday the Academy of Sciences at Berlin has elected you to be one of the first possessors of the Helmholtz medal. At the same time the medal has been given to Mr. du Bois-

Reymond, to Robert Bunsen, and to our Mathematician Professor, Professor Weierstrass.'

Some experiments on Electrical Standards, which Helmholtz was proposing to undertake with Lord Rayleigh, were the cause of the following request to the Ministry for leave of absence on July 19, 1892 :—

' I have the honour respectfully to inform Your Excellency that I propose to betake myself to England on Thursday, the 28th inst., for the purpose of testing, with Lord Rayleigh and Prof. Glazebrook of Cambridge, the results of the experiments on the Comparison of Resistances which will have already been carried out by Dr. Lindeck in the Cambridge Laboratory. The Meeting (of the British Association) in Edinburgh will last from August 3 to 11, after which we shall assemble in the Laboratory of the Board of Trade in London to compare the German resistances and standard cells with those of the Board of Trade.'

Returned from England, after working off the most important of his official duties, Helmholtz prepared Parts 6 and 7 of the new edition of *Physiological Optics* for the press, so that they were able to appear the same year, and then left Berlin for a few days to celebrate the 50th year of his doctorate, on November 2, in the retirement of his family. Some of the many congratulations which poured in upon him, and Helmholtz's answers, are of great interest.

The Medical Faculty in Berlin, before whom he had passed his doctor's examination 50 years before, sent him a renewed diploma with cordial congratulations. Helmholtz's answer, dated from Charlottenburg, November 3, ran as follows :—

' I must beg to return my warmest thanks to the Medical Faculty of this University for the gratifying and cordial words that accompanied the renewal of the diploma granted 50 years ago. I have always been aware, and have often said expressly, that I owe much to the study of medicine, even in regard to my later career as a physicist. It gave me a much wider knowledge of Nature than I could otherwise have obtained from studies limited to inorganic nature and to mathematics ; and the grave responsibilities that devolve upon the physician to ensure the success of his professional treatment accustomed me at an early period to strive after an exact knowledge of the actual facts and their consequences. For this reason I have always felt my-self closely connected with medicine, my first intellectual home, even though in later years I have made no direct contributions to this subject. The assurances contained in the letter from the Faculty have accordingly given me much pleasure.'

The cordial and inspiring Address from the Academy of Berlin was also a source of great delight to Helmholtz. In his reply he says :—

' I cannot wholly suppress a doubt whether I am worthy of such high praise, but the Address will be a valued document for my descendants, telling them to the farthest generation that their ancestor had but one aim : to make the best use of his time.'

Helmholtz had conjectured from the elegance of its style and contents that du Bois was the author of this address, and du Bois replied on November 7 :—

' You know the marksman, no need to look elsewhere ; it was I, too, who murdered the Latin on your renewed diploma. When it was too late, I discovered that you had spoken of yourself as Arminius in your dissertation, where it is the fashion nowa-days to say Hermannus.'

Meantime, Hertz (who was obliged by illness to break off his great experimental researches for increasingly long periods) was expanding Helmholtz's work on the principle of least action, and its significance in electrodynamics, in theoretical memoirs of the utmost importance. In December, 1892, he writes to Helmholtz :

' Of late I have been devoting myself entirely to theoretical work, to which I was incited by the study of your papers on the Law of Least Action. I asked myself what shape must be given to Mechanics from the outset, that the principle of least action may be stated at the beginning, and that its different forms may appear not as the result of com-plicated calculations, but as illuminating truths of primary significance, and be recognized as the clear and unmistakable aspects of one and the same law. I am satisfied with my results up to a certain point, but I have still a half or whole year's work on the subject, and since my illness now makes an interruption, I must appear idle to many. But I beg Your Excellency to believe that I am not more idle than my illness makes me.

' A very remarkable discovery has been made here during

the last few weeks by Dr. Lenard, my Assistant. He covered some Geissler's Tubes with excessively thin plates of aluminium, and succeeded in obtaining plates of such a thickness that they are completely air-tight, and are yet so thin that a perceptible portion of the kathode rays that excite phosphorescence can traverse them. He then found that these rays, once generated, can be propagated in spaces filled with gas with greater or less ease in different gases, which opens up a whole new field of research, since the production of these rays can now be entirely separated from their observation. I have advised him to mark the importance of his results by sending a short report to the Berlin Academy. I hope it may be considered worthy of acceptance for the Proceedings.'

Helmholtz was greatly distressed by the conviction that Hertz was rapidly approaching his end.

On December 6, 1892, a heavy blow descended on him in the death of his faithful friend, Werner von Siemens. The noble character and sympathy of this distinguished man (who rightly stated in his *Reminiscences*, that he had never undertaken any work with the sole object of enriching himself, but had always kept the common good in view) had been an abiding stimulus to Helmholtz. His immense energy, and invariable success in bringing high and ideal aims into the realities of practical life, had supported Helmholtz throughout his whole life, and had but recently prepared the ground for his present labours. The irreparable loss of this gifted and practical friend brought isolation to Helmholtz in many a department of intellectual work, as well as in the intercourse of daily life.

Close on this followed anxiety for the health of his son Fritz, whose recurrent bodily suffering paralysed his energy, and permanently obstructed his mental development. Helmholtz was once more driven to find calm and resignation to his lot in arduous intellectual labour.

He took the keenest interest in all new discoveries and researches. Thus on November 20 he writes to his old Heidelberg pupil, Lippmann, who had sent his colour-photographs from Paris :—

'I had not previously seen any proofs of your famous invention, and am amazed at the saturation and depth of these colours. . . . The principles of your theoretical account of the phenomenon appear to be indubitably correct, but there are some things which I do not altogether understand, e. g. that the reflection of the green leaves of a plant are only seen in one given direction when the plate is rotated in its plane. . . .

'I had hoped to present myself in person to my new colleagues at the Academy this August, but was deterred by the fear of cholera quarantine.'

On December 15, 1892, Helmholtz gave a paper to the Berlin Academy which he called 'The Electromagnetic Theory of Colour Dispersion', at which he had been working for a long time.

The prevailing theories of Optics had rejected the notion that light waves could be other than elastic in their nature. Maxwell, in the treatise published in 1865 with the title *Electromagnetic Theory of Light*, had linked together two conjectures, originally far apart, in such a way that they gave each other mutual support. Electricity in motion produces magnetic forces, magnetism in motion produces electrical forces, but these effects are only perceptible with very great velocities. The constant which controls the reciprocal relations between electricity and magnetism is a very high velocity, which proves equal to the velocity of light. The explanation of colour dispersion on the ground of the electromagnetic theory of light is only possible with regard to the ponderable masses which are embedded in the ether, since the dispersion of light belongs to those processes, which, like refraction, galvanic conductivity, the accumulation of true electricity, and the existence of magnetic poles, never take place in the pure ether of a vacuum, but only in, or at, the border of spaces which contain ponderable masses as well as the ether. It was recognized by Helmholtz that, according to Maxwell's mathematical theory, pondero-motive forces must be active within ether that was permeated by electrical oscillations, and might set the heavy atoms that lie within the ether in motion. But if the ponderable particles are not themselves electrical, these forces must be proportional to the squares of the electrical and magnetic momentum of the oscillating ether, and therefore would have the same magnitude and direction for negative as for positive values. During each vibration period, accordingly, they would twice reach their maximal and twice their minimal value, so that they could not as a rule produce nor maintain vibrations of the length of a single period. It is only when the ponderable particles carry charges of true electricity that the periodic alternations of electrical momentum in the ether can produce pondero-motive forces of the same period. The corresponding view that the embedded atoms can only contain northern or southern magnetism was rejected by Helmholtz as too improbable. On the other hand, the electrolytic phenomena, especially Faraday's law of electrolytic equivalents, had long ago convinced him that electric charges of definite size are attached to the valency points of chemically combined ions, which may either be positive or negative, but must everywhere have the same absolute magnitude for each valency point of every atom.

Helmholtz therefore assumes that the embedded atoms are the carriers of definite quantities of true electricity, as required by Faraday's law. If the ether in the vicinity of a pair of associated ions is acted on and dielectrically polarized by electrical forces, the axis of the pair of ions will be prolonged or shortened, and bent towards or away from the direction of the lines of force. It must be presupposed that the forces which spread out into space from the ions as their centres, alter in correspondence with the alterations occurring in the position of the molecules, and are displaced in space, in the manner required by Maxwell's equations. The only thing demanded by the electrochemical theory beyond what Maxwell's equations imply is the possibility that these centres of the electrical forces shall be able to shift in chemical reactions from one ion to the other, and that with a great expenditure of work, as if they were bound up with a material carrier, which is attracted by the valency points of different ions with different degrees of force. If the ether surrounding a pair of associated ions is acted on by electrical forces, and polarized dielectrically, the antagonistically polarized ions will be exposed to the tensions falling in the direction of the lines of force, i. e. two equal but opposite forces, forming together a couple, which does not throw the centre of gravity of the molecule into motion, but prolongs or shortens the electric axis of the molecule, and deflects it to or from the direction of the lines of force.

The problem, as mathematically determined by this assumption, gives a kinetic potential, the exact discussion of which presents a correct account of anomalous dispersion. Helmholtz shows that in the equations of motion to be established, electrical momentum must (since there is as yet no electrical force, no inertia, no friction, &c.) be distinguished from that of the free ether, and the undulatory vibrations must be investigated separately in the free ether and in that charged with mobile molecules, deducing from the mathematical expressions here developed, that the normal dispersion spectrum can be produced by absorptions in the ultra-violet. An error in the mathematical development which led to contradictions between Helmholtz's theory and the earlier theories of dispersion, was detected by Reiff at a later time.

A peculiarly interesting corollary is that phase-differences exist between the electrical and the magnetic vibrations, as well as between the electrical vibrations and those of the ions, so that intense vibrations might conceivably tear the ions away from their combinations, especially where there is also an electrostatic charge of the substance. It would follow that the escape of electricity under the influence of the violet rays, as observed by Hertz, might obtain for all substances in which there is strong absorption at the limits of the ultra-violet. For non-absorbent media the theory leads to a dispersion formula which approximates to that of Cauchy; complete polarization is produced by refraction, and if the electrical vibrations are assumed to be in the plane of incidence, Fresnel's value for the intensity of the reflected ray is obtained in the other direction of polarization. An appendix gives the verification of the dispersion formula by Fraunhofer's experiments, which yielded very satisfactory results.

On the Jubilee for the fiftieth year of the doctorate of his oldest friend, du Bois-Reymond, Helmholtz composed an address, in February of the same year, at the request of the Academy of Sciences, in which he gave expression to his own deep affection, and to the high appreciation which he felt for the work of his former colleague in physiology.

After Helmholtz had brought the winter lectures to a close, and had attended an interesting meeting of the Aeronautic Commission (he was present at the third great ascent, which took place in the early days of March, but was not entirely satisfactory), he went in April to Ruhrort for the wedding of his niece, the daughter of his brother Otto, and was so fresh and vigorous in mind and body that eyewitnesses could not say enough of his conversational powers and fresh spirits.   He went through the spring, after passing a few weeks at Baden-Baden, in full vigour.   As usual, many evenings at his house were devoted to music, and the best artists exerted themselves for his approval.   After Steinway sent him a new piano from America, he often sat down to it himself to study his Wagner Scores: he was not, he said, a good performer on any instrument, but knew something of all, having paid so much attention to them, while his ear had become very acute from his constant preoccupation with tones.

His old friend Knapp sent him a pressing invitation from New York, to visit the World's Fair at Chicago, and entrust himself to his guidance. Helmholtz, however, replied: ' If Werner von Siemens were still alive I might perhaps have done it, in which case I should of course have accepted your kind invitation, and become acquainted with you in your new fatherland, and the circle of activities you have made for yourself there.   For me, also, that would have been the best and most interesting introduction to American life.   I have always felt a strong wish to make acquaintance with America and her doings under ordinary normal conditions.   Great Exhibitions, on the contrary, have never attracted me, nor have I found that they taught one anything of importance that one did not know before, or that was worth the disturbance and excitement that it cost one. So I have decided not to go to Chicago. I have been persuaded, by the advice of Dr. A. Koenig, to give up my lectures on mathematical physics, a course that lasts six semesters.   You will see that I am clearing the decks.   But when one sees how the friends round one are departing, one feels it is time to begin doing so.' The pressure from all sides, however, was so great (on the plea that he, as the greatest authority and most influential representative of German Science, should not be missing in the splendidly planned concourse of delegates from all the theoretical and technical sciences), that after much hesitation Helmholtz took the momentous decision to go to America.

' It has gone so far,' he writes to Knapp on June 30, 'that I have been approached by the Government and invited to go as the German Delegate to the Electrical Congress, which opens at Chicago on August 21. The final decision was a little difficult, since, though I do not yet feel myself an old man, or recognize the manifold little infirmities of advancing years as any serious hindrance, my wife and my friends are somewhat perturbed over my resolution to undertake such a journey in my seventy-second year.

' I am convinced that America represents the future of civilized Humanity, and that it contains a vast number of interesting men, while in Europe we have only chaos or the supremacy of Russia to look forward to.'

The anxiety of Helmholtz's family and of his friends was, however, so great that the Ministry, at his request, increased the allowance made for travelling expenses, so that his wife was able to accompany him.

And thus Helmholtz prepared for the journey. He concluded his Lectures earlier than usual, and made an important communication to the Academy on July 6, with the title ' Conclusions from Maxwell's Theory as to the Motions of Pure Ether '.

In Maxwell's Theory of Electrodynamics, mobility was ascribed to the ether as the carrier of electrical and magnetic forces, and values were also given for the direction and intensity of the motive forces which act upon it. This assumption entails no difficulty, so long as we conceive the ether as permeated by ponderable substances, which move with it. Helmholtz, however, maintains that the case is different for space that is free from ponderable bodies, and filled with ether only, such as we imagine interstellar space, and also the interstices between the molecules of heavy bodies, to be. In these cases we must ask whether pure ether is altogether free from all inertia, and able to satisfy the equations of Maxwell, and what are the motions it must perform. This is closely related to the question whether it yields to the ponderable bodies moving through it, or permeates them ; that is, whether it is wholly at rest, or partly moves with them, partly yields to them, according to Fresnel's hypothesis.

Helmholtz makes the assumption that pure ether, regarded mechanically, has the properties of a frictionless, incompressible fluid, but that it is wholly without inertia, and finds that the laws proposed by Maxwell, and completed by Hertz with the explicit introduction of velocity-components, are adequate on this assumption to give a full explanation of the laws that govern the alterations and motion of the ether. The summing-up of the laws of electrodynamics in the principle of least action presents a system of action and reaction that is complete in itself, and requires no farther complement than the introduction of the hypothesis of incompressibility. Helmholtz succeeded in showing this by adding to the expression which he had previously given for the electro-kinetic potential, another which, for every motion of an incompressible fluid, does not alter the value of that potential. He finds that if ether that is not freely mobile is at rest, the pondero-motive forces derived partly from electrical tensions, partly from a magnetic origin, which cannot be referred back to a potential but evoke recurrent lines of force, are only present in the ether when the flow of energy in unit time increases or diminishes; that, further, they are not annulled by the incompressibility of the ether, and must throw the ether itself into motion. On the other hand, in fully mobile ether, cyclical forces which cannot be held in equilibrium by the pressure must call forth instantaneous streaming motions of the ether, which attain every degree of velocity, and may augment until the induced forces cancel the pondero-motive forces.

On August 6 began the momentous journey to America. Frau von Helmholtz could not shake off a certain feeling of anxiety. She wrote to her daughter on July 28:—

'I hope the journey will do your father good. He looks so pale and tired now . . . and I dread any extra exertion for him. He is getting more and more like his bust, as though Hildebrand had suspected what was coming, and had fixed it in his expression and attitude. To me it is inexpressibly sad to realize that this signifies the coming of old age, the idea which I have so long kept at a distance.'

Arrived at Bremerhaven the Helmholtzes embarked on the SS. *Lahn*. 'Fate,' writes Felix Klein to the author, 'ordained that I should be with Helmholtz not only on the outward voyage upon the *Lahn*, from August 8 to 17, but also on the return upon the *Saale*. On the voyage out Helmholtz was escorted by a regular staff of physicists, Dr. Lummer in particular. Kindly as Helmholtz endeavoured to answer lay questions, I found it very difficult to get into scientific relations with him. Nor was there much opportunity, as we had frequent bad weather. One day we discussed the monodromic axioms of spatial geometry, Helmholtz having been very pleased with the explanation I gave in the *Math. Ann.*, vol. 37, p. 565, the relation of which to Lie's own position I had discussed a little time before in Part II of my Lectures on Higher Geometry.   Next day Frau von Helmholtz told me I must not discuss such hard problems with her husband; it fatigued him too much.'

In her letters to her daughter, Frau von Helmholtz gave a lively account of the events of the American tour, to which Helmholtz contributed a few very interesting comments.

'Thorwood, Dobbes Ferry, N. Y., August 19, 1893.

'If I did not know that it is we who are sitting here in an ideal room above a mild English park-landscape—looking away to the broad Hudson, on which white steamers pass up and down like swans,—with splendid trees, a lawn (that is not English, but yellow) sloping downwards in front of the fine house, humming-birds, real humming-birds, darting to and fro, and butterflies of the same size; that I have enjoyed a true water orgy here of warm and cold baths; that yesterday morning we all huddled together on the ship at 5 a.m. for breakfast, and landed without any laurel wreaths or nymphs, or other appropriate reception, and wrestled for two hours with our trunks, &c., I should not believe it! Knapp came with his servant and coachman, and Clara Gross was there, and Dr. Pringsheim with roses, and there was a general bustle and leave-taking, and then we went in a kind of covered ferry boat across an arm of the sea, and through half New York, from the slums to the most beautiful quarter, to Fifth Avenue, &c., till at last we found Knapp and this handsome and very comfortable house—as quiet as if one were in Carlton Gardens, with everything at hand.'

'Denver, Colorado, September 2, 1893.

'Thirty hours across the prairies to get here from Chicago was a great undertaking, after which we are having a whole day's rest.   Denver is a wonderful spot, 5,000 odd feet above the sea, a city of palaces, villas and log cabins, with a Capitol on the heights, of course, for the wise governors of the State of Colorado and its silver mines.   A villa quarter of Norman castles, colonial farmhouses with huge verandas, beautiful turf, trees, and some few flowers where the soil had been irrigated: electric light, electric tramways, arena, boulevards, and a magnificent mountain range in the background, with peaks 14,000 feet high—which are really long snowy ridges, up which one climbs by a cog-wheel railway, as we propose doing to-morrow. . . .

'Providence must have taken a holiday while the interior of America was being made. Such a horrible squalid monotony, and such unbroken monotony, as the journey between Chicago and Denver never was seen. It is as flat as a table; the first part, endless stretches of maize fields, miles and miles of them, always the same, enclosed here and there, alternating endlessly with miles of dry stubble, where the wheat had been; here and there a log house with veranda, a few scanty trees, a few fowls, or a wooden village, with a wooden lunch-room, or saloon, and avenues and a hotel, more fit, however, for fowls than men; then a log city with great sheds for cattle and corn, waiting to be carried away, and then more maize, more stubble, more lean cows and black pigs,—till on the evening of the first day we reached the city of Burlington. There we went to bed in that horrible Pullman Sleeping Car; I opened my window, which let in dust as deep as my finger, but with it some air into my compartment, and was waked by the damp smell in the night, when we came to the Missouri, a great wide river shining in the moonlight. The Mississippi was yellow and squalid as the Vistula, but the evening sky with its gorgeous colours made up for the weariness of the day. The courage of the men who settle in these wildernesses—whether fruitful or not is not to the point—impressed me enormously. One sees smart buggies darting about in the neighbourhood of the so-called locations, with female creatures driving them, and there is an occasional child—rarely, however; the men are all pale, and stoop, all chewing something, all unspeakably repulsive, not the least like our idea of rustics, only vulgar and weary, whether out of doors, or in the cars, in the Exposition, or in the streets.' . . .

Glenwood Springs, Colorado, Sept. 6, 1893.

'It was insane to make the Rocky Mountains, or Rockies, as they are called, our object: instead of rushing to Newport, we ought, like other reasonable people, to have gone to Niagara, and thence to Chicago, and from there by the Yellowstone Park to the East; or straight through from Chicago to San Francisco, and then back across the Rocky Mountains.

Now we have a long, long railway journey in slow trains with no good cars, which certainly shows one the country and the people, but one travels in dirt and discomfort with impossible passengers. Considering that every one travels in the same class, most of them behave admirably; they cannot help being unsympathetic, and having a hideous lingo and way of gesticulating. That they let their children swarm upon their fellow-travellers, and never check them, is less attractive, considering the great desire for amusement and the shrill voices of these darlings; but one hears and sees more of human interest than in the Palace Car, and taking them as a whole the long journeys are less fatiguing than with us. . . .

'From Manitou we went, partly by road, to a health resort, Colorado Springs, which as a matter of fact possesses no springs, but has a good hotel, and thence for twelve hours' railway journey through a dry land in which it never rains, although there are pastures, to this place in the mountains, our westernmost point. The railway is the Rio-Grande-Denver, constructed by an English engineer, Palmer, who has built an English cottage for himself and his family in a remote valley, where he has coaxed green stretches of lawn, and flower beds, bushes and creepers out of the wilderness, which without destroying the characteristics of the landscape has none the less created a bit of Old England that excited our admiration and delight. He built no Cyclopean erections in the kitchen garden, no Norman castles with a little front garden to the street, but he sunk an Artesian well, watered his land, and now has turf, and the whole dark blue world of mountains above him, with the prairie sufficiently accentuated to afford a view. . . .

'Hentschel is shortly going to leave us, as he wishes to travel farther West, and with Knapp we shall only go as far as St. Louis. From there we are to go on alone to Niagara and Boston, and thence back to New York. There we shall put up at the Waldorf Hotel, Fifth Avenue; then a few days at the Villards', a visit to Mr. Phelps, in order to see the cities of Washington, Philadelphia, and Baltimore, with their Institutes and Universities, and then the homeward journey, at the idea of which I partly tremble, partly rejoice at getting away from this country. Out here in the West one turns into a fanatical European. . . . Your father is well, somewhat thinner, but that is no wonder, in view of our "fodder" here, for one cannot call it anything else.'

Helmholtz writes to his daughter from St. Louis, September 12, 1893 : 'Our journey was interesting to a degree, more interesting than beautiful or pleasant. The beautiful parts are separated by endless dreary deserts, and are dearly paid for by an infinite amount of *ennui*, heat, and dust, notwithstanding all the extraordinary conveniences of the Pullman Cars. As a whole, America astonishes one by its vast dimensions, and the tremendous enterprises that have already been carried out there. And yet this is little in comparison with what yet remains to be done, and doubtless will be done in the next century. At present everything is unfinished, even in many respects unreasonable and paradoxical . . . [*Continuation at Niagara*] which is not to be wondered at in a civilization that begins with electric light and steam engines, while the elements of cookery and other simple domestic arts, and the organization of all the mutual good offices of society, are extraordinarily imperfect, and the newspapers are daily filled with fresh reports of the most outrageous brigandage. We travelled last night from St. Louis to the Niagara Falls. On the previous evening the night express on the same line between Chicago and St. Louis was held up by a band of twenty robbers, as it was known that there were large sums of money on board. Besides these tales of murder the newspapers only contain excited declamations about the gold or silver currency question, over which they have gone quite mad, and about which I was interviewed in St. Louis by a nocturnal reporter, although I assured the man that I had never studied questions of political economy. While I was getting ready for bed your mother sent away two other gentlemen of the same sort. It had got known through a letter from Dr. Knapp to an oculist there that we were coming. Niagara is the first thing in America that has really given us a deep impression both of grandeur and of beauty.

'We must, however, admit that we have been received with the utmost courtesy, both in private and in public, wherever we were known. From the point of view of geography and political economy the journey has been most interesting. I am afraid your mother has suffered more from its annoyances.

I myself have held out very well so far, and hope that I have got over the most fatiguing part.'

From Boston, Frau von Helmholtz writes :—

' *Vendôme Hotel, September* 17, 1893. We got here the day before yesterday at midnight, after twenty-eight hours' journey from that wonderful Niagara ; we were alone, and did not leave our luggage behind. At any rate I have learned this much, that in this country one must always stand by it, and cannot rely on any organization, least of all on the potency of the " baggage-check".

' Boston is wonderfully fine, quite English in its correctness and self-respect : nice clean streets, fine houses overgrown with ivy, wonderful churches, a big river, the Charles River, and on the other side the University suburb of Cambridge, with Harvard University.

' The Falls of Niagara are simply wonderful, and grow on one from hour to hour. We had to put up at the Cataract House, but still it was beautiful, although our view of the river was obstructed by wash-houses and an incredible amount of lumber, and the front of the house with a fine portico opened on to the grimy street.

' We saw the Falls from above, looking down ; from below, looking up ; went round both sides on foot and also travelled by a fascinating electric railway over hanging bridges, and then by a cog-railway sheer down to a tiny steamer, while the trans-parent grey mass of water poured silently over all the while, not with such a tremendous roar, but so magnificent! The spray, and the seething and heaving of it all, was so unspeak-ably beautiful and poetical, that the impression it made on us will never be wiped out. The surrounding scenery is much prettier than we expected. The Falls are so wide that they seem low at first, till one realizes the whole thing. We had very good weather, though it poured before and after. Here we are rejoicing in beds and a bath-room, and congratulating ourselves on our escape from the squalid West. We are towed about from morning till night by learned gentlemen, who show us laboratories, gymnasiums, dormitories, buildings for eating and sleeping (all admirable), memorial halls, &c.: sometimes it is like Edinburgh, sometimes like London, sometimes quite different, and it is really refreshing to read the date 1657 on a church. Some intellectual interest attaches to this city, unlike that awful Chicago. We remained here four whole days, because Professor Bowditch, a physiologist, had travelled a long way to see your father. We drove for an hour in the country to-day with his charming daughter.'

On October 7, Helmholtz and his wife set out on the return journey to Europe. Klein writes:—

'I can supply some details of the tragic close of the journey, and Helmholtz's disastrous fall. We were sitting in the smoking-room till about 10 p.m., with a perfectly calm sea,—Helmholtz, a young physician, Dr. Morton from Boston (son of the famous Morton, who first made practical use of ether as an anaesthetic), Captain Rings, and I,—when Helmholtz, remarking that it was time to go to bed, went down the fairly steep stairway leading to the saloon. Then we heard a heavy fall, to which at the moment I paid no attention, till Dr. Morton cried out, "Something has happened to the *Geheimrath*," on which we all hurried below, and were in time to see Helmholtz lifted by a number of stewards at the foot of the gangway, and carried into his cabin: there was a pool of blood on the floor.'

His wife writes, on board the *Saale*, October 14, 1893:—

'In defiance of superstition, we embarked late on Friday, the 6th, started at 7 a.m. and at once got on to the edge of a cyclone which stood by us all the time—warm, misty, depressing. I suffered unspeakably till to-day; your father, well, energetic, and particularly kind and dear about my sickness, told me on Thursday, as on all the other days, what he had been talking about with our nice captain, and then took Kuno Fischer's *Schopenhauer* into the smoking-room—while I lay more wretched than ever. Then Professor Klein came in, and broke to me that your father had fallen down the companion, and was bleeding from forehead and nose, and that two doctors were with him; and then led me into the ship doctor's cabin. There lay your father covered with blood, but he appeared to be conscious, and was able to answer all questions. At first they feared an apoplectic stroke, which I never believed for a moment, but I think one of his old and long-forgotten swoons must have suddenly come upon him. Evidently he had become unconscious before the fall, since he did not put his hands out to protect himself, but fell heavily on his face.'

At last they reached Bremen, on October 17, where Helmholtz

received the best medical attention, while the most affectionate sympathy was tendered both to him and to his wife from the entire city, and from the friends who hastened to them, and others at a distance. After a stay of eight days they were able to undertake the journey to Berlin. Although the scalp wound was visible externally for a long while, Helmholtz, thanks to the unremitting attention of Bardeleben and Renvers, was so far recovered after a few weeks, that he was able to resume his official duties in November. On December 4 he writes himself to his friend Knapp about the accident: 'The scalp wound has healed externally, and seems to be keeping so; and I can read pretty continuously, without getting vertigo or headache. At the outset it was quite otherwise. I not only felt great weakness and vertigo on attempting to walk, but had to cut any attempt at reading very short, and my face was disfigured and suffused with blood. The loss of blood, estimated by weighing me ten days after the accident in Berlin, must have been four to five kilos. Dr. Morton (who travelled with us at your suggestion) took the very greatest care of me, and I am most deeply indebted to him. It seems to me quite a moot point whether without his prompt and constant attentions I might not have bled to death directly after the accident. . . . Viewed from this somewhat greater distance, the American journey has left a very interesting and pleasant picture on my mind.'

Helmholtz frequently declared during the winter that succeeded his return from America that he required twice as much time as before for any piece of work. He often complained of seeing two different pictures with his two eyes, and attributed this to a wrench of the muscles. During the course of the winter, however, he was able to resume all his official and scientific work.

Hertz, meantime, had hardly completed three years (from the spring of 1889) at the University of Bonn, when he had been attacked by a painful disease of the bones, which after long suffering prostrated him anew at the beginning of December, 1893. The announcement of his death, January 1, 1894, was a great blow to Helmholtz: it was the ominous commencement of a fateful year for all his friends.

'All,' said Helmholtz, 'who are accustomed to gauge the

progress of Humanity by the widest range of its intellectual faculties, and by the supremacy of intellect over the natural passions, and the resistant forces of Nature, were deeply affected by the intelligence of the death of this pre-eminent genius. Endowed with the rarest gifts of mind and character, he had reaped in his sadly brief career a harvest of almost unhoped for results, the discovery of which during the preceding century had been vainly attempted by the most gifted of his colleagues. In the old classical days, it would have been said that he had fallen a victim to the envy of the gods. Nature and Destiny here seemed in quite unusual fashion to have conspired in the development of a human mind, which combined all requisites for solving the most complex problems of science. His was a mind as capable of the keenest acumen and lucidity of logical thought, as of supreme efforts of attention in observing the more obscure phenomena. The uninitiated often pass these by easily without attending to them; to the more acute observer they indicate the way in which he may penetrate into new and unknown depths of Nature.

'Heinrich Hertz seemed predestined to give men such new insight into many depths of Nature hitherto concealed from us. But all these hopes were wrecked by the insidious malady, which as it crept slowly and pitilessly forward, consumed this precious life, and cruelly destroyed the many hopes depending on it. I have personally felt this as a deep grief; for of all my pupils I had ever held Hertz to be the one who had penetrated deepest into my own range of scientific thought, and on him I had founded my surest hopes of its further development and extension.'

Whether Helmholtz himself, in the heavy fate that befell him in his lifetime in the sickness of both his sons, was not in classical parlance a victim to the envy of the gods, was a question that frequently occurred to many of his friends—but all who knew his noble and modest demeanour must reply in the negative.

The grief felt by the scientific world upon the death of Hertz is expressed in the lines which Boltzmann addressed to Helmholtz on January 6, 1894, which show the respect felt for the physicist whose life was thus prematurely cut short, and are also characteristic of the temper of the eminent investigator by whom they were written :—

'On hearing of the sudden death of Hertz, I asked myself how the German people can show their respect for his memory. Might it not be possible to address a petition to the Reichstag, to vote a national gift to those whom Hertz has left behind him? . . . One should emphasize the extraordinary import of Hertz's discoveries in relation to our whole conception of Nature, and the fact that beyond a doubt they have pointed out the only true direction that investigation can take for many years to come: and insist that it would be as uncalled for to do anything out of the common for an investigator (such as myself, for example) who does his duty and has the good fortune to discover two or three new laws, as it would be inexcusable not to do something out of the common for Hertz.'

Boltzmann was convinced by Helmholtz's answer of the impracticability of his proposition.

On February 24, 1894, Helmholtz published Vol. I of the Scientific Transactions of the Deutsche Physikalisch-Technische Reichsanstalt.

In the spring he sought rest and refreshment from the harassing experiences of the past year at Abbazia. But fate made new gaps in the circle of his friends and acquaintants.

His successor in the University Chair of Experimental Physics in 1888 had been Kundt. It was a great distress to Helmholtz to learn that this distinguished physicist and amiable man, who was still in the prime of life, was suffering from a severe form of heart disease. When Kundt informed him that he wanted leave of absence, Helmholtz, who was at Klagenfurt on his return journey (April 18), wrote him words of sympathy and consolation :—

'I can but approve of your decision, since I too have long felt how exhausting it is to expend one's intellectual time and strength on tiring details, when one is conscious of the capacity for better work, and is actually made responsible by the nature of one's post for carrying it out. I myself went through a stage at the beginning of my life in Berlin when I felt very infirm, and believed myself to be suffering from acute disease of the heart. But I came to Berlin later than you, and was already case-hardened, so that I took it less to heart when I was told to give up the more wearing parts of my work, and was thus able to recover comparatively quickly, and after a shorter break. So that from my own experience I recommend you to live entirely for your health for some time to come. The weakness that remained from my great loss of blood in October has almost entirely disappeared, and the strained eye-muscles have made good progress in accustoming themselves to new orientation of the visual images. It is only in rapid turns and motions of the body that I still occasionally feel a vertigo.'

Helmholtz had scarcely returned to Berlin when he received the news of the death of Kundt. He had esteemed him highly as a scholar and a man, and would not be dissuaded at the funeral on May 21, 1894, from expressing his feelings of deep regret at his decease. The emotion under which he was labouring is unmistakable in the notes for this funeral oration, which were found among his papers: the heavy blows which fate had dealt him of late years—the death of his beloved son Robert, the constant illness in mind and body of his son Fritz, his own deplorable accident on the ship, the death of his great pupil Hertz, so swiftly followed by the loss of the friend and colleague, taken in the midst of his mental and bodily vigour—were almost more than he could bear.

On April 28, Lenard approached Helmholtz with a request as follows :—

' My request concerns Hertz's *Principles of Mechanics*, the publication of which he confided to me. As you know, Hertz had brought the book so nearly to a conclusion in his last days that he was himself able to give the larger portion of it to the publisher. But he sent the MS. off regretfully, since he would have liked to hold the book back for six months longer, in order to work through the Second Part of it again. The desire to omit nothing, and to do the best that is possible for the book, decided me to apply to you when the time came, with the request that you would be so good as to look through the two passages indicated, and to advise me in regard to them. I should only consider myself justified in making any important alteration if you were to advise it. . . .'

Helmholtz replied on May 21 :—

' Forgive me for not having answered your questions sooner. But since I returned from my journey I have had little spare time for the tranquil consideration and thorough understanding of anything that deviates so much from the beaten track, and is so subtly interwoven, as this work of Hertz. I can only say that I am just beginning to see what his aim is, and this merely since I received the last set of proof-sheets a few days ago. Till then I had not the least inkling of what he was driving at. Under these conditions I cannot at present undertake to criticize the text, or to approve of a criticism of it, and should suppose that it will be some weeks before I have got far enough to embark upon it. I quite appreciate the difficulty you are in. But it seems to me that you can get out of it simply, without compromising yourself, if you mark the points that seem to you dubious, and add a footnote to the effect that " the text is an accurate reproduction of the original MS." This will indicate to the reader that he must pay attention in these places, and that these points may require consideration.'

Helmholtz now immersed himself in the study of Hertz's *Mechanics*, and wrote a Preface to this extraordinarily original work in July, 1904, which gives much insight into his own views of the development of mechanics.

After sketching the position of the Theory of Electricity at the time when Hertz first took it up, and after commending his great physical discoveries, he says :—

'The extent to which Hertz's reflections were focused upon the most universal points of view in science, appears once more from this last memorial of his earthly activity, his book on the Principles of Mechanics. In this he endeavoured to give a logical statement of a perfect and consistent system of mechanics, and to deduce all the particular special laws of this science from one single fundamental law, which, logically speaking, must of course be regarded merely as a plausible assumption. In this he reverted to the oldest theoretical views, which must be regarded as the simplest and most natural, and asks whether these are not adequate to enable us to deduce from them, in the strictest and most logical manner, all the recently discovered universal principles of mechanics, even where these had till now been regarded merely as inductive generalizations.'

Helmholtz points out that the laws of mechanics have all been developed on the assumption of Newton's attributes of the forces of attraction (independent of time, and hence conservative) that exist between material points, and the existence of fixed associations between the same, and that they were discovered and proved on this assumption only.

'At a later time it was found by observation that the propositions thus derived command a much wider application in Nature than follows from the proof which is given of them, and it was thence concluded that certain universal characteristics of the Newtonian conservative forces of attraction obtain for all natural forces, although no one succeeded in reducing this generalization to a common basis.'

Helmholtz then points out that Hertz had endeavoured to discover this fundamental conception, inasmuch as, in order to give a perfectly logical derivation for all the laws of mechanical processes that have hitherto been recognized as universal, he had selected the outlook of the oldest mechanical theories as his sole standpoint, and had imagined all mechanical processes to proceed as though the several associations between the interacting parts were fixed, explaining the forces that exist between bodies not in direct contact by means of the hypothesis that there are a great number of imperceptible masses and invisible motions. Helmholtz's cyclical systems with invisible motions were employed by Hertz for the working out of examples; indeed the whole structure of his mechanics rests upon the foundation laid by Helmholtz, but the death of this brilliant investigator stopped the advance of mechanics in this direction, possibly for many years.

'English physicists like Lord Kelvin in his theory of vortex atoms, and Maxwell in his assumption of a system of cells with rotating contents on which he based his attempt at a mechanical explanation of electromagnetic processes, had obviously found greater satisfaction in explanations of this kind, than in the mere general representation of facts, and the laws that govern them, such as is given by the systems of the differential equations in physics. I confess that, for my own part, I have hitherto adhered to this last kind of representation, and regarded it as the safest; but I have no substantial objections to make to a method recommended by such prominent physicists as the three above named. Certainly there are still great difficulties to be overcome in the attempt to explain particular sections of physics on the basis proposed by Hertz. But, as a whole, the Hertzian representation of the fundamental laws of mechanics is a book which must be of immense interest to every reader who takes pleasure in a logical system of dynamics, presented in the most complete and ingenious mathematical form. It is conceivable that this book may be of great heuristic value in the future as a clue to the discovery of new and universal characteristics of the Forces of Nature.'

On June 14, Helmholtz communicated a paper to the Academy, entitled 'Appendix to the Treatise: On the Principle of Least Action in Electrodynamics', which was only published by Planck after his death, on account of his manuscript annotations.

The memoir presented to the Academy in 1892 on the 'Law of Least Action in Electrodynamics' had led to great mathematical complications, and Helmholtz had been almost incessantly occupied ever since with the thought of how best to simplify the statement of the variations, and thus render the problem, as he conceived it, more perspicuous and lucid.

He intended to prepare a complete digest of his investigations for Vol. III of his *Scientific Papers*, hoping that a more simple and tangible representation of the kinetic potential, and the variation of the corresponding Hamiltonian integral required for electrodynamics, might prepare the way for the extension of the principle of least action to all forces of Nature. Many introductory notes were found among his papers, which were intended to be introduced into an extensive treatise of this kind.

All these attempts, however, broke down when he tried to apply the results (arrived at by the solution of the great mathematical difficulties which he had surmounted in his famous memoir of 1892) to obtaining a clear conception of the complicated calculations: and he could not believe there was any other way than this by which Nature could lead him to the development of his profound ideas. In the paper communicated to the Academy on June 14, 1894, he succeeded in getting a little nearer his goal.

Helmholtz had previously included the laws of electro-dynamics, as proposed by Clerk Maxwell and Hertz, in a generalized form of the principle of least action, and had referred the problem back to the question whether the known value of the total energy of electromagnetic processes agrees with that of Maxwell's system of pondero-motive forces, or must be further supplemented by a function linear with respect to the velocities. If, however, the pondero-motive forces can be derived from the above principle, this would, according to Helmholtz's statement, involve certain variations with respect to the co-ordinates and to the corresponding components of velocity, resulting in very complex calculations. This work, which remained unfinished, aimed at proposing a more simple and obvious method of solving the problem, and was fitted to eliminate these purely formal difficulties, while its results were, as he stated, confirmatory of his earlier conclusions.

On Sunday, July 9, the corrected proof of his Preface to Hertz's *Mechanics* was read aloud to him at his daughter's house at the Wannsee, and later Frau von Siemens (after searching for him in vain through the house to take him out for a walk) found him sitting by a quiet window, his little notebook and pencil in his hand, lost in thought. ' His eyes were bright, and his whole bearing was wonderfully happy.' He explained that he had been fortunate enough that day to discover something which he, and for a long time many before him, had been seeking ; but he would have no time before Wednesday to work out his ideas, which he hoped to lay before the Academy on Thursday. By the 10th he was hesitating again whether there might not be some fallacy in his argument—but to the day of his death he remained convinced that all the phenomena of Nature were comprised in the Principle of Least Action, under the universal form in which he expressed it—a view which Hertz had adopted from him, and on the universal validity of which the future only can pronounce.

During the summer a contribution from Helmholtz appeared in the *Zeitschrift f. Psych. u. Physiol. d. Sinnesorg.*, entitled ' On the Origin of the Correct Interpretation of our Sense-impressions ', subsequently rewritten by himself for the second edition of his *Physiological Optics*, then being issued ; the concluding parts only came out in the following year. This, his last contribution to Physiological Psychology, has a peculiar interest, because it re-states and re-establishes the very same opinions which Helmholtz put forward in his first lectures at Königsberg ; and because he thus proclaims himself, at the close of his long and fruitful career, to be the faithful adherent of empiricism, without denying that the nativistic position is tenable under certain limitations. In all directions whatsoever, he is still the definite opponent of every kind of metaphysical speculation. Elsewhere, however, Helmholtz guards himself against the accusation that his antagonism to all kinds of metaphysical speculation extended to philosophical inquiry in general :—

'In thus confining the name of Metaphysics to that so-called science which strives by pure thought to formulate conclusions as to the ultimate principles of the coherency of the Universe, I must protest against my objections to metaphysics being transferred to philosophy in general. In my opinion nothing has been so pernicious to philosophy as its repeated confusion with metaphysics. The latter has played much the same part in relation to the former as that which astrology has borne to astronomy. It has been metaphysics that turned the attention of the great majority of scientific amateurs to philosophy, and attracted troops of proselytes and disciples, who no doubt in many cases have wrought more harm than the bitterest opponents could have effected. They were led on by the delusive hope of obtaining insight, with little expenditure of time or trouble, into the deepest order of things and the nature of the human spirit, into the past and future of the world—in which lay the main interest that incited so many to take up the study of philosophy, just as the hope of obtaining prognostications for the future formerly led to the fostering of astronomy. What philosophy has so far been able to teach us, or with continued study of the facts involved may one day be able to teach us, is of the utmost interest to the scientific thinker, who must know the exact capabilities of the instrument with which he has to work, that is, the human intellect. But as regards the satisfaction of this dilettante curiosity, or the still more frequent egoism of the individual, these severe and abstract studies will continue to yield only a small and reluctant response : just as the mathematical mechanics of the planetary system, and the calculations of perturbation, are far less popular, despite their admirable systematic completeness, than was the astrological superstition of old days.'

And it was this position, thus clearly defined some twenty years before, that Helmholtz now took up in the wholly remodelled section of his *Physiological Optics*, entitled 'On Perceptions in General'.

In giving a more exact definition of the views of Nativism and Empiricism, which he had stated fifty years ago, he illustrates his position by the example of a man learning a new language. Here the frequent repetition of similar experiences teaches us to recognize and establish a regularly recurrent association between two different perceptions, which at the outset had no natural relation to each other. An association between two observed facts recurs with the fewest exceptions when it ensues in obedience to a natural law, which requires either the coincidence or the regular sequence of the association in a given interval. He returns in detail to the antithesis previously stated between the cognition of an object, by means of which we retain a conceptual image derived from sensory impressions, and that knowledge of it which can be expressed in words, and illustrates this contrast by divers examples from physiological optics. After an exact definition of the concepts, intuition and thought, he reverts naturally to his far earlier theory of inductive inferences and unconscious inferences, and then passes to fallacious inductions and sensory illusions, with some interesting comments upon the degree of illusion, in which from the very outset he makes the concept of attention play an important part.

'I think I may sum up the preceding considerations and experiences as follows:—

'1. As the evidence of innate organization in man, we find reflex motions and instincts, the latter presenting the antithesis of pleasure in certain impressions, pain in others.

'2. Inductive inferences, as acquired by the unconscious work of memory, play a prominent part in the building up of concepts.

'3. It seems doubtful whether the ideation of adults includes any forms of cognition not derived from these sources.'

On July 11, his mind was still in full vigour. He had previously (on May 12) recommended Lipschitz and Königsberger to the President of the Peter-Wilhelm-Müller Institute, Herr August Müller, of Frankfurt-a.-M., as judges in the distribution of a prize of 15,000 marks, and he now wrote to the author:—

'May I suggest that the prize be given to Heinrich Hertz, who died at the commencement of this year. I think all our contemporaries will agree as to the value of his discoveries and their scientific results. The circumstance of his death does not, as I interpret the statutes, preclude the allotting to him of the prize, and his life was prolonged into this year.

'If you agree with this proposition, which seems to remove a reproach from our nation, inasmuch as during his lifetime Hertz was much less honoured by the German people than by other countries, we can make the award by a brief communication in writing.'

On July 11 (the day on which he wrote) he accompanied his daughter and her children in the evening to the train which was to take them to Holland for the vacation.

'On the morning of the 12th,' writes Wachsmuth, 'I was summoned from the Reichsanstalt. Helmholtz had crossed the vestibule, but suddenly became incapable of going farther; the servant sprang forward, led him back into his room, and put him on the sofa. The paralysis, due no doubt to some increasing cerebral haemorrhage, crept on slowly. In the forenoon he was still able to talk calmly about all necessary arrangements, and I wrote a number of letters at his dictation. The first physician who came was Bardeleben, followed by Gerhardt and Leyden, but Helmholtz himself knew too much about medicine not to grasp the situation fully. Then came a time of wandering and lucid intervals, with anxious nursing, reminiscences of America and the Falls of Niagara,— lastly a decided improvement.'

On July 18, Frau von Helmholtz writes to her sister: 'His thoughts ramble on confusedly, real life and dream life, time and scene, all float mistily by in his brain—for the most part he does not know where he is—thinks himself travelling—in America—on the ship, and so on. I was obliged to bring him the pictures of Niagara. It is as if his soul were far, far away, in a beautiful ideal world, swayed only by science and the eternal laws. Then his surroundings jar on him, and he gets confused and wanders.'

His birthday, on Aug. 31, could be kept with a spark of hope; 'he rejoiced in the more cheerful spirit which pervaded his home on this last day of comparative brightness, though the pressure of the coming calamity was already heavy on all who left or entered the house.' Even on the next day he was feebler, talked anxiously of being compelled to resign, and was only calmed when his wife told him that the Under Secretary of

State, von Rottenburg, had called on his birthday, and declared that the Emperor would never consent to his resignation.

On the following day new symptoms of paralysis set in; a succession of weary days and nights began, in which his vital forces were gradually exhausted, till after the unspeakable sufferings of the last day the end came on September 8, at eleven minutes past one in the afternoon.

'His early death, which removed him in the midst of his full working powers,' said du Bois Reymond, 'was felt not merely as an irreparable loss to Science, but as a national misfortune.'

The scientific men of Europe had been looking forward to the end of September with keen anticipation, since it was known that Helmholtz had consented to give a lecture to the Naturforscher-Versammlung in Vienna, 'On Persistent Forms of Motion and Apparent Substances.' In a letter addressed to Siegmund Exner, the President of the Congress, Helmholtz had declared his willingness to address the Meeting, but added that it would not be easy at his advanced age to pledge himself definitively, 'so I end with the well-known riddle:—

> Das erste ist nicht wenig,
> Das zweite ist nicht schwer,
> Das Ganze macht Dir Hoffnung,
> Doch trau' ihm nicht zu sehr.'

Some brief notes headed 'Naturforscher-Rede' may be given here, as they are in close relation to the subject which Helmholtz had chosen as the theme of his lecture:—

'. . . I hold that the fittest theme for any speaker who has undertaken to address one of the General Meetings of the Association is to call attention from time to time to the changes that have taken place in the general aspects of Science. In sciences which have already attained a high degree of elaboration, these alterations can only take place slowly, and in little isolated steps. It is after comparatively long periods that they first become plainly perceptible, and then only to those who can look back over the experiences of a long life, passed in the midst of scientific work and the frequent reflections and doubts attaching to it, or to those who have acquired a corresponding knowledge of the historical development of Science by special historical studies.

'In thus undertaking to speak to you of these alterations in the scientific standpoint, I must beg to make my excuses for mentioning not only the most recent discoveries, but also many that are old and familiar to you, which however, in the course of time, have so entirely altered in significance that they appear under quite a different aspect.

'I may define the capital aim of my lecture by calling it a discourse on the nature of substances, using this word, however, in its older and wider sense.

'According to modern use the word substance denotes exclusively material bodies, which are located in definite points of space, and can neither be destroyed nor added to; which have a definite mass, that is, a definite inertia in their motion, but are also, as far as we know, subject to the universal force of gravitation—i. e. their weight is proportional to their mass; and which bodies are the carriers of unalterable forces, with which they act upon other masses. In virtue of their mechanical forces and inertia, i. e. their resistance to motion, they are perceptible to our tactile sense; they also affect our other senses upon many occasions and in diverse ways, so that it has been, and is, easy to learn their properties and the conditions of their rest and motion. We know of a fairly large but still limited number of such indestructible substances, the chemical elements, and an ever-increasing number of others which are compound, the chemical compounds, which latter, however, are not incapable of being destroyed or increased, since they are composed of the former and can be resolved into them again.

'In its older sense the concept of substance was more comprehensive. It corresponded more to the etymology of the term *id quod substat*, that which subsists in the background, or behind the mutable phenomena; in Greek ἡ οὐσία, Being or Essence, by which was understood not merely material things, but the concepts of categories of things, subject to one common law, of which, indeed, nothing very definite could be said, and the attributes of which depended principally on the play of fancy. The prototype which was for the most part adopted in this was the human mind, and the principle that regulated the processes in the living organism, the vital essence or vital force. The nomenclature was governed by analogy with the least material things that were known in the world.

The vital principle was successively the ἔμφυτον θερμόν, the inherent heat of Hippocrates, deriving from the sacred fire which Prometheus stole from Zeus, later the πνεῦμα, the breath of Galen, the *anima inscia*, the unconscious soul of G. E. Stahl, or the *archaeus* of Paracelsus, a kind of helpful kobold. The conscious soul of man, again, and even the Holy Ghost, were defined conceptually as the breath or wind, the *pneuma*, the imparting of it being an inspiration, an inbreathing.

' Intangible as might be this concept of immaterial substance, and obscure as were its attributes, it was none the less firmly believed in, and the dispute over the substantiality or insubstantiality of the human soul is vigorously kept up to the present day. And there is no mistaking the cardinal point of the discussion, the essential attribute of substance, its indestructibility, the immortality of the conscious soul; and, if the vital principle be distinguished from this, the idea of metempsychosis.

' How far the form given to these ideas among the different nations and sects of the human race, has been arbitrary, fantastic, contradictory, and tasteless, need not here be dwelt on. It has been fully discussed in preceding centuries, nor do I here make any claim to solve the ultimate riddles of psychology and the ruling of the Universe. But some actual knowledge of magnitudes, so far agreeing with the old conception of immaterial substances, that they are indestructible, incapable of being added to, active in space, but not necessarily divisible with it, has been obtained in the last century.

' I am not referring to the so-called imponderables, which played an important part in the earlier physics. For these were represented as material substances, like gases, filling space, only not subject to the force of gravity, though endowed with inertia like the heavy masses. Modern physics assumes another such imponderable substance, the so-called luminiferous ether, the medium by which space is filled between the ponderable bodies contained in it, which it also penetrates—the presence of which is apparent to us, since its oscillations appear as light to our eyes, and produce heat, or electrical and magnetic tensions in the heavy bodies, on which they impinge.

'Conceptually the luminiferous ether will always come under the same category as the ponderable bodies.

'Of the magnitudes comprised in the concept of immaterial substances I will here only mention the one we are most fully acquainted with, that of which you have in all probability heard most frequently, and the idea of which will be the most familiar. I mean the supply of energy, of effective working power, which is operating in the world, a Proteus capable of being manifested under the most various forms, and of changing from one to another while still unalterable in its quantity, indestructible, incapable of being added to.

'A weight lifted from the earth represents to us energy which we can utilize to drive a clock and all manner of small machines. A stream flowing down from a mountain can drive powerful engines. From these instances we obtain the fundamental unit of energy; we measure it by the weight raised, multiplied by the height to which it is lifted, and by the force of gravity, i.e. by kilogrammetres.

'The velocity of a mass in motion is again the equivalent of a driving force, which we denote by an old term as its *vis viva*. A falling weight descends with increasing velocity, i.e. the energy of its height is converted into *vis viva* while the height itself is lost, and if eventually compelled to convert its falling motion by a curved path back into a rising motion, it can thereby regain the height whence it descended. The stretched spring of a clock contains a store of energy, and so does a compressed volume of gas or steam. The latter drives our steam-engines and hot-air machines.

'We obtain the proper quantity of compressed gas and steam in these last machines by addition of heat. Heat is energy. It may be derived from mechanical motion when this is destroyed by friction and inelastic impact, and is reconverted into mechanical energy in the above machines.

'Chemical force is energy, and of a very high equivalent. It provides us with the largest part of our artificially produced supply of heat for practical purposes. It can also be converted directly through electricity into mechanical driving power without any equivalent production of heat, and thus reproduce chemical energy.

'The more carefully these thousandfold interchanges between

the diverse forces of Nature have been studied, the more exact has been the confirmation of the law that in none of them has energy been destroyed or increased. It always remains the same immutable amount which changes only in its mode of manifestation.

'The same law holds even in the most complex and delicate of all the natural processes, in those of organized life. Animals obtain the energy which they develop from the slow combustion of the food they take in with the inspired oxygen of the air, giving out heat and mechanical work in exchange. For plants, on the contrary, the principal source of energy is the sunlight, and in exchange they produce the combustible substances of which they consist, and free oxygen, which they give back to the air.

'This immense, immutable store of energy, notwithstanding the fact that it participates in the indestructibility of the material substances, and of the luminiferous ether, is yet no substance analogous to them. It is inherent in no particular substances, although from time to time it may permeate and abide in ponderable matter, whether as elastic tension, or as heat, or as chemical affinity. Nor, again, is energy simply bound to any position in space, or divisible with space, like a material substance. There are indeed certain forms which can be shown to have their seat in some definite natural body, when, that is to say, such a body is thrown into agitation by violent motion, or is very hot, or strongly compressed. But along with these we have a whole series of forms of energy, which arise only from the relations of two bodies to one another. The greatest supply of energy known to us is in the gravitation of the celestial bodies to one another, and depends on the magnitude of their reciprocal distances, being smaller the nearer the mutually attracting bodies come to one another.

'So too for chemical affinities. The energy which appears in the combination of oxygen and carbon exists neither in oxygen alone nor in carbon alone. It exists only in the relation of these to one another, whether this be regarded as direct, or as due to the intervention of electrical forces. Since it is neither contained in the space which is occupied by the oxygen nor in that occupied by the carbon, it is impossible to locate it in any precise spot.

'We know of other quantities of a similar kind, such as the energy-supply of a mechanical system protected from external influences, but otherwise arbitrarily constituted. You will have heard of this in popular lectures on astronomy, in connexion with the planetary system, since this is actually so far removed from even the nearest fixed stars, that their action has been unable to produce any perceptible effect during the whole course of the history of astronomical observations. In a closed system of this kind, the centre of gravity may have a motion which proceeds, undisturbed by all reciprocal actions of the system, at constant velocity, in an eternally unaltered direction. The corresponding velocity may also have zero value, i. e. the centre of gravity may be at rest; then it will never set up motion.

'We do not as yet know with any degree of certainty whether the centre of gravity of the planetary system is at rest or in motion. So far, the assertion of the constancy of its velocity and its direction is only based on theoretical grounds.

'But there is another similar quantity, the amount of which can actually be controlled by observation; that is the so-called momentum of the rotary motion of the planetary system, which embraces the mechanical total of all the individual revolutions of the planets round the sun, and of the satellites round the planets, and of the planets round their own axes of rotation. The sum of these magnitudes can be calculated by suitable means, the rotations being referred to any required direction in space as the axis.

'For every such axis of constant direction, which passes through the centre of gravity of the system, and moves with it through space, remaining parallel with itself, the entire rotational momentum is constant. It is greatest for one of these axes; the "invariable plane" of the system is conceived as being perpendicular to this, occupying a mean position between all the planes of rotation of the system and the equatorial planes of the several planets. The direction of this plane, and the amount of the rotational momentum of the system taken round the normal to it, cannot be modified by any reciprocal interaction whatsoever between the bodies of the system.

'This inertia of rotation may be demonstrated on a small

scale, though never wholly free from external disturbances, upon every rapidly rotating top that stands firm upon its point with a vertical axis so long as it is in rapid rotation, and falls over as soon as it loses the motion.

'Accordingly these quantities, the velocity of the centre of gravity of the planetary system and its direction, the direction of the invariable plane and the value of the greatest rotational momentum of the system, are, under the given conditions of our universe, as much unalterable magnitudes as its supply of energy. If perturbations from the fixed stars are present their cumulative effect may conceivably, after a very great lapse of time, become perceptible to posterity; and they perhaps may have to take into account the motions of the centre of gravity of these fixed stars and their rotary momenta. So long as we reckon by millenniums only, the calculation may be confined to the planetary system.

'And now we may say that we have come to the end of our knowledge of these immutable motor magnitudes. To the end of our knowledge, to the end of the list of things whose values we can exactly reckon and determine, but not to the end of the tale of all existing magnitudes of this kind. The number of these, on the contrary, is so great that we can scarcely think that the human race can ever succeed in recognizing and enumerating all of them.

'Let us now take counsel with the mathematician, who is engaged upon mechanical problems. All that I have been describing to you are known to him as Integration Constants; "Constants" because they are unalterable. And he terms his method of resolving the equations that express the laws of motion, and of discovering their final result for any later point in time, "Integration." For him accordingly there are constants which he meets in the integration of the equations of motion, and the value of which he must find some means of determining, in order to adapt his solution of the universal law of motion to the special case of the given system of bodies, with which he is occupied at the moment,—the parts of which had all, at the commencement of the time embraced in the calculation, their definite position in space, and their velocities of definite value and direction.

'Now ask the mathematician how many integration constants

he requires for one problem, in which a single indivisible heavy particle moves under the influence of known forces, unalterably distributed in space. He will reply that he requires three. Their value is expressed in the measurements by which he has determined the initial and final position of the particle, and by the energy which it possessed in the first moment of its motion.

'If, however, there are ten such heavy particles exerting reciprocal force upon each other, he will have to calculate thirty integration constants—that is, he has to discover how these constant and (during the further undisturbed course of the motion) unalterable values are constructed and calculated from spatial measurements.

'In the case of smaller groups, formed from natural bodies, with reciprocal interaction, perturbations from without, which alter the course of the motion, will be more frequent. But the general form of the solution remains the same, even if the calculations prove impossible for the human intellect, and for the resources of our present mathematics, which is unable even to construct the nine integration constants for three heavy particles.

'We must, however, conclude from these considerations, that these magnitudes, which can neither be destroyed nor added to . . .'

.   .   .   .

On December 14 a Memorial Ceremony was held in the Singakademie at Berlin at the instigation of the Physical and Physiological Societies. The Emperor, the Empress, and the Empress Frederick, with the nearest relatives of the deceased, as well as a large and distinguished assembly, were present at the ceremony. As an introduction to the whole, the Choir of the *Königliche Hochschule für Musik* performed a chorale under the direction of Professor Adolf Schulze. Then followed a solemn discourse, delivered by his friend and colleague of many years, Wilhelm von Bezold. Immediately after its conclusion Joachim played Schumann's *Abendlied*, with organ accompaniment, to which the departed had so often listened with emotion. Another chorale terminated the solemn service. Once more the Master was vividly recalled to the inward vision of all who were present. 'His contemporaries and successors,' says du Bois-Reymond (whose pen was to the last devoted to his friend's memory), 'will realize and retain the outward features of Helmholtz from the pictures and busts of the first artists of Germany. For those unacquainted with him it may be said that the external aspect wholly corresponded with the greatness of his mind. His skull was immense, but perfect in form; his splendid eyes did not betray the effort they had endured unscathed in subjective experiments, while the delicacy and refinement of the lower half of his face revealed the subtlety of his intellect. He was of a dark complexion, above the middle height, and powerfully built, with a noble bearing.'

After the Commemoration the Emperor informed the Minister von Delbrück that it was his intention that a public memorial should immediately be erected to Helmholtz, towards which he would contribute 10,000 marks, and grant a site.

Helmholtz had consented, shortly before Easter, 1892, at the request of his pupils, to publish the Lectures in Mathematical Physics, which he had delivered at the University of Berlin, and had revised certain portions of them before his death in 1894, although they were not ready for the press. These were subsequently edited by his distinguished pupils A. Koenig, O. Krigar-Menzel, C. Runge, and F. Richarz, and constitute the most important textbook for certain departments of mathematical physics.

Before his death, Helmholtz had also seen in type some two-thirds of Vol. iii of his *Wissenschaftliche Abhandlungen* (Scientific Papers), which appeared in the following year; and the printing of the Fourth Edition of his *Vorträge und Reden* (Essays and Addresses), which was only published in 1896, had just begun when he died.

The Head of the Central Committee in charge of the erection of the Monument was Rudolph von Delbrück, 'the last witness —himself now dead—of that glorious epoch of our race.' The man in whom Dryander applauded 'the might of his all-conquering intellect, the lucidity of his mind, which penetrated all confusions, the marvellous and enlightened composure of his wisdom', was for two decades among the truest friends and most devoted adherents of Helmholtz. Accordingly, both he and Arthur Koenig, Helmholtz's pupil and collaborator, gladly took up the task assigned to them by the Emperor.

The unveiling of the Monument, for which the Emperor

selected a site in front of the University Building, took place on June 6, 1899, in the presence of the Empress, the Crown Prince, and Prince Henry as the Emperor's representative, as well as the members of Helmholtz's family, and the most prominent personages of the artistic and scientific circles of Berlin. On the evening of the same day Frau von Helmholtz invited the promoters of this act of friendship and devotion to assemble round her table. It was a moment never to be forgotten when in large-hearted simple words, broken by emotion, she thanked them for procuring her this last happy hour out of their great love for the departed.

The next day she accompanied her invalid son Fritz to his stanch friends, Kussmaul and Fleiner in Heidelberg, while she herself went to Baden to make arrangements for the modest house in which she established him.

After a brief sojourn with her daughter, grandchildren, and friends, she went at the end of November, 1899, to Abbazia to her sister, to comfort her at her husband's deathbed. A fortnight later, on the day of her projected journey homeward, she was taken very ill in her sister's house, and died at Volosca, December 1, 1899. Her last words were, ' Forgive me for dying here.'

' In recalling the years,' writes Frau von Schmidt-Zabiérow, ' in which the social life of my sister in Berlin and myself in Austria was steadily widening in consequence of the positions of our husbands and our improving circumstances, my sister's image stands out as a guiding light, to which I looked confidently in all complications and difficulties. Her sure judgement, her rich intellectual life, her cheerful temperament overflowed in the energy which her influence, often unbeknown to her, infused into those surrounding her, both high and low, . . . into all who ever came into contact with her. The homely working-woman found understanding for the trials of her life, and help and comfort, from my sister, while Princesses, remote from the sorrows and cares of everyday existence, learned the possibilities of fundamental social reform from her rich experiences. In a word, nothing human was strange to her.'

On December 4, 1899, Eduard Zeller wrote to Frau von Siemens :—

' Many hundreds, and those of the highest intellectual and

social standing, will grieve with you for the rare woman—with whom none can compare among all the German women of the day—for this beneficent life that spent its treasures on all sides with such generosity. Only those, however, who were privileged, like ourselves, to live in long intimacy with your ever memorable parents and their family—only those can fully realize what and how much you have lost in your mother, as so lately by your father's death. In comparison with such a loss all words of comfort are cold and trite. There is but one thing left, to resign ourselves to the inevitable, and to cherish those who are torn from our eyes the more closely in the perpetual inner communion of the spiritual vision.'

On November 17, 1901, the youngest son, Fritz, ended his life of sorrow in Heidelberg, at the age of 33, after spending the last years in quiet retirement on his little property in Baden. True friends stood round his coffin in the Hospital at Heidelberg, deeply moved at the contemplation of all that had befallen the House of Helmholtz.

. . . .

And thus we part from the Mighty Dead, and from his works, which amaze us by the depth and universality of their ideas and arouse our admiration as works of art, and which sprang from a noble and truly moral intellect. We feel ourselves in the grip of the emotions which Helmholtz himself expressed so grandly in his tribute to Goethe and Beethoven: in words which may as justly be applied to himself, and to his creations of pure reason and aesthetic criticism, as to the great poet and musician:—

'We venerate in him a genius, a spark of the divine creative energy, transcending the limits of our rational and self-conscious thought. And yet the artist is a man as we are, in him the same intellectual forces are at work as in ourselves, save that their aim is purer and more enlightened, and their balance is less disturbed: and in proportion as we comprehend the language of the artist more or less perfectly and completely, we feel that we have in ourselves some share of the forces that have brought forth such marvels.'

CATALOGUE OF DOVER BOOKS

The more difficult books are indicated by an asterisk (*)

Books Explaining Science and Mathematics

WHAT IS SCIENCE?, N. Campbell. The role of experiment and measurement, the function of mathematics, the nature of scientific laws, the difference between laws and theories, the limitations of science, and many similarly provocative topics are treated clearly and without technicalities by an eminent scientist. "Still an excellent introduction to scientific philosophy," H. Margenau in PHYSICS TODAY. "A first-rate primer . . . deserves a wide audience," SCIENTIFIC AMERICAN. 192pp. 5⅜ x 8.   S43 Paperbound **$1.25**

THE NATURE OF PHYSICAL THEORY, P. W. Bridgman. A Nobel Laureate's clear, non-technical lectures on difficulties and paradoxes connected with frontier research on the physical sciences. Concerned with such central concepts as thought, logic, mathematics, relativity, probability, wave mechanics, etc. he analyzes the contributions of such men as Newton, Einstein, Bohr, Heisenberg, and many others. "Lucid and entertaining . . . recommended to anyone who wants to get some insight into current philosophies of science," THE NEW PHILOSOPHY. Index. xi + 138pp. 5⅜ x 8.   S33 Paperbound **$1.25**

EXPERIMENT AND THEORY IN PHYSICS, Max Born. A Nobel Laureate examines the nature of experiment and theory in theoretical physics and analyzes the advances made by the great physicists of our day: Heisenberg, Einstein, Bohr, Planck, Dirac, and others. The actual process of creation is detailed step-by-step by one who participated. A fine examination of the scientific method at work. 44pp. 5⅜ x 8.   S308 Paperbound **75¢**

THE PSYCHOLOGY OF INVENTION IN THE MATHEMATICAL FIELD, J. Hadamard. The reports of such men as Descartes, Pascal, Einstein, Poincaré, and others are considered in this investigation of the method of idea-creation in mathematics and other sciences and the thinking process in general. How do ideas originate? What is the role of the unconscious? What is Poincaré's forgetting hypothesis? are some of the fascinating questions treated. A penetrating analysis of Einstein's thought processes concludes the book. xiii + 145pp. 5⅜ x 8.   T107 Paperbound **$1.25**

THE NATURE OF LIGHT AND COLOUR IN THE OPEN AIR, M. Minnaert. Why are shadows sometimes blue, sometimes green, or other colors depending on the light and surroundings? What causes mirages? Why do multiple suns and moons appear in the sky? Professor Minnaert explains these unusual phenomena and hundreds of others in simple, easy-to-understand terms based on optical laws and the properties of light and color. No mathematics is required but artists, scientists, students, and everyone fascinated by these "tricks" of nature will find thousands of useful and amazing pieces of information. Hundreds of observational experiments are suggested which require no special equipment. 200 illustrations; 42 photos. xvi + 362pp. 5⅜ x 8.   T196 Paperbound **$2.00**

THE UNIVERSE OF LIGHT, W. Bragg. Sir William Bragg, Nobel Laureate and great modern physicist, is also well known for his powers of clear exposition. Here he analyzes all aspects of light for the layman: lenses, reflection, refraction, the optics of vision, x-rays, the photoelectric effect, etc. He tells you what causes the color of spectra, rainbows, and soap bubbles, how magic mirrors work, and much more. Dozens of simple experiments are described. Preface. Index. 199 line drawings and photographs, including 2 full-page color plates. x + 283pp. 5⅜ x 8.   T538 Paperbound **$1.85**

SOAP-BUBBLES: THEIR COLOURS AND THE FORCES THAT MOULD THEM, C. V. Boys. For continuing popularity and validity as scientific primer, few books can match this volume of easily-followed experiments, explanations. Lucid exposition of complexities of liquid films, surface tension and related phenomena, bubbles' reaction to heat, motion, music, magnetic fields. Experiments with capillary attraction, soap bubbles on frames, composite bubbles, liquid cylinders and jets, bubbles other than soap, etc. Wonderful introduction to scientific method, natural laws that have many ramifications in areas of modern physics. Only complete edition in print. New Introduction by S. Z. Lewin, New York University. 83 illustrations; 1 full-page color plate. xii + 190pp. 5⅜ x 8½.   T542 Paperbound **95¢**

CATALOGUE OF DOVER BOOKS

THE STORY OF X-RAYS FROM RONTGEN TO ISOTOPES, A. R. Bleich, M.D. This book, by a member of the American College of Radiology, gives the scientific explanation of x-rays, their applications in medicine, industry and art, and their danger (and that of atmospheric radiation) to the individual and the species. You learn how radiation therapy is applied against cancer, how x-rays diagnose heart disease and other ailments, how they are used to examine mummies for information on diseases of early societies, and industrial materials for hidden weaknesses. 54 illustrations show x-rays of flowers, bones, stomach, gears with flaws, etc. 1st publication. Index. xix + 186pp. 5⅜ x 8. T622 Paperbound **$1.35**

SPINNING TOPS AND GYROSCOPIC MOTION, John Perry. A classic elementary text of the dynamics of rotation — the behavior and use of rotating bodies such as gyroscopes and tops. In simple, everyday English you are shown how quasi-rigidity is induced in discs of paper, smoke rings, chains, etc., by rapid motions; why a gyrostat falls and why a top rises; precession; how the earth's motion affects climate; and many other phenomena. Appendix on practical use of gyroscopes. 62 figures. 128pp. 5⅜ x 8. T416 Paperbound **$1.00**

SNOW CRYSTALS, W. A. Bentley, M. J. Humphreys. For almost 50 years W. A. Bentley photographed snow flakes in his laboratory in Jericho, Vermont; in 1931 the American Meteorological Society gathered together the best of his work, some 2400 photographs of snow flakes, plus a few ice flowers, windowpane frosts, dew, frozen rain, and other ice formations. Pictures were selected for beauty and scientific value. A very valuable work to anyone in meteorology, cryology; most interesting to layman; extremely useful for artist who wants beautiful, crystalline designs. All copyright free. Unabridged reprint of 1931 edition. 2453 illustrations. 227pp. 8 x 10½. T287 Paperbound **$3.00**

A DOVER SCIENCE SAMPLER, edited by George Barkin. A collection of brief, non-technical passages from 44 Dover Books Explaining Science for the enjoyment of the science-minded browser. Includes work of Bertrand Russell, Poincaré, Laplace, Max Born, Galileo, Newton; material on physics, mathematics, metallurgy, anatomy, astronomy, chemistry, etc. You will be fascinated by Martin Gardner's analysis of the sincere pseudo-scientist, Moritz's account of Newton's absentmindedness, Bernard's examples of human vivisection, etc. Illustrations from the Diderot Pictorial Encyclopedia and De Re Metallica. 64 pages. **FREE**

THE STORY OF ATOMIC THEORY AND ATOMIC ENERGY, J. G. Feinberg. A broader approach to subject of nuclear energy and its cultural implications than any other similar source. Very readable, informal, completely non-technical text. Begins with first atomic theory, 600 B.C. and carries you through the work of Mendelejeff, Röntgen, Madame Curie, to Einstein's equation and the A-bomb. New chapter goes through thermonuclear fission, binding energy, other events up to 1959. Radioactive decay and radiation hazards, future benefits, work of Bohr, moderns, hundreds more topics. "Deserves special mention . . . not only authoritative but thoroughly popular in the best sense of the word," Saturday Review. Formerly, "The Atom Story." Expanded with new chapter. Three appendixes. Index. 34 illustrations. vii + 243pp. 5⅜ x 8. T625 Paperbound **$1.45**

THE STRANGE STORY OF THE QUANTUM, AN ACCOUNT FOR THE GENERAL READER OF THE GROWTH OF IDEAS UNDERLYING OUR PRESENT ATOMIC KNOWLEDGE, B. Hoffmann. Presents lucidly and expertly, with barest amount of mathematics, the problems and theories which led to modern quantum physics. Dr. Hoffmann begins with the closing years of the 19th century, when certain trifling discrepancies were noticed, and with illuminating analogies and examples takes you through the brilliant concepts of Planck, Einstein, Pauli, Broglie, Bohr, Schroedinger, Heisenberg, Dirac, Sommerfeld, Feynman, etc. This edition includes a new, long postscript carrying the story through 1958. "Of the books attempting an account of the history and contents of our modern atomic physics which have come to my attention, this is the best," H. Margenau, Yale University, in "American Journal of Physics." 32 tables and line illustrations. Index. 275pp. 5⅜ x 8. T518 Paperbound **$1.50**

SPACE AND TIME, E. Borel. Written by a versatile mathematician of world renown with his customary lucidity and precision, this introduction to relativity for the layman presents scores of examples, analogies, and illustrations that open up new ways of thinking about space and time. It covers abstract geometry and geographical maps, continuity and topology, the propagation of light, the special theory of relativity, the general theory of relativity, theoretical researches, and much more. Mathematical notes. 2 Indexes. 4 Appendices. 15 figures. xvi + 243pp. 5⅜ x 8. T592 Paperbound **$1.45**

FROM EUCLID TO EDDINGTON: A STUDY OF THE CONCEPTIONS OF THE EXTERNAL WORLD, Sir Edmund Whittaker. A foremost British scientist traces the development of theories of natural philosophy from the western rediscovery of Euclid to Eddington, Einstein, Dirac, etc. The inadequacy of classical physics is contrasted with present day attempts to understand the physical world through relativity, non-Euclidean geometry, space curvature, wave mechanics, etc. 5 major divisions of examination: Space; Time and Movement; the Concepts of Classical Physics; the Concepts of Quantum Mechanics; the Eddington Universe. 212pp. 5⅜ x 8. T491 Paperbound **$1.35**

CATALOGUE OF DOVER BOOKS

*THE EVOLUTION OF SCIENTIFIC THOUGHT FROM NEWTON TO EINSTEIN, A. d'Abro. A detailed account of the evolution of classical physics into modern relativistic theory and the concomitant changes in scientific methodology. The breakdown of classical physics in the face of non-Euclidean geometry and the electromagnetic equations is carefully discussed and then an exhaustive analysis of Einstein's special and general theories of relativity and their implications is given. Newton, Riemann, Weyl, Lorentz, Planck, Maxwell, and many others are considered. A non-technical explanation of space, time, electromagnetic waves, etc. as understood today. "Model of semi-popular exposition," NEW REPUBLIC. 21 diagrams. 482pp. 5⅜ x 8.
T2 Paperbound **$2.00**

EINSTEIN'S THEORY OF RELATIVITY, Max Born. Nobel Laureate explains Einstein's special and general theories of relativity, beginning with a thorough review of classical physics in simple, non-technical language. Exposition of Einstein's work discusses concept of simultaneity, kinematics, relativity of arbitrary motions, the space-time continuum, geometry of curved surfaces, etc., steering middle course between vague popularizations and complex scientific presentations. 1962 edition revised by author takes into account latest findings, predictions of theory and implications for cosmology, indicates what is being sought in unified field theory. Mathematics very elementary, illustrative diagrams and experiments informative but simple. Revised 1962 edition. Revised by Max Born, assisted by Gunther Leibfried and Walter Biem. Index. 143 illustrations. vii + 376pp. 5⅜ x 8.
S769 Paperbound **$2.00**

PHILOSOPHY AND THE PHYSICISTS, L. Susan Stebbing. A philosopher examines the philosophical aspects of modern science, in terms of a lively critical attack on the ideas of Jeans and Eddington. Such basic questions are treated as the task of science, causality, determinism, probability, consciousness, the relation of the world of physics to the world of everyday experience. The author probes the concepts of man's smallness before an inscrutable universe, the tendency to idealize mathematical construction, unpredictability theorems and human freedom, the supposed opposition between 19th century determinism and modern science, and many others. Introduces many thought-stimulating ideas about the implications of modern physical concepts. xvi + 295pp. 5⅜ x 8.
T480 Paperbound **$1.65**

THE RESTLESS UNIVERSE, Max Born. A remarkably lucid account by a Nobel Laureate of recent theories of wave mechanics, behavior of gases, electrons and ions, waves and particles, electronic structure of the atom, nuclear physics, and similar topics. "Much more thorough and deeper than most attempts . . . easy and delightful," CHEMICAL AND ENGINEERING NEWS. Special feature: 7 animated sequences of 60 figures each showing such phenomena as gas molecules in motion, the scattering of alpha particles, etc. 11 full-page plates of photographs. Total of nearly 600 illustrations. 351pp. 6⅛ x 9¼.
T412 Paperbound **$2.00**

THE COMMON SENSE OF THE EXACT SCIENCES, W. K. Clifford. For 70 years a guide to the basic concepts of scientific and mathematical thought. Acclaimed by scientists and laymen alike, it offers a wonderful insight into concepts such as the extension of meaning of symbols, characteristics of surface boundaries, properties of plane figures, measurement of quantities, vectors, the nature of position, bending of space, motion, mass and force, and many others. Prefaces by Bertrand Russell and Karl Pearson. Critical introduction by James Newman. 130 figures. 249pp. 5⅜ x 8.
T61 Paperbound **$1.60**

MATTER AND LIGHT, THE NEW PHYSICS, Louis de Broglie. Non-technical explanations by a Nobel Laureate of electro-magnetic theory, relativity, matter, light and radiation, wave mechanics, quantum physics, philosophy of science, and similar topics. This is one of the simplest yet most accurate introductions to the work of men like Planck, Einstein, Bohr, and others. Only 2 of the 21 chapters require a knowledge of mathematics. 300pp. 5⅜ x 8.
T35 Paperbound **$1.75**

SCIENCE, THEORY AND MAN, Erwin Schrödinger. This is a complete and unabridged reissue of SCIENCE AND THE HUMAN TEMPERAMENT plus an additional essay: "What Is an Elementary Particle?" Nobel Laureate Schrödinger discusses such topics as nature of scientific method, tne nature of science, chance and determinism, science and society, conceptual models for physical entities, elementary particles and wave mechanics. Presentation is popular and may be followed by most people with little or no scientific training. "Fine practical preparation for a time when laws of nature, human institutions . . . are undergoing a critical examination without parallel," Waldemar Kaempffert, N. Y. TIMES. 192pp. 5⅜ x 8.
T428 Paperbound **$1.35**

CONCERNING THE NATURE OF THINGS, Sir William Bragg. The Nobel Laureate physicist in his Royal Institute Christmas Lectures explains such diverse phenomena as the formation of crystals, how uranium is transmuted to lead, the way X-rays work, why a spinning ball travels in a curved path, the reason why bubbles bounce from each other, and many other scientific topics that are seldom explained in simple terms. No scientific background needed—book is easy enough that any intelligent adult or youngster can understand it. Unabridged. 32pp. of photos; 57 figures. xii + 232pp. 5⅜ x 8.
T31 Paperbound **$1.35**

*THE RISE OF THE NEW PHYSICS (formerly THE DECLINE OF MECHANISM), A. d'Abro. This authoritative and comprehensive 2 volume exposition is unique in scientific publishing. Written for intelligent readers not familiar with higher mathematics, it is the only thorough explanation in non-technical language of modern mathematical-physical theory. Combining both history and exposition, it ranges from classical Newtonian concepts up through the electronic theories of Dirac and Heisenberg, the statistical mechanics of Fermi, and Einstein's relativity theories. "A must for anyone doing serious study in the physical sciences," J. OF FRANKLIN INST. 97 illustrations. 991pp. 2 volumes.
T3 Vol. 1, Paperbound **$2.00**
T4 Vol. 2, Paperbound **$2.00**

CATALOGUE OF DOVER BOOKS

SCIENCE AND HYPOTHESIS, Henri Poincaré. Creative psychology in science. How such concepts as number, magnitude, space, force, classical mechanics were developed and how the modern scientist uses them in his thought. Hypothesis in physics, theories of modern physics. Introduction by Sir James Larmor. "Few mathematicians have had the breadth of vision of Poincaré, and none is his superior in the gift of clear exposition," E. T. Bell. Index. 272pp. 5⅜ x 8.
S221 Paperbound **$1.35**

THE VALUE OF SCIENCE, Henri Poincaré. Many of the most mature ideas of the "last scientific universalist" conveyed with charm and vigor for both the beginning student and the advanced worker. Discusses the nature of scientific truth, whether order is innate in the universe or imposed upon it by man, logical thought versus intuition (relating to mathematics through the works of Weierstrass, Lie, Klein, Riemann), time and space (relativity, psychological time, simultaneity), Hertz's concept of force, interrelationship of mathematical physics to pure math, values within disciplines of Maxwell, Carnot, Mayer, Newton, Lorentz, etc. Index. iii + 147pp. 5⅜ x 8.
S469 Paperbound **$1.35**

THE SKY AND ITS MYSTERIES, E. A. Beet. One of the most lucid books on the mysteries of the universe; covers history of astronomy from earliest observations to modern theories of expanding universe, source of stellar energy, birth of planets, origin of moon craters, possibilities of life on other planets. Discusses effects of sunspots on weather; distance, age of stars; methods and tools of astronomers; much more. Expert and fascinating. "Eminently readable book," London Times. Bibliography. Over 50 diagrams, 12 full-page plates. Fold-out star map. Introduction. Index. 238pp. 5¼ x 7½.
T627 Clothbound **$3.50**

OUT OF THE SKY: AN INTRODUCTION TO METEORITICS, H. H. Nininger. A non-technical yet comprehensive introduction to the young science of meteoritics: all aspects of the arrival of cosmic matter on our planet from outer space and the reaction and alteration of this matter in the terrestrial environment. Essential facts and major theories presented by one of the world's leading experts. Covers ancient reports of meteors; modern systematic investigations; fireball clusters; meteorite showers; tektites; planetoidal encounters; etc. 52 full-page plates with over 175 photographs. 22 figures. Bibliography and references. Index. viii + 336pp. 5⅜ x 8.
T519 Paperbound **$1.85**

THE REALM OF THE NEBULAE, E. Hubble. One of great astronomers of our day records his formulation of concept of "island universes." Covers velocity-distance relationship; classification, nature, distances, general types of nebulae; cosmological theories. A fine introduction to modern theories for layman. No math needed. New introduction by A. Sandage. 55 illustrations, photos. Index. iv + 201pp. 5⅜ x 8.
S455 Paperbound **$1.50**

AN ELEMENTARY SURVEY OF CELESTIAL MECHANICS, Y. Ryabov. Elementary exposition of gravitational theory and celestial mechanics. Historical introduction and coverage of basic principles, including: the ecliptic, the orbital plane, the 2- and 3-body problems, the discovery of Neptune, planetary rotation, the length of the day, the shapes of galaxies, satellites (detailed treatment of Sputnik I), etc. First American reprinting of successful Russian popular exposition. Follow actual methods of astrophysicists with only high school math! Appendix. 58 figures. 165pp. 5⅜ x 8.
T756 Paperbound **$1.25**

GREAT IDEAS AND THEORIES OF MODERN COSMOLOGY, Jagjit Singh. Companion volume to author's popular "Great Ideas of Modern Mathematics" (Dover, $1.55). The best non-technical survey of post-Einstein attempts to answer perhaps unanswerable questions of origin, age of Universe, possibility of life on other worlds, etc. Fundamental theories of cosmology and cosmogony recounted, explained, evaluated in light of most recent data: Einstein's concepts of relativity, space-time; Milne's a priori world-system; astrophysical theories of Jeans, Eddington; Hoyle's "continuous creation;" contributions of dozens more scientists. A faithful, comprehensive critical summary of complex material presented in an extremely well-written text intended for laymen. Original publication. Index. xii + 276pp. 5⅜ x 8½.
T925 Paperbound **$1.85**

BASIC ELECTRICITY, Bureau of Naval Personnel. Very thorough, easily followed course in basic electricity for beginner, layman, or intermediate student. Begins with simplest definitions, presents coordinated, systematic coverage of basic theory and application: conductors, insulators, static electricity, magnetism, production of voltage, Ohm's law, direct current series and parallel circuits, wiring techniques, electromagnetism, alternating current, capacitance and inductance, measuring instruments, etc.; application to electrical machines such as alternating and direct current generators, motors, transformers, magnetic amplifiers, etc. Each chapter contains problems to test progress; answers at rear. No math needed beyond algebra. Appendices on signs, formulas, etc. 345 illustrations. 448pp. 7½ x 10.
S973 Paperbound **$2.95**

ELEMENTARY METALLURGY AND METALLOGRAPHY, A. M. Shrager. An introduction to common metals and alloys; stress is upon steel and iron, but other metals and alloys also covered. All aspects of production, processing, working of metals. Designed for student who wishes to enter metallurgy, for bright high school or college beginner, layman who wants background on extremely important industry. Questions, at ends of chapters, many microphotographs, glossary. Greatly revised 1961 edition. 195 illustrations, tables. ix + 389pp. 5⅜ x 8.
S138 Paperbound **$2.25**

BRIDGES AND THEIR BUILDERS, D. B. Steinman & S. R. Watson. Engineers, historians, and every person who has ever been fascinated by great spans will find this book an endless source of information and interest. Greek and Roman structures, Medieval bridges, modern classics such as the Brooklyn Bridge, and the latest developments in the science are retold by one of the world's leading authorities on bridge design and construction. BRIDGES AND THEIR BUILDERS is the only comprehensive and accurate semi-popular history of these important measures of progress in print. New, greatly revised, enlarged edition. 23 photos; 26 line-drawings. Index. xvii + 401pp. 5⅜ x 8.   T431 Paperbound **$2.00**

FAMOUS BRIDGES OF THE WORLD, D. B. Steinman. An up-to-the-minute new edition of a book that explains the fascinating drama of how the world's great bridges came to be built. The author, designer of the famed Mackinac bridge, discusses bridges from all periods and all parts of the world, explaining their various types of construction, and describing the problems their builders faced. Although primarily for youngsters, this cannot fail to interest readers of all ages. 48 illustrations in the text. 23 photographs. 99pp. 6⅛ x 9¼.   T161 Paperbound **$1.00**

HOW DO YOU USE A SLIDE RULE? by A. A. Merrill. A step-by-step explanation of the slide rule that presents the fundamental rules clearly enough for the non-mathematician to understand. Unlike most instruction manuals, this work concentrates on the two most important operations: multiplication and division. 10 easy lessons, each with a clear drawing, for the reader who has difficulty following other expositions. 1st publication. Index. 2 Appendices. 10 illustrations. 78 problems, all with answers. vi + 36 pp. 6⅛ x 9¼.   T62 Paperbound **60¢**

HOW TO CALCULATE QUICKLY, H. Sticker. A tried and true method for increasing your "number sense" — the ability to see relationships between numbers and groups of numbers. Addition, subtraction, multiplication, division, fractions, and other topics are treated through techniques not generally taught in schools: left to right multiplication, division by inspection, etc. This is not a collection of tricks which work only on special numbers, but a detailed well-planned course, consisting of over 9,000 problems that you can work in spare moments. It is excellent for anyone who is inconvenienced by slow computational skills. 5 or 10 minutes of this book daily will double or triple your calculation speed. 9,000 problems, answers. 256pp. 5⅜ x 8.   T295 Paperbound **$1.00**

MATHEMATICAL FUN, GAMES AND PUZZLES, Jack Frohlichstein. A valuable service for parents of children who have trouble with math, for teachers in need of a supplement to regular upper elementary and junior high math texts (each section is graded—easy, average, difficult —for ready adaptation to different levels of ability), and for just anyone who would like to develop basic skills in an informal and entertaining manner. The author combines ten years of experience as a junior high school math teacher with a method that uses puzzles and games to introduce the basic ideas and operations of arithmetic. Stress on everyday uses of math: banking, stock market, personal budgets, insurance, taxes. Intellectually stimulating and practical, too. 418 problems and diversions with answers. Bibliography. 120 illustrations. xix + 306pp. 5⅝ x 8½.   T789 Paperbound **$1.75**

GREAT IDEAS OF MODERN MATHEMATICS: THEIR NATURE AND USE, Jagjit Singh. Reader with only high school math will understand main mathematical ideas of modern physics, astronomy, genetics, psychology, evolution, etc. better than many who use them as tools, but comprehend little of their basic structure. Author uses his wide knowledge of non-mathematical fields in brilliant exposition of differential equations, matrices, group theory, logic, statistics, problems of mathematical foundations, imaginary numbers, vectors, etc. Original publication. 2 appendixes. 2 indexes. 65 illustr. 322pp. 5⅜ x 8.   S587 Paperbound **$1.75**

*****MATHEMATICS IN ACTION, O. G. Sutton.** Everyone with a command of high school algebra will find this book one of the finest possible introductions to the application of mathematics to physical theory. Ballistics, numerical analysis, waves and wavelike phenomena, Fourier series, group concepts, fluid flow and aerodynamics, statistical measures, and meteorology are discussed with unusual clarity. Some calculus and differential equations theory is developed by the author for the reader's help in the more difficult sections. 88 figures. Index. viii + 236pp. 5⅜ x 8.   T440 Clothbound **$3.50**

*****INTRODUCTION TO SYMBOLIC LOGIC AND ITS APPLICATIONS, Rudolph Carnap.** One of the clearest, most comprehensive, and rigorous introductions to modern symbolic logic, by perhaps its greatest living master. Not merely elementary theory, but demonstrated applications in mathematics, physics, and biology. Symbolic languages of various degrees of complexity are analyzed, and one constructed. "A creation of the rank of a masterpiece," Zentralblatt für Mathematik und Ihre Grenzgebiete. Over 300 exercises. 5 figures. Bibliography. Index. xvi + 241pp. 5⅜ x 8.   S453 Paperbound **$1.85**

*****HIGHER MATHEMATICS FOR STUDENTS OF CHEMISTRY AND PHYSICS, J. W. Mellor.** Not abstract, but practical, drawing its problems from familiar laboratory material, this book covers theory and application of differential calculus, analytic geometry, functions with singularities, integral calculus, infinite series, solution of numerical equations, differential equations, Fourier's theorem and extensions, probability and the theory of errors, calculus of variations, determinants, etc. "If the reader is not familiar with this book, it will repay him to examine it," CHEM. & ENGINEERING NEWS. 800 problems. 189 figures. 2 appendices; 30 tables of integrals, probability functions, etc. Bibliography. xxi + 641pp. 5⅜ x 8.   S193 Paperbound **$2.25**

CATALOGUE OF DOVER BOOKS

THE FOURTH DIMENSION SIMPLY EXPLAINED, edited by Henry P. Manning. Originally written as entries in contest sponsored by "Scientific American," then published in book form, these 22 essays present easily understood explanations of how the fourth dimension may be studied, the relationship of non-Euclidean geometry to the fourth dimension, analogies to three-dimensional space, some fourth-dimensional absurdities and curiosities, possible measurements and forms in the fourth dimension. In general, a thorough coverage of many of the simpler properties of fourth-dimensional space. Multi-points of view on many of the most important aspects are valuable aid to comprehension. Introduction by Dr. Henry P. Manning gives proper emphasis to points in essays, more advanced account of fourth-dimensional geometry. 82 figures. 251pp. 5⅜ x 8.   T711 Paperbound **$1.35**

TRIGONOMETRY REFRESHER FOR TECHNICAL MEN, A. A. Klaf. A modern question and answer text on plane and spherical trigonometry. Part I covers plane trigonometry: angles, quadrants, trigonometrical functions, graphical representation, interpolation, equations, logarithms, solution of triangles, slide rules, etc. Part II discusses applications to navigation, surveying, elasticity, architecture, and engineering. Small angles, periodic functions, vectors, polar coordinates, De Moivre's theorem, fully covered. Part III is devoted to spherical trigonometry and the solution of spherical triangles, with applications to terrestrial and astronomical problems. Special time-savers for numerical calculation. 913 questions answered for you! 1738 problems; answers to odd numbers. 494 figures. 14 pages of functions, formulae. Index. x + 629pp. 5⅜ x 8.   T371 Paperbound **$2.00**

CALCULUS REFRESHER FOR TECHNICAL MEN. A. A. Klaf. Not an ordinary textbook but a unique refresher for engineers, technicians, and students. An examination of the most important aspects of differential and integral calculus by means of 756 key questions. Part I covers simple differential calculus: constants, variables, functions, increments, derivatives, logarithms, curvature, etc. Part II treats fundamental concepts of integration: inspection, substitution, transformation, reduction, areas and volumes, mean value, successive and partial integration, double and triple integration. Stresses practical aspects! A 50 page section gives applications to civil and nautical engineering, electricity, stress and strain, elasticity, industrial engineering, and similar fields. 756 questions answered. 556 problems; solutions to odd numbers. 36 pages of constants, formulae. Index. v + 431pp. 5⅜ x 8.
T370 Paperbound **$2.00**

PROBABILITIES AND LIFE, Emile Borel. One of the leading French mathematicians of the last 100 years makes use of certain results of mathematics of probabilities and explains a number of problems that for the most part, are related to everyday living or to illness and death: computation of life expectancy tables, chances of recovery from various diseases, probabilities of job accidents, weather predictions, games of chance, and so on. Emphasis on results not processes, though some indication is made of mathematical proofs. Simple in style, free of technical terminology, limited in scope to everyday situations, it is comprehensible to laymen, fine reading for beginning students of probability. New English translation. Index. Appendix. vi + 87pp. 5⅜ x 8½.   T121 Paperbound **$1.00**

POPULAR SCIENTIFIC LECTURES, Hermann von Helmholtz. 7 lucid expositions by a preeminent scientific mind: "The Physiological Causes of Harmony in Music," "On the Relation of Optics to Painting," "On the Conservation of Force," "On the Interaction of Natural Forces," "On Goethe's Scientific Researches" into theory of color, "On the Origin and Significance of Geometric Axioms," "On Recent Progress in the Theory of Vision." Written with simplicity of expression, stripped of technicalities, these are easy to understand and delightful reading for anyone interested in science or looking for an introduction to serious study of acoustics or optics. Introduction by Professor Morris Kline, Director, Division of Electromagnetic Research, New York University, contains astute, impartial evaluations. Selected from "Popular Lectures on Scientific Subjects," 1st and 2nd series. xii + 286pp. 5⅜ x 8½.   T799 Paperbound **$1.45**

SCIENCE AND METHOD, Henri Poincaré. Procedure of scientific discovery, methodology, experiment, idea-germination—the intellectual processes by which discoveries come into being. Most significant and most interesting aspects of development, application of ideas. Chapters cover selection of facts, chance, mathematical reasoning, mathematics, and logic; Whitehead, Russell, Cantor; the new mechanics, etc. 288pp. 5⅜ x 8.   S222 Paperbound **$1.35**

HEAT AND ITS WORKINGS, Morton Mott-Smith, Ph.D. An unusual book; to our knowledge the only middle-level survey of this important area of science. Explains clearly such important concepts as physiological sensation of heat and Weber's law, measurement of heat, evolution of thermometer, nature of heat, expansion and contraction of solids, Boyle's law, specific heat. BTU's and calories, evaporation, Andrews's isothermals, radiation, the relation of heat to light, many more topics inseparable from other aspects of physics. A wide, non-mathematical yet thorough explanation of basic ideas, theories, phenomena for laymen and beginning scientists illustrated by experiences of daily life. Bibliography. 50 illustrations. x + 165pp. 5⅜ x 8½.   T978 Paperbound **$1.00**

Classics of Science

THE DIDEROT PICTORIAL ENCYCLOPEDIA OF TRADES AND INDUSTRY, MANUFACTURING AND THE TECHNICAL ARTS IN PLATES SELECTED FROM "L'ENCYCLOPEDIE OU DICTIONNAIRE RAISONNE DES SCIENCES, DES ARTS, ET DES METIERS" OF DENIS DIDEROT, edited with text by C. Gillispie. The first modern selection of plates from the high point of 18th century French engraving, Diderot's famous Encyclopedia. Over 2000 illustrations on 485 full page plates, most of them original size, illustrating the trades and industries of one of the most fascinating periods of modern history, 18th century France. These magnificent engravings provide an invaluable glimpse into the past for the student of early technology, a lively and accurate social document to students of cultures, an outstanding find to the lover of fine engravings. The plates teem with life, with men, women, and children performing all of the thousands of operations necessary to the trades before and during the early stages of the industrial revolution. Plates are in sequence, and show general operations, closeups of difficult operations, and details of complex machinery. Such important and interesting trades and industries are illustrated as sowing, harvesting, beekeeping, cheesemaking, operating windmills, milling flour, charcoal burning, tobacco processing, indigo, fishing, arts of war, salt extraction, mining, smelting iron, casting iron, steel, extracting mercury, zinc, sulphur, copper, etc., slating, tinning, silverplating, gilding, making gunpowder, cannons, bells, shoeing horses, tanning, papermaking, printing, dying, and more than 40 other categories. 920pp. 9 x 12. Heavy library cloth.   T421 Two volume set **$18.50**

THE PRINCIPLES OF SCIENCE, A TREATISE ON LOGIC AND THE SCIENTIFIC METHOD, W. Stanley Jevons. Treating such topics as Inductive and Deductive Logic, the Theory of Number, Probability, and the Limits of Scientific Method, this milestone in the development of symbolic logic remains a stimulating contribution to the investigation of inferential validity in the natural and social sciences. It significantly advances Boole's logic, and describes a machine which is a foundation of modern electronic calculators. In his introduction, Ernest Nagel of Columbia University says, "(Jevons) . . . continues to be of interest as an attempt to articulate the logic of scientific inquiry." Index. liii + 786pp. 5⅜ x 8.
S446 Paperbound **$2.98**

*DIALOGUES CONCERNING TWO NEW SCIENCES, Galileo Galilei. A classic of experimental science which has had a profound and enduring influence on the entire history of mechanics and engineering. Galileo based this, his finest work, on 30 years of experimentation. It offers a fascinating and vivid exposition of dynamics, elasticity, sound, ballistics, strength of materials, and the scientific method. Translated by H. Crew and A. de Salvio. 126 diagrams. Index. xxi + 288pp. 5⅜ x 8.   S99 Paperbound **$1.75**

DE MAGNETE, William Gilbert. This classic work on magnetism founded a new science. Gilbert was the first to use the word "electricity," to recognize mass as distinct from weight, to discover the effect of heat on magnetic bodies; invented an electroscope, differentiated between static electricity and magnetism, conceived of the earth as a magnet. Written by the first great experimental scientist, this lively work is valuable not only as an historical landmark, but as the delightfully easy-to-follow record of a perpetually searching, ingenious mind. Translated by P. F. Mottelay. 25 page biographical memoir. 90 fix. lix + 368pp. 5⅜ x 8.   S470 Paperbound **$2.00**

*OPTICKS, Sir Isaac Newton. An enormous storehouse of insights and discoveries on light, reflection, color, refraction, theories of wave and corpuscular propagation of light, optical apparatus, and mathematical devices which have recently been reevaluated in terms of modern physics and placed in the top-most ranks of Newton's work! Foreword by Albert Einstein. Preface by I. B. Cohen of Harvard U. 7 pages of portraits, facsimile pages, letters, etc. cxvi + 412pp. 5⅜ x 8.   S205 Paperbound **$2.25**

A SURVEY OF PHYSICAL THEORY, M. Planck. Lucid essays on modern physics for the general reader by the Nobel Laureate and creator of the quantum revolution. Planck explains how the new concepts came into being; explores the clash between theories of mechanics, electrodynamics, and thermodynamics; and traces the evolution of the concept of light through Newton, Huygens, Maxwell, and his own quantum theory, providing unparalleled insights into his development of this momentous modern concept. Bibliography. Index. vii + 121pp. 5⅜ x 8.
S650 Paperbound **$1.15**

A SOURCE BOOK IN MATHEMATICS, D. E. Smith. English translations of the original papers that announced the great discoveries in mathematics from the Renaissance to the end of the 19th century: succinct selections from 125 different treatises and articles, most of them unavailable elsewhere in English—Newton, Leibniz, Pascal, Riemann, Bernoulli, etc. 24 articles trace developments in the field of number, 18 cover algebra, 36 are on geometry, and 13 on calculus. Biographical-historical introductions to each article. Two volume set. Index in each. Total of 115 illustrations. Total of xxviii + 742pp. 5⅜ x 8.   S552 Vol I Paperbound **$1.85**
S553 Vol II Paperbound **$1.85**
The set, boxed **$3.50**

CATALOGUE OF DOVER BOOKS

*THE THIRTEEN BOOKS OF EUCLID'S ELEMENTS, edited by T. L. Heath. This is the complete EUCLID — the definitive edition of one of the greatest classics of the western world. Complete English translation of the Heiberg text with spurious Book XIV. Detailed 150-page introduction discusses aspects of Greek and medieval mathematics: Euclid, texts, commentators, etc. Paralleling the text is an elaborate critical exposition analyzing each definition, proposition, postulate, etc., and covering textual matters, mathematical analyses, refutations, extensions, etc. Unabridged reproduction of the Cambridge 2nd edition. 3 volumes. Total of 995 figures, 1426pp. 5⅜ x 8. S88, 89, 90 — 3 vol. set, Paperbound **$6.75**

*THE GEOMETRY OF RENE DESCARTES. The great work which founded analytic geometry. The renowned Smith-Latham translation faced with the original French text containing all of Descartes' own diagrams! Contains: Problems the Construction of Which Requires Only Straight Lines and Circles; On the Nature of Curved Lines; On the Construction of Solid or Supersolid Problems. Notes. Diagrams. 258pp. S68 Paperbound **$1.60**

*A PHILOSOPHICAL ESSAY ON PROBABILITIES, P. Laplace. Without recourse to any mathematics above grammar school, Laplace develops a philosophically, mathematically and historically classical exposition of the nature of probability: its functions and limitations, operations in practical affairs, calculations in games of chance, insurance, government, astronomy, and countless other fields. New introduction by E. T. Bell. viii + 196pp. S166 Paperbound **$1.35**

DE RE METALLICA, Georgius Agricola. Written over 400 years ago, for 200 years the most authoritative first-hand account of the production of metals, translated in 1912 by former President Herbert Hoover and his wife, and today still one of the most beautiful and fascinating volumes ever produced in the history of science! 12 books, exhaustively annotated, give a wonderfully lucid and vivid picture of the history of mining, selection of sites, types of deposits, excavating pits, sinking shafts, ventilating, pumps, crushing machinery, assaying, smelting, refining metals, making salt, alum, nitre, glass, and many other topics. This definitive edition contains all 289 of the 16th century woodcuts which made the original an artistic masterpiece. It makes a superb gift for geologists, engineers, libraries, artists, historians, and everyone interested in science and early illustrative art. Biographical, historical introductions. Bibliography, survey of ancient authors. Indices. 289 illustrations. 672pp. 6¾ x 10¾. Deluxe library edition. S6 Clothbound **$10.00**

GEOGRAPHICAL ESSAYS, W. M. Davis. Modern geography and geomorphology rest on the fundamental work of this scientist. His new concepts of earth-processes revolutionized science and his broad interpretation of the scope of geography created a deeper understanding of the interrelation of the landscape and the forces that mold it. This first inexpensive unabridged edition covers theory of geography, methods of advanced geographic teaching, descriptions of geographic areas, analyses of land-shaping processes, and much besides. Not only a factual and historical classic, it is still widely read for its reflections of modern scientific thought. Introduction. 130 figures. Index. vi + 777pp. 5⅜ x 8.
  S383 Paperbound **$2.95**

CHARLES BABBAGE AND HIS CALCULATING ENGINES, edited by P. Morrison and E. Morrison. Friend of Darwin, Humboldt, and Laplace, Babbage was a leading pioneer in large-scale mathematical machines and a prophetic herald of modern operational research—true father of Harvard's relay computer Mark I. His Difference Engine and Analytical Engine were the first successful machines in the field. This volume contains a valuable introduction on his life and work; major excerpts from his fascinating autobiography, revealing his eccentric and unusual personality; and extensive selections from "Babbage's Calculating Engines," a compilation of hard-to-find journal articles, both by Babbage and by such eminent contributors as the Countess of Lovelace, L. F. Menabrea, and Dionysius Lardner. 11 illustrations. Appendix of miscellaneous papers. Index. Bibliography. xxxviii + 400pp. 5⅜ x 8. T12 Paperbound **$2.00**

*THE WORKS OF ARCHIMEDES WITH THE METHOD OF ARCHIMEDES, edited by T. L. Heath. All the known works of the greatest mathematician of antiquity including the recently discovered METHOD OF ARCHIMEDES. This last is the only work we have which shows exactly how early mathematicians discovered their proofs before setting them down in their final perfection. A 186 page study by the eminent scholar Heath discusses Archimedes and the history of Greek mathematics. Bibliography. 563pp. 5⅜ x 8. S9 Paperbound **$2.25**

History of Science and Mathematics

THE STUDY OF THE HISTORY OF MATHEMATICS, THE STUDY OF THE HISTORY OF SCIENCE, G. Sarton. Two books bound as one. Each volume contains a long introduction to the methods and philosophy of each of these historical fields, covering the skills and sympathies of the historian, concepts of history of science, psychology of idea-creation, and the purpose of history of science. Prof. Sarton also provides more than 80 pages of classified bibliography. Complete and unabridged. Indexed. 10 illustrations. 188pp. 5⅜ x 8.   T240 Paperbound **$1.25**

A HISTORY OF PHYSICS, Florian Cajori, Ph.D. First written in 1899, thoroughly revised in 1929, this is still best entry into antecedents of modern theories. Precise non-mathematical discussion of ideas, theories, techniques, apparatus of each period from Greeks to 1920's, analyzing within each period basic topics of matter, mechanics, light, electricity and magnetism, sound, atomic theory, etc. Stress on modern developments, from early 19th century to present. Written with critical eye on historical development, significance. Provides most of needed historical background for student of physics. Reprint of second (1929) edition. Index. Bibliography in footnotes. 16 figures. xv + 424pp. 5⅜ x 8.   T970 Paperbound **$2.00**

A HISTORY OF ASTRONOMY FROM THALES TO KEPLER, J. L. E. Dreyer. Formerly titled A HISTORY OF PLANETARY SYSTEMS FROM THALES TO KEPLER. This is the only work in English which provides a detailed history of man's cosmological views from prehistoric times up through the Renaissance. It covers Egypt, Babylonia, early Greece, Alexandria, the Middle Ages, Copernicus, Tycho Brahe, Kepler, and many others. Epicycles and other complex theories of positional astronomy are explained in terms nearly everyone will find clear and easy to understand. "Standard reference on Greek astronomy and the Copernican revolution," SKY AND TELESCOPE. Bibliography. 21 diagrams. Index. xvii + 430pp. 5⅜ x 8.   S79 Paperbound **$1.98**

A SHORT HISTORY OF ASTRONOMY, A. Berry. A popular standard work for over 50 years, this thorough and accurate volume covers the science from primitive times to the end of the 19th century. After the Greeks and Middle Ages, individual chapters analyze Copernicus, Brahe, Galileo, Kepler, and Newton, and the mixed reception of their startling discoveries. Post-Newtonian achievements are then discussed in unusual detail: Halley, Bradley, Lagrange, Laplace, Herschel, Bessel, etc. 2 indexes. 104 illustrations, 9 portraits. xxxi + 440pp. 5⅜ x 8.
T210 Paperbound **$2.00**

PIONEERS OF SCIENCE, Sir Oliver Lodge. An authoritative, yet elementary history of science by a leading scientist and expositor. Concentrating on individuals—Copernicus, Brahe, Kepler, Galileo, Descartes, Newton, Laplace, Herschel, Lord Kelvin, and other scientists—the author presents their discoveries in historical order, adding biographical material on each man and full, specific explanations of their achievements. The full, clear discussions of the accomplishments of post-Newtonian astronomers are features seldom found in other books on the subject. Index. 120 illustrations. xv + 404pp. 5⅜ x 8.   T716 Paperbound **$1.65**

THE BIRTH AND DEVELOPMENT OF THE GEOLOGICAL SCIENCES, F. D. Adams. The most complete and thorough history of the earth sciences in print. Geological thought from earliest recorded times to the end of the 19th century—covers over 300 early thinkers and systems: fossils and hypothetical explanations of them, vulcanists vs. neptunists, figured stones and paleontology, generation of stones, and similar topics. 91 illustrations, including medieval, renaissance woodcuts, etc. 632 footnotes and bibliographic notes. Index. 511pp. 5⅜ x 8.
T5 Paperbound **$2.25**

THE STORY OF ALCHEMY AND EARLY CHEMISTRY, J. M. Stillman. "Add the blood of a red-haired man"—a recipe typical of the many quoted in this authoritative and readable history of the strange beliefs and practices of the alchemists. Concise studies of every leading figure in alchemy and early chemistry through Lavoisier, in this curious epic of superstition and true science, constructed from scores of rare and difficult Greek, Latin, German, and French texts. Foreword by S. W. Young. 246-item bibliography. Index. xiii + 566pp. 5⅜ x 8.
S628 Paperbound **$2.45**

HISTORY OF MATHEMATICS, D. E. Smith. Most comprehensive non-technical history of math in English. Discusses the lives and works of over a thousand major and minor figures, from Euclid to Descartes, Gauss, and Riemann. Vol. I: A chronological examination, from primitive concepts through Egypt, Babylonia, Greece, the Orient, Rome, the Middle Ages, the Renaissance, and up to 1900. Vol. 2: The development of ideas in specific fields and problems, up through elementary calculus. Two volumes, total of 510 illustrations, 1355pp. 5⅜ x 8. Set boxed in attractive container.   T429,430 Paperbound the set **$5.00**

CATALOGUE OF DOVER BOOKS

A CONCISE HISTORY OF MATHEMATICS, D. Struik. A lucid, easily followed history of mathematical ideas and techniques from the Ancient Near East up to modern times. Requires no mathematics but will serve as an excellent introduction to mathematical concepts and great mathematicians through the method of historical development. 60 illustrations including Egyptian papyri, Greek mss., portraits of 31 eminent mathematicians. Bibliography. xix + 299pp. 5⅜ x 8.   T255 Paperbound **$1.75**

A SHORT ACCOUNT OF THE HISTORY OF MATHEMATICS, W. W. Rouse Ball. Last previous edition (1908) hailed by mathematicians and laymen for lucid overview of math as living science, for understandable presentation of individual contributions of great mathematicians. Treats lives, discoveries of every important school and figure from Egypt, Phoenicia to late nineteenth century. Greek schools of Ionia, Cyzicus, Alexandria, Byzantium, Pythagoras; primitive arithmetic; Middle Ages and Renaissance, including European and Asiatic contributions; modern math of Descartes, Pascal, Wallis, Huygens, Newton, Euler, Lambert, Laplace, scores more. More emphasis on historical development, exposition of ideas than other books on subject. Non-technical, readable text can be followed with no more preparation than high-school algebra. Index. 544pp. 5⅜ x 8.   S630 Paperbound **$2.00**

ON MATHEMATICS AND MATHEMATICIANS, R. E. Moritz. A ten year labor of love by the discerning and discriminating Prof. Moritz, this collection has rarely been equalled in its ability to convey the full sense of mathematics and the personalities of great mathematicians. A collection of anecdotes, aphorisms, reminiscences, philosophies, definitions, speculations, biographical insights, etc., by great mathematicians and writers: Descartes, Mill, De Morgan, Locke, Berkeley, Kant, Coleridge, Whitehead, Sylvester, Klein, and many others. Also, glimpses into the lives of mathematical giants from Archimedes to Euler, Gauss, and Weierstrass. To mathematicians, a superb book for browsing; to writers and teachers, an unequalled source of quotation; to the layman, an exciting revelation of the fullness of mathematics. Extensive cross index. 410pp. 5⅜ x 8.   T489 Paperbound **$1.95**

SIR ISAAC NEWTON: A BIOGRAPHY, Louis Trenchard More. Standard, definitive biography of Newton, covering every phase of his life and career in its presentation of the renowned scientific genius as a living man. Objective, critical analysis of his character as well as a careful survey of his manifold accomplishments in many areas of science, and in theology, history, politics, finance. Text includes letters by Newton and acquaintances, many other papers, some translated from Latin to English by the author. Scientists, teachers of science will especially be interested in this book, which will appeal to all readers concerned with history of ideas, development of science. Republication of original (1934) edition. 1 full-page plate. Index. xii + 675pp. 5⅜ x 8½.   S79 Paperbound **$2.50**

GUIDE TO THE LITERATURE OF MATHEMATICS AND PHYSICS, N. G. Parke III. Over 5000 entries included under approximately 120 major subject headings, of selected most important books, monographs, periodicals, articles in English, plus important works in German, French, Italian, Spanish, Russian (many recently available works). Covers every branch of physics, math, related engineering. Includes author, title, edition, publisher, place, date, number of volumes, number of pages. A 40-page introduction on the basic problems of research and study provides useful information on the organization and use of libraries, the psychology of learning, etc. This reference work will save you hours of time. 2nd revised edition. Indices of authors, subjects. 464pp. 5⅜ x 8.   S447 Paperbound **$2.49**

Dover publishes books on art, music, philosophy, literature, languages, history, social sciences, psychology, handcrafts, orientalia, puzzles and entertainments, chess, pets and gardens, books explaining science, intermediate and higher mathematics mathematical physics, engineering, biological sciences, earth sciences, classics of science, etc. Write to:

                        Dept. catrr.
                        Dover Publications, Inc.
                        180 Varick Street, N. Y. 14, N. Y.